The Institute of British Geographers
Special Publications Series

20   Sea-level Changes

The Institute of British Geographers
Special Publications Series

Sea-level Changes

Edited by
Michael J. Tooley and Ian Shennan

Basil Blackwell

Copyright © The Institute of British Geographers, 1987

First published 1987

Basil Blackwell Ltd
108 Cowley Road, Oxford, OX4 1JF, UK

Basic Blackwell Inc,
432 Park Avenue South, Suite 1503
New York, NY 10016, USA

British Library Cataloguing in Publication Data

Sea-level changes. – (Institute of British
  Geographers special publication, ISSN
  0073–9006; v. 20).
  1. Sea level
  I. Tooley, M. J.   II. Shennan, Ian
  III. Series
  551.46   GC89

  ISBN 0–631–15402–7

Library of Congress Cataloging in Publication Data

Sea-level changes.
  (Special publications series; 20)
  Includes indexes.
  1. Sea level.   2. Coast changes.   I. *Tooley, M. J.*
II. Shennan, Ian.   III. Series: Special publications
series (Institute of British Geographers); 20.
GC89.S4 1987   551   87–6553
ISBN 0–631–15402–7

Typeset in 11 on 13 pt Plantin
by Columns, Reading
Printed in Great Britain
by Page Bros (Norwich) Ltd

Contents

Preface

International Geological Correlation Programme (IGCP) Project 200 on sea-level correlations and applications was scheduled to run from 1983 until 1987. The main objective of this book is to contribute to the aims of this project. Three main lines of approach have been adopted by the International Working Group to realise the aims of the project:

1 To collect, analyse, interpret and correlate new and existing sea-level data.
2 To survey and analyse data from the world's coasts and continental shelves to provide information on resource exploitation, coastal land use planning, land subsidence, reclamation, aquaculture and ecology.
3 To analyse tide-gauge records and to model other short-term sea-level fluctuations, such as palaeotides, storm surges, tsunamis, using computer simulation techniques controlled by reliable sea-level data.

The chapters in this book cover, to a greater or lesser extent, all these lines of approach, although there is a greater emphasis on the first.

The occasion for this *Special Publication* was a suggestion by Professor Denys Brunsden and Dr. David Stoddart that a collection of research papers on current work on sea-level changes might be a suitable theme for one of the Institute of British Geographers' publications, complementing the material and approach in *Special Publication* 16 on *Shorelines and Isostasy*, edited by Professor David Smith and Dr Alistair Dawson. The suggestion, made in April 1982, was opportune, for eight years of research on different aspects of sea-level changes under the auspices of ICGP 61 'Holocene Sea-level Changes' had ended, and a proposal for a successive project (200) had been made. At the end of IGCP 61, many national working groups had seen through to publication reports on the results of research carried out between 1974 and 1982 (see chapter 1). It was a useful opportunity to take stock of the achievements and advances in sea-level methodology, data analysis and geographical cover, to consider problems that had arisen, and to draw together a group of scientists to contribute chapters on aspects of sea-level changes at different geographical and temporal scales. The contributors are all associated with IGCP 200, and include the international project leader (P.A.P.), the secretary of the international working group (I.S.) and several national representatives of national working groups. Notwithstanding this commonality, each author has adopted his own approach within editorial guidelines in terms of geographical and temporal scale and of methodology.

The exploratory approach to sea-level data analysis, which holds out the most satisfactory route to correlation and which evolved during IGCP 61 and was applied during IGCP 200, has not been employed universally. Each regional chapter bears witness to this.

The chapters of the book are grouped together loosely at different geographical scales. At the local scale, the sedimentary record during the Holocene along coastlines about 40km long is considred for a tropical coast in the southern hemisphere and a temperate coast in the northern hemisphere: part of the coast of Rio de Janeiro state is described by Stephen Ireland and part of the coast of North-east Scotland by Andrew Haggart. Both authors critically apply the exploratory route of coastal evolution developed in the Fenland of England and North-west England, and consider the results in relation to coastal and sea-level changes in Brazil and Scotland respectively.

At a reduced level of geographical resolution, but over the same time period, Ian Shennan considers sea-level changes in the North Sea Region, providing a context for Andrew Haggart's work in North-east Scotland, and an application for the methodology outlined in *Shorelines and Isostasy*.

A further reduction in geographical resolution permits sea-level changes in the Mediterranean Sea to be reviewed by Paolo Pirazzoli. The whole of the Quaternary is considered, and special attention is given to marine deposits of the last interglacial age – the 'Tyrrhenian' – high sea levels during the last glaciation and sea-level changes during the Holocene. Recent sea-level trends from tide gauge records are also considered.

Yoko Ota and Hiroshi Machida describe sea-level changes in the tectonically active coast of Japan since the Bruhnes-Matuyama boundary, *c*.700 000 years ago.

Tom Cronin provides an historical and methodological perspective for a consideration of sea-level changes along the eastern seaboard of the United States of America, at a geographical scale comparable to that employed by

Yoko Ota and Hiroshi Machida, but for a shorter time period from *c*.140 000 years ago.

At a continental scale, Pierre Giresse and Lars-Erik Åse treat of the coasts of West and East Africa respectively, and John Chappell considers methodological and interpretational problems applied to the Australian region during the Late Quaternary.

Finally, at the scale of the world ocean, Niklas Mörner considers models of global sea-level changes, adopting an historical approach and Jim Clark and John Primus consider the prediction of future sea-level changes resulting from the retreat of the Antarctic ice sheet and the partial melting of the Greenland ice sheet arising from the carbon dioxide warming of the atmosphere.

The essays are introduced by a chapter on sea-level studies, in which fundamental and strategic aspects of sea-level research are considered, and the contribution to the sea-level investigations of INQUA, IGU, ICGP and IBG is critically reviewed. There is a concluding chapter in which current work on sea-level changes is reviewed, and an agenda for future research considered.

Invitations to contribute to the special publication were sent out to 23 potential authors in February 1983 from whom 15 contributors submitted single or joint-authored chapters. The initial deadline for the receipt of copy was October 1984 and a new deadline was occasioned by the transfer of the publication of the IBG *Special Publications Series* from Academic Press to Basil Blackwell. All the contributors were given the opportunity to revise their chapters, and the last revised chapter was received in July 1986. The editors have taken advantage of this to incorporate new material on strategic aspects of sea-level research that has been published during the past six months.

We should like to thank the contributors for their manuscripts and the referees for their valuable comments and observations. We are grateful to Professor Ian Simmons, Chairman of the Board of Studies in Geography, University of Durham, for allowing access to technical facilities in the Department of Geography to enable the typescripts and artwork to be produced. We are particularly grateful to Vicky Innes and Louise Shennan for assistance in the final stages of the preparation of the typescripts.

Michael J. Tooley
Ian Shennan
Durham

Acknowledgements

We are grateful for permission to reproduce the following figures:

Figure 5.2. M. F. Barlier, Centre d'Etudes de Recherches Géo-dynamique et Astronomique, Grasse, France.

Figure 5.3. Elsevier Scientific Publishing Company, Amsterdam.

Figure 5.4. The editor, *Quaternary Research*, Quaternary Research Centre, Seattle, Washington.

Figure 9.3. The editor, *Geografiska Annaler*, Stockholm.

Figure 9.5. The editor, *Geografiska Annaler*, Stockholm.

Figure 9.6. The editor, *Geografiska Annaler*, Stockholm.

Figure 9.7. The editor, *Geologischen Jahrbuches*, Hannover.

1

Sea-level studies

Michael J. Tooley

1.0 INTRODUCTION

Fundamental and strategic research have characterized sea-level investigations during the past 30 years, and strategic research has recently become particularly prominent since the interest shown in sea-level changes and prediction in the United States of America by the Environmental Protection Agency (Hoffman *et al.* 1983, Barth and Titus 1984). Prior to this, extreme events, such as the catastrophic storm surge in the North Sea in 1953, in which more than 1800 people lost their lives in the Netherlands (von Ufford 1953) and 307 in the United Kingdom (Steers 1953), resulted in fundamental research in two systematic areas: long term sea-level changes, particularly in subsiding areas in north-west Europe (e.g. Anon. 1954a,b, Dunham and Gray 1972, Jelgersma 1961), and the development of storm surge models and forecasting (Heaps 1967, 1983). In the tropics, except for advances in forecasting and the development of models of tide-surge interaction (for example, Johns *et al.* 1985), comparable studies have not followed the catastrophic storms there, which have been accompanied by much greater losses of life than in temperate latitudes. Losses of more than 200 000 lives in Bangladesh following the 1970 storm surge in the Bay of Bengal (Chowdhury 1977, Flierl and Robinson 1972, Frank and Husain 1971), and of more than 15 000 lives following the 1985 storm surge also in the Bay of Bengal (Maddox 1985), have been estimated. The magnitudes and effects of storm surges in the past have been well-documented in parts of Europe (for example on the North Sea coasts (Lamb 1980); in north-west England (Tooley 1978b, 1985); in the Netherlands (Gottschalk 1971, 1975, 1977)), and one of the most devastating sea floods recorded in Europe on 18 November 1421 in the Netherlands resulted in the death of an estimated 10 000 people (Jensen 1953a,b). Frank and Husain (1971) have listed the estimated number of deaths in the tropics associated with cyclones between 1780 and 1970. The link between long period secular sea-level changes and storm surges lies in the increased probability of damaging storm surges as sea-level rises: Rossiter (1962) showed for the British coasts that a rise of mean sea-level as little as 15 cm would double the probability of storm surges exceeding danger level on the east coast of England and treble the probability on the west coast.

Strategic or applied sea-level research is concerned, in the first instance, with projecting future secular sea-level rise or fall on the scale of decades and centuries, and evaluating the likely environmental impact on the areas that are expected to be affected both directly and indirectly. This requires, secondly, an exploration of the linkages between sea level and ice volumes, the concentration of carbon dioxide and other radiatively active gases in the atmosphere, and oceanic and atmospheric temperatures (Robin 1985). Thirdly, in a complementary investigation, the cumulative area that would be affected both directly and indirectly by incremental changes in sea level could be established from topographic maps and an assessment made of the social and economic consequences, particularly the effects on agriculture, biotic communities, drainage works, ground-water levels and water quality, low altitude dumping of wastes, water intakes and effluent outlets and sedimentary regimes. Fourthly, the redistribution of load from high latitude ice sheets to the ocean basins, continental shelves and newly transgressed land areas would set up stresses in the crust and mantle and initiate earth movements (Mörner 1979a, 1979b, 1980). A fifth effect on sea-level changes would be on the location of hypersaline ecosystems: biogeochemical cycles would be disrupted by movements of sea level, and the present-day location of mineral and hydrocarbon deposition associated with evaporation cycles and specialised biotic communities in coastal lagoons would be shifted (Krumbein 1985).

There is clearly a need, within strategic sea-level investigations, to consider the human response to sea-level change, in the past and in the future, and to evaluate ways in which sea-level movements could be managed. One route has recently been proposed by Newman and Fairbridge (1986) and further elaborated in *The Economist* (Anon. 1986): the projected rise of sea level could be countered by recharging aquifers, storing fresh water in reservoirs and flooding continental depressions with sea-water.

Such strategic studies rely on fundamental or academic research and the collection of basic data in the field is as imperative today as it was 30 years ago when Steers (1956), in his presidential address to the Institute of British Geographers, made a plea for more measurements of, *inter alia*, vertical movements that may be affecting our coasts and the possible results of a slow but continuous change of sea level. Fundamental research comprises the measurement of unequivocal sea-level index points throughout the Earth at different geographical and temporal scales in order to determine not only the direction, rate and magnitude of sea-level change, within homogeneous areas, but also the strength and behaviour of the crust and mantle. These processes have expression in terms of landforms and sediments, the mapping of which provides a spatial framework. There is a need to consider not only uplifted areas of Fennoscandinavia (Mörner 1969) and Laurentia (Andrews 1970), but also subsiding areas such as the Netherlands (Jelgersma 1961), and to consider them not in isolation, but together (for example, in Britain, this has been attempted recently by Shennan *et al.* (1983), and for the North Sea by Shennan (chapter 4, this volume). The data of sea-level studies can be increased significantly by considering archaeological evidence (Flemming 1979–80) and not restricting investigations to present land areas adjacent to the coast, but to the continental shelf seas, including the epicontinental shelf seas such as the North Sea, the Mediterranean and Beringia (Masters and Flemming 1983).

Fundamental research has been pursued along many routes, the results of which from the older literature have been very adequately reviewed by Daly (1929, 1934), Fairbridge (1961), Flint (1947, 1957), Mörner (chapter 11, this volume), West (1968), Wright (1914) and Zeuner (1959), and recent literature relating to sea-level changes during the past 10 000 years has been considered by Kidson (1982).

In the past 15 years, considerable advances have been made in systematic, methodological and geographical sea-level investigations at different time scales, fostered by learned societies, international organisations, *ad hoc* meetings of specialists and individual scientists. Of the international organisations, the International Association for Quaternary Research (INQUA) and the International Geographical Union (IGU) have promoted, through their commissions and subcommissions, interdisciplinary and collaborative work on sea-level and coastal changes for many years. Since 1974, two sea-level projects have run sequentially under the auspices of the International Geological Correlation Programme (IGCP), the principles and programme of which were agreed in 1968 as a joint Unesco/IUGS enterprise (Anon. 1972). The contribution of these organisations is considered as a context for a description and assessment of the effort made by the Institute of British Geographers to advance sea-level studies. Aspects of strategic sea-level research are considered in the final chapter on a conspectus of sea-level studies.

2.0   INQUA, IGU AND IGCP AND SEA-LEVEL STUDIES

INQUA and IGU, through their respective commissions and sub-commissions, have promoted studies on sea-level and coastal changes since their inception, but it was only in 1974, under the auspices of the IGCP, that a specific sea-level project was promulgated. The objectives of the commissions and of IGCP 61 and 200 have not been mutually exclusive, and the same scientists have often participated in all the projects. It is perhaps an over-simplification to conclude that the INQUA Commission on Quaternary Shorelines was concerned with changes of land and sea level around the world's coastlines, whereas the IGU Commissions and working group were concerned with the advance or retreat of coasts (Bird 1985b): the data are complementary, and the palaeographic maps of The Netherlands showing the distribution of tidal flat and lagoonal sediments are explained in terms of sea-level movements, coastal change, coastal landforms and sediment supply (Jelgersma 1961; Pons *et al*. 1963; Jelgersma *et al* 1979). In the succeeding sections, the objectives and achievements of each organisation are evaluated.

2.1   *International Union for Quaternary Research*

The INQUA Commission on Quaternary Shorelines was set up during the IV INQUA Congress in Rome in 1953, under the presidency of Professor A. C. Blanc. The commission had eight objectives, which were reiterated at the VII INQUA Congress in Boulder-Denver, Colorado, USA in 1965 (Richmond 1965). These were:

1   To establish the criteria for defining reference shorelines (maximum).
2   To determine and study those favourable and more stable shorelines where a sequence of such features occur.
3   To establish the number of shorelines between the Calabrian and Tyrrhenian in the most diverse settings and correlate them in different parts of the world.
4   To determine the minimum drop of sea level during the Würm.
5   To demonstrate the erosion stages after Tyrrhenian I.
6   To extend correlations to the coasts of Africa and the Indian Ocean.
7   To correlate between marine, fluvial and fluvio-glacial terraces.

8   To describe the stratigraphic alternation of marine and continental facies encountered in borings in coastal plains and deltas.

In order to prosecute these objectives, four regional subcommissions were set up in 1961 at the VI INQUA Congress in Warsaw, at which Professor R. W. Fairbridge became the president of the commission. A subcommission on Mediterranean and Black Sea Shorelines had been established at the V INQUA Congress in Madrid and Barcelona in 1957, and this was supplemented by four further subcommissions on Baltic and Scandinavian Shorelines, on Eurafrican-Atlantic Shorelines, on American Shorelines and on Pacific-Indian Ocean Shorelines. By the eleventh inter-congress period 1977–81, after the commission has been reconstituted at the X INQUA Congress in Birmingham, the area covered by two of the subcommissions had been altered: the subcommission on Baltic and Scandinavian Shorelines had been enlarged to encompass north-west Europe, and an African subcommission replaced the large Eurafrican-Atlantic Shorelines' subcommission. Each subcommission oversees a geographical area of different size and it could be posited that if the Mediterranean merits its own subcommission, the Arabian Sea, the Red Sea–Gulf of Aqaba–Gulf of Suez, and the Caribbean merit their own sub-commissions. Although the objectives of the Commission on Quaternary Shorelines have been clearly enunciated, rather surprisingly the principal objective has been given as the preparation of a world-wide Annotated Bibliography of Quaternary Shorelines (Fairbridge and Richards 1967). Whilst the five volumes of annotated bibliographies that have been published for each inter-congress period represent a major reference source, they disguise the fact that the commission's and subcommissions' works are more than clerkly. To this end, working groups of the commission have been established – in 1972, to produce a World Shorelines Map at the scale of 1:30 million and an atlas of regional shorelines; in 1977, on hydro-isostasy and on coastal management (Grant 1978). Jardine (1982) has described the activities of the INQUA subcommission on shorelines of northwestern Europe for inter-congress perid 11, 1977–82, and Streif (1985) has described one of the field conferences held at sites along the south-east coast of the North Sea in 1984 and part of the activities of inter-congress period 12, 1982–7.

2.2   International Geographical Union

The International Geographical Union, through two of its commissions and working groups, has had an interest in similar or related aspects of sea level, shorelines and coasts. The first commission for the study of littoral and fluvial terraces, particularly along the coasts of Western Europe and in the Mediterranean Basin was established at the second IGU Congress in Cambridge in 1926 (de Martonne 1950). By 1950 the chairman of the terrace commission was Henri Baulig, whilst Emm. de Martonne remained chairman of a commission on erosion surfaces. The history of and relationship between these two commissions have been described by Lefevre (1960). At the IGU Congress in Washington in 1950, the terrace commission was succeeded by a new commission for the study and correlation of erosion surfaces around the Atlantic chaired by Francis Ruellan of the University of Paris. The new commission was particularly concerned with erosion levels and planation surfaces. Erosion levels included peneplanes and marine shorelines connected with the sea or regulated directly by sea level. Planation surfaces, such as pediments and river terraces, were not connected directly with sea level. Correlation of surfaces across the Atlantic was an aim of the commission. Examples of levels and surfaces from each geological period were considered in groups the third of which comprised the marine shorelines of glaciated regions, as a category of erosional levels (Lougee 1955). Concurrently, at the 1952 Congress another new commission on coastal sedimentation had been instituted under the chairmanship of Axel Schou, and had as its aims the collection of data on sedimentation in coastal areas, the quantitative assessment of coastal changes and the dynamics of cliff shorelines (Schou 1954). The misleading name of the commission and the wide interest in coastal geomorphology, which included research on the post-glacial eustatic rise of sea level, led to a proposal to dissolve the commission on coastal sedimentation and replace it with a new commission (Schou and Steers 1960). This was effected at the Xth General Assembly in Stockholm in 1960, when the Commission on Coastal Geomorphology came into existence with terms of reference surprisingly redolent of those enunciated in 1952 (Anon. 1961). At the 1972 IGU Congress in Montreal, coastal studies lost their commission status, and a Working Group on the Dynamics of Shoreline Erosion was set up to compile data on the advance and recession of sandy shorelines in order to determine if there was evidence of increasing erosion around the world's coasts. Sectors of sandy shorelines which had prograded during the past 100 years and the reasons for their advancement were of particular interest (Anon. 1974). At the 1976 IGU Congress in Moscow, the working group evolved into the Commission on the Coastal Environment and was chaired by Eric Bird of the University of Melbourne. Work on five projects was prosecuted (Bird 1980):

1   changes in progress on sandy shorelines around the world;
2   dynamics of salt marshes and mangrove swamps;
3   effects of artificial structures on coasts;
4   recognition and delineation of coastal sites of scientific interest;
5   management of coastal dune systems.

During the subsequent inter-congress period, work on four projects was undertaken: coastal changes, the impact of man on coasts, man's response to coastal changes and coastal management. The results of eight years' collaborative research have been two seminal collations: one on coastal changes (Bird 1985a) and the second on the world's coastline (Bird and Schwartz 1985), realising in part one of Helmut Valentin's aspirations for a handbook on regional coastal geomorphology of the world (Schou, 1967, 1968).

Continuation of the Commission on the Coastal Environment was approved for another four years under the chairmanship of Roland Paskoff at the IGU Congress in Paris in 1984. The five projects to be pursued during the inter-congress period are: beach-dune system interactions, coastal lagoons, recreation use in coastal areas, coastal hazards and the nature and impact of national policies for coastal open space. In addition, working papers are to be prepared on sediment budget calculation, shore response to sea-level rise, human-induced effects on coral reef evolution, dynamics and morphological responses of coarse-clastic beaches, and cheniers (Psuty 1986).

The shift in emphasis from fundamental to strategic research that has characterised the evolving aims of the IGU Commissions that treat of the world's coastlines, was influential in the process leading to the establishment of the International Geological Correlation Programme (IGCP) and in determining its aims.

2.3   *International Geological Correlation Programme*

The IGCP was finally established in 1973 as a joint enterprise of Unesco and the International Union of Geological Sciences (IUGS). It was designed to encourage international research on geological problems (Reinemund and Watson 1983). Problems identified included desertification, environmental contamination and geological hazards, but there was concern that the scientific content of IGCP covering time and strateigraphy, major geological events in time and space, the distribution of mineral deposits and the processes of ore formation, and data processing in geological correlation, would be compromised (Bally and Hoover 1983, Martinsson 1973).

The development of the Earth during the Quaternary and sea-level changes in particular were identified as priority areas of the programme. A project on Holocene sea-level movements was amongst the first 20 projects, already approved by the International Union of Geological Societies (IUGS) and incorporated into IGCP (Martinsson 1973). Project 61, Holocene Sea-level Changes, represented a melding of two projects, one proposed in 1973 by Dr. J. C. Schofield of the New Zealand Geological Survey and the other proposed in 1974 by Dr. A. A. Thiadens of the Geological Survey of the Netherlands. The sea-level project was assigned key project status in 1974 and leading project status in 1977. The objectives of the project were to establish a graph of the trend of mean sea level during the last deglaciation and continuing to the present time. The graph would express the changing hydrologic balance between ice and water in response to climatic change, and individual records of relative sea-level movements in different parts of the world would permit conclusions about local crustal movements and the strength and elasticity of the Earth's outer layers (Martinsson 1974). In the project proposal of 1974, a further objective was the prediction of future trends of sea level, particularly in low-lying, densely populated coastal areas (Thiadens 1974, Bloom 1983). Project 61 ran from 1974 until 1982 with Professor A. L. Bloom of Cornell University as the international project leader, and by the final year of the project there were 30 participating countries with national representatives and working groups, of which nine were in developing countries (Hoover 1983). Two information bulletins, *Sea-level* and *Nivmer*, were circulated to more than 800 recipients once or twice each year. Bloom (1983) has summarised the achievements of IGCP 61. The first phase was the compilation of several thousand radiocarbon dates from coastal sites. Data capture was facilitated by the use of a sea-level documentation computer form for the collection of sample dates, three editions of which were produced by the working group of the Federal Republic of Germany, together with explanatory guidelines (Preuss 1979, van de Plassche and Preuss 1978, Tooley 1978a). By 1978, what was available comprised magnetic tape storage, line printer output of sea-level documentation lists, line printer plots and graphical displays on age-altitude graphs of raw data or selected and corrected data (Preuss 1979, Preuss and Streif 1979). The ability to display selected and corrected data taking into account consolidation, the indicative meaning of the sampled material in terms of water level, and the tendencies of sea-level change, promised that not only could large numbers of sea-level data be handled in a uniform and consistent way, but also the output of sea-level graphs would permit comparisons between and within areas and explanations of differences could be sought. Progress was hampered by both a poor return of completed computer forms and an uneven quality in the content of the forms. Of 2000 computer forms sent out initially, only 700 were returned (Preuss 1979), and in the UK it soon became clear that the process of data capture, verification, storage and retrieval far outstretched the available resources. The process of verification alone was formidable, and on the first trawl of computer forms, more than 18 per cent were rejected because of data defects (Tooley 1978c). Data capture and their display subsequently relied almost entirely upon the energy of Dr Ian Shennan, who with others at the University of Durham, using a simplified tabulated form assembled 782 data points ostensibly related to sea level from unpublished and published sources, such as *Radiocarbon*. Verification of each point led to the rejection of just under half the points, because they provided no evidence that they were related to sea level. The retained 374 dates were radiocarbon dates from peats showing some relationship to sea level and were displayed on maps of the UK, as frequency histograms showing the temporal pattern of dates and as cumulative frequency histograms showing positive and negative sea-level tendencies (Tooley 1978c, 1982a,b). These diagrams show the unevenness in space and time of sea-level index points in the UK (see also Flemming 1982), and this applies elsewhere, as the atlas of Holocene sea-level records in Japan (Ota *et al.* 1981) shows.

On a global scale compilation of published sea-level curves yielded an atlas (Bloom 1977, 1982) which revealed a similar unevenness of cover. The curves also lacked concurrence in age and altitude, and revealed considerable regional variations. Mörner (1971) had remarked regional variations and noted a convergence of eustatic sea-level graphs at about 7000 BP, which led him to the conclusion that the sea-level curve from the west coast of Sweden (Mörner 1969) was an expression of regional eustasy, later (Mörner 1976) ascribed to geoidal changes. It has been suggested (Tooley 1985) that lack of concurrence also arises from the failure to employ a unified methodology from which would arise an homogeneous data base.

Theoretical studies supported and reinforced the conclusion that eustasy was neither a valid concept nor a reality, except in the terms defined by Mörner (1976, 1980). Walcott (1972) demonstrated that because the Earth is not rigid, the addition of water to the world ocean during deglaciation did not produce a uniform global rise of sea level; for example, in the central Pacific Ocean, of an expected 127 m observed rise in sea level 27 m would be contributed by vertical displacement due to elastic deformation of the Earth. Clark (1980) and Clark *et al.* (1978)

showed that there was a non-uniform rise of sea level during deglaciation resulting from a deformation of the ocean floor and a distortion of the geoid caused by a redistribution of water and ice on the Earth's surface and a consequential redistribution of mass within the Earth. Clark *et al.* (1978) subdivided the world ocean into six zones characterized by a specific form of sea-level curve: in four zones emergence was predicted and in two zones submergence. The predicted sea-level histories were supported, to a certain extent, by empirical data.

It was inevitable that such considerations would lead to criticisms of the objectives of IGCP Project 61. At the International Geological Congress in Paris in 1980, it was concluded that 'we are no longer seeking to define a single globally-valid curve of sea-level variation. The new goal is to define the history of local or regional sea level. It is now clear that many local factors modulate the variation of global ocean volume' (Faure *et al.* 1980). This shift in emphasis, unremarked by some (e.g. Bloom 1983), vindicated Schofield's proposal, accepted by IUGS, to test whether or not Holocene sea-level changes had been the same throughout the world, rather than to establish a single graph of the trend of mean sea level for the whole world.

IGCP 61 was dominated by participants from the developed world and there were few tangible results in terms of technological transfer and the training of personnel from developing countries. Furthermore the aims of the project were perforce adjusted in the light of the growing body of empirical data from local studies in different parts of the world and the challenging theoretical studies. Nevertheless, the project drew together a large number of scientists from different disciplines and national working groups and stimulated research on a wide range of topics, the results of which were published towards the end of the project period. Much of the eastern coast of South America and the continental shelf off the South American coast was treated during the 1978 International Symposium on Coastal Evolution in the Quaternary in Sao Paulo (Suguio *et al.* 1979). The Quaternary history of the epicontinental seas of north-west Europe and their coasts was treated in three books (Kidson and Tooley 1977, Oele *et al.* 1979, Gudelis and Königsson 1979). National working groups stimulated the publication of essays on sea-level changes in national regions, such as Australia (Hopley 1983), the United Kingdom (Greensmith and Tooley 1982) and Japan (Fujii *et al.* 1982). The proceedings of symposia on aspects of sea-level changes were also published after meetings in Paris (*Nivmer* 1979–80) and Columbia, South Carolina (Colquhoun 1982).

IGCP 61 ended at the INQUA Congress in Moscow in 1982, and was succeeded in 1983 by project 200. Its aim was to identify and quantify the processes of sea-level change by producing detailed local histories that can be analysed and correlated for tectonic, climatic, tidal and oceanographic fluctuations (Pirazzoli 1985a). The ultimate aim is to provide a basis for prediction of near-future sea-level changes especially in densely populated low-lying areas (Hoover 1983). The international project leader is Dr P. A. Pirazzoli of CNRS-INTERGEO, Paris. Participation in Project 200 is wider than that in Project 61, eclipsing, numerically, participation in the INQUA and IGU commissions and subcommissions. By the end of 1985, there were 560 participants from 65 countries (Pirazzoli 1986), of which 25 were developing countries (Merriam 1985). The organisation of the project has been structured geographically and thematically: most of the world's coastline is covered and themes treated are data banks, physical models, tidal variations, shelf research, geoidal research, evolution of ice caps and glaciers, water-mass balance, ocean/climate changes and sea level, astronomical influences on sea level, neotectonics, human impact on sea level, evolution of coastal landforms and applied aspects of sea level. Notwithstanding the devolved functions and fissiparous tendencies, to achieve the aims of the project a series of co-ordinated and instructive field excursions and conferences have been held in Japan, France, Argentina, French Polynesia, Norway, Ireland, Senegal and Brazil and reported in Pirazzoli (1984, 1985b, 1986). Other meetings are to be held in Australia, Israel, China and Canada during the XII INQUA Congress in 1987, when IGCP 200 will terminate. In terms of publications, IGCP 200 took over from IGCP 61 the guidance to publication of the *Manual for sample collection and evaluation of sea-level data*, part of which appeared in draft form during the X INQUA in Birmingham, UK in 1977. The *Manual* (edited by O. van de Plassche) is designed to assist investigators in developing countries, and hence fulfils one of the main aims of the IGCP. Tangible evidence of the activities of IGCP 200 is the publication of the *Directory of Sea-level Research 1984* (Shennan and Pirazzoli 1984), and *IGCP 200 Newsletter and Annual Report 1986* (Shennan 1986).

Whilst it is premature to evaluate the results of IGCP 200, it is possible to conclude that both IGCP projects added a zest, vigour and geniality to sea-level investigations and collaborative research, out of proportion of the resources available, and that this collaborative research will long outlive both projects. It is unlikely that any individual or national group could have mounted and sustained an effort on the scale of these two projects, and research on the global and local scale has been stimulated by them.

Sea-level studies are a fertile area for fundamental and strategic reserach, and during the past twelve years have experienced a kind of *épanouissement*, from which other international organisations, such as INQUA and IGU, and national organisations, such as the IBG, will benefit from the wide participation now channelled in their direction.

3.0   THE INSTITUTE OF BRITISH GEOGRAPHERS AND SEA-LEVEL STUDIES

The Institute was founded in 1933, and an original or founder, and council, member was J. A. Steers (Steel 1984), whose interests in coastal physiography, coastline and sea-level changes, raised beaches, coral reefs and coastal planning (Steers 1929, 1933, 1934, 1939, 1944, 1946, 1964, 1973) created the right climate for the publication of studies on sea-level and coastal changes. One of the earliest *Transactions* of the Institute was the publication of four lectures given by Henri Baulig at the University of London in November 1933 and entitled *The Changing Sea Level* (Baulig 1935). A thousand copies were printed in 1935 and a reprinting was undertaken in 1956 (Steel 1961). Baulig (1877–1962) had been a student of Vidal de la Blache and had gone to the United States of America in 1905 and studied under W. M. Davis at Harvard. He introduced the ideas of W. M. Davis, G. K. Gilbert and D. W. Johnson to France and linked the ideas of erosional surfaces and eustatic sea-level changes to explain the surfaces in the Central Plateau of France. *The Changing Sea Level* is an exposition and development of these ideas, in which stratigraphic and palaeontological investigations of marine and terrestrial strata were considered, but were regarded as inferior as a basis for division and correlation to levels of erosion studied in geomorphology. Baulig (1935) followed Johnson (1933) in stressing the importance of establishing a link between shore features and a water plane, of the margin of error, exactly determined and explicitly stated, and of understanding contemporary shore processes to explain fossil features such as wave-cut platforms and barrier beaches and their relationship to a former sea level. It is not surprising that the study of erosion surfaces became a popular focus of geomorphological study in the United Kingdom, and for the anonymous writer of Baulig's obituary to write that 'the influence of (*The Changing Sea Level*) on the younger generation of British geomorphologists has been quite remarkable, and even today is not yet spent' (Anon. 1963). Four years after the publication of Baulig's lectures, two volumes of the *Transactions* were given over to the monograph by Wooldridge and Linton (1939) on *Structure, Surface and Drainage in South-east England*, and papers on erosion surfaces and denudation chronology appeared regularly in the *Transactions* until 1964 when Baulig's influence appears at last to have been 'spent'. Sixteen years later, Wooldridge and Linton's interpretations were re-evaluated and their simple model of landscape evolution in southern England, involving a mid-Tertiary Alpine folding phase, the evolution of a Mio-Pliocene peneplain and the effects of a widespread Plio-Pleistocene marine transgression, was replaced by alternative models of landform and drainage evolution (Jones 1980). Whilst interpretations may change, as new data emanating from the techniques of Quaternary Studies accumulate, any continuing interest in the papers on denudation chronology lies in the attention they gave to pre-Quaternary events, particularly marine transgressions of the Tertiary and earlier periods and the effects of these transgressions on sedimentary regimes and landforms. In this context, it is inviting to consider the implications of those rapid relative sea-level changes during the Phanerozoic described by Vail et al. (1977).

Baulig (1935) referred to stratigraphic and micropalaeontological investigations of marine and terrestrial sediments in *The Changing Sea Level* as a basis for correlation, but it was left to botanists such as von Post, Erdtman, Iversen and Godwin (1975, 1978, 1981; Godwin *et al.* 1933; see also Tooley 1986) to apply these techniques to sea-level studies. The first geographer to use such techniques was Frank Oldfield (1958) who contributed a valuable appendix in a paper, published in the *Transactions*, by R. K. Gresswell on the post-glacial raised beach in Furness and Lyth, North Morecambe Bay. Although this was followed by a few others (for example Oldfield 1960, Brooks 1972), sea-level studies were pursued indirectly through investigations of raised beaches, which were mapped and their altitudes measured. Borings through raised beach sediments were ostensibly undertaken to determine the nature of the buried topography and its genesis, not to determine the environments under which the sediments were laid down. The marine unit was best expressed as erosional remnants to be mapped and the altitude measured, confirming Baulig's conclusion that 'geomorphology seems to open more promising ways', 'erosional forms are as a rule much better indicators of long phases of stability than constructional forms . . . '.

In 1966, the Institute promoted a special number of the *Transactions* on *The vertical displacement of shorelines in Highland Britain*. Of the eleven papers, eight were concerned with erosional and depositional landforms determined largely by measurement and mapping, and two (Newey 1966, Ritchie 1966) with stratigraphic and micropalaeontological investigations of coastal lithology. In the next 20 years, papers on elevated shorelines in Scotland by J. B. Sissons or inspired by his seminal investigations appeared in the *Transactions* (Sissons 1966, 1969, 1972, 1982), although some problems of elevated shorelines in Scotland and the methodology of raised beach investigations were treated elsewhere (Sissons 1962, 1963). By 1982, geomorphological and biological techniques were combined to resolve problems of sea-level changes in north-east Scotland (Smith *et al*. 1982).

Whilst little work on coastal and sea-level changes in subsiding areas in Britain and elsewhere was published in the *Transactions* during this period and earlier (notable exceptions were Carr and Blackley 1973, Carr and Baker 1968, Nunn 1983) there was the occasional paper that directed attention to changes elsewhere in the world such as the east coast of the USA (Hails and Hoyt 1969), the Indian coast (Geddes 1960, Stoddart and Gopinadha Pillai 1972), the Malaysian coast (Carter 1959), the Australian coast (Hails 1968, Ollier 1979), the coast of Sierra Leone (Gregory 1962) and of British Honduras (Stoddart 1965).

About 6 per cent of all articles published in the *Transactions* between 1935 and 1985 treated some aspect of sea level (raised shorelines, coastal processes, denudation chronology) in Britain and abroad. For the 21-year period from 1961 to 1981, if the chapters of the two IBG special publications (Andrews 1970, Smith and Dawson 1983) are included, the proportion of sea-level papers increases to about 10 per cent, which is close to the average for British publications in research area F (Geochronological Studies 9.5 per cent) calculated by Embleton (1983) from entries in *Geoabstracts*. This proportion is not reflected in the research effort indicated in the British Geomorphological Research Group's 11 *Registers in Current Research in Geomorphology* 1963–79 from which Embleton (1983) had calculated that in 1979 about 35 per cent of research undertaken by members of the BGRG was on some aspect of coasts, glaciation, Quaternary studies and sea-level changes, for which publication outlets were found elsewhere. Embleton's data do show a sustained decline in research in these areas from a peak of *c*.70 per cent in 1968, and this continues into the 1980s, reflecting, in part, persistent underfunding.

The Institute, throughout its history, has promoted studies of sea-level change through its publications from Henri Baulig's collection of lectures on *The Changing Sea Level* in 1935 to the special number of the *Transactions* devoted to vertical displacement of shorelines in Highland Britain in 1966, and two numbers of the special publications – number 2 on *A geomorphological study of post-glacial uplift, with particular reference to Canada* (Andrews 1970) and number 16 *Shorelines and Isostasy* (Smith and Dawson 1983). The present volume continues this pattern of publications, and it is to be hoped that the Institute will continue to reflect research activity in sea-level and coastal changes, and vertical movements by sustaining its publications record.

4.0 CONCLUSIONS

Strategic research has succeeded fundamental research as the main contemporary thrust in sea-level investigations, and this is reflected in the change in emphasis of the objectives of IGCP Project 61 compared with IGCP Project 200. A similar shift is discernible in the IGU commissions and to a lesser extent in the INQUA commission, but has yet to find expression in the publications of the IBG. This change in emphasis reflects the development and function of a science.

Braithwaite (1953) argued that 'the function of a science . . . is to establish general laws covering the behaviour of the empirical events or objects with which the science in question is concerned, and thereby to enable us to connect together our knowledge of the separately known events, and to make reliable predictions of events . . . '. In sea-level investigations, no general laws have emerged and generalisations will have to suffice as the basis for prediction. Harvey (1969) identified two routes to scientific explanation. The first or 'Baconian' route proceeds from perceptual experiences to unordered facts, followed by definition, classification and measurement to ordered facts, inductive generalisation, laws and theory construction and thence to explanation. The second or alternative route again begins with perceptual experiences and thence to images of real world structures, *a priori* models, hypotheses, experimental design, facts and verification, at which point unsuccessful verification carries the route back to an earlier stage and successful verification to laws and theory construction that can be tested in the real world. Once tested, the route leads to explanation.

In sea-level investigations, during the past 50 years or so, several routes to explanation have been enunciated, but are now largely forgotten by contemporary investigators. Johnson (1933) proposed eight principles of marine level correlation at the IGU Congress in Paris and Gill (1967, 1971) described ten criteria for the description of Quaternary shorelines at the INQUA Congress also in Paris. Shennan (1983) has described the route taken by most sea-level investigators prior to 1980: the eight stages could be considered as a form of the 'Baconian' route of which there are many examples (Tooley 1978b, Devoy 1979). An increase in the number of reliable radiocarbon dates on Holocene marine episodes, standardised methods of empirical data collection and analysis, an overhaul of the nomenclature of sea-level studies, particularly the use of terms, sea-level index point, indicative meaning, tendencies of sea-level movement and transgressive and regressive overlap, encouraged Shennan (1983) to develop an alternative route to explanation in sea-level investigations. This route is sympathetic to the alternative route to general scientific explanation proposed by Harvey (1969), and has been successfully applied to within and between area correlations (e.g. Shennan *et al.* 1983). Correlations using heterogeneous data sets and different routes to explanation will be at best less robust and will at worst yield erroneous results. As these results serve as a basis for prediction, routes to explanation should be explicit and few in number. It is suggested that the model of sea-level research methods with explicit allowances for errors as elaborated by Shennan (1983), the computer form for sea-level document-ation (Preuss 1979) and the *Manual for sample collection and evaluation of sea-level data* (van de Plassche 1977, 1986) are used in conjunction to provide an homogeneous data base and subsequent analyses leading to explanation.

INQUA, IGU, IGCP and IBG have fulfilled a crucial catalytic role of providing the opportunities for collaborative, imaginative and innovatory research into many aspects of coastal and sea-level changes, both nationally and internationally, through working groups, commissions and publications. At the same time, individual effort has not been trammelled: in several countries, inspiring research has been undertaken individually and independently, overtaking and eclipsing research pursued under the aegis of national and regional commissions, committees and working groups, and effecting radical changes in both emphasis and direction. It is to be hoped that research on fundamental and strategic aspects of sea level will continue to be prosecuted by all scientists working individually or within the institutionalised framework of INQUA, IGU, IGCP and IBG.

Revised typescript received 1986, July.

REFERENCES

Andrews, J. T. 1970: A geomorphological study of post-glacial uplift, with particular reference to Arctic Canada. *Institute of British Geographers Special Publication*, no. 2: xxi + 1–56, London.
Anon. 1954a: *Report of departmental committee on coastal flooding*. Cmd 9165. London: HMSO.
Anon, 1954b: Quaternary changes in level, especially in the Netherlands. *Geol. Mijnbouw*, 16, 147–267.
Anon. 1961: Commission on coastal geomorphology. *The IGU Newsletter* 12 (17), 43–4.

Anon. 1963: Obituary – Henri Baulig. *Trans. Inst. Br. Geogr.* 33, vii–ix.

Anon. 1972: *Final Report Intergovernmental Conference of experts for preparing an International Geological Correlation Programme (IGCP)*, Paris 19–28 October 1971. Paris: Unesco.

Anon. 1974: Reports of Working Groups. Dynamics of Shoreline Erosion. *IGU Bulletin*, 25 (1), 11.

Anon. 1986: Sea level: rolling back the waves. *The Economist*, 299, 92.

Bally, A. W. and Hoover, L. (eds) 1983: Science, Resources and Developing Nations: a review and a look into the future 1978–1982. *Geological Correlation Special Issue*. Paris: IGCP/Unesco.

Barth, M. C. and Titus, J. G. (eds) 1984: *Greenhouse Effect and Sea Level Rise: a challenge for this generation*. New York: Van Nostrand Reinhold Company Inc.

Baulig, H. 1935: The Changing Sea Level. *Institute of British Geographers. Publication* 3, 1–46.

Bird, E. C. F. 1980: Coastal environment. *IGU Bulletin*, 31 (1–2), 42–4.

Bird, E. C. F. 1985a: *Coastline Changes: a global review*. Chichester: John Wiley and Sons.

Bird, E. C. F. 1985b: The study of coastline changes. *Z. Geomorph. Suppl.*, 57, 1–9.

Bird, E. C. F. and Schwartz, M. L. (eds) 1985: *The World's Coastline*. New York: Van Nostrand Reinhold Company Inc.

Bloom, A. L. 1977: *Atlas of Sea-level Curves*. ICGP Project 61. Ithaca, New York: Cornell University.

Bloom, A. L. 1982: Atlas of Sea-level Curves: Supplement. IGCP Project 61, unpublished typescript.

Bloom, A. L. 1983: Sea-level movements during the last deglacial hemicycle: Project 61 in Science, Resources and Developing Nations: a review and a look into the future 1978–1982. *Geological Correlation Special Issue*, Paris: IGCP/Unesco, 98–100.

Braithwaite, R. B. 1953: *Scientific Explanation: a study of the function of theory, probability and law in science*. Cambridge: Cambridge Univerity Press.

Brooks, C. L. 1972: Pollen analysis and the Main Buried Beach in the western part of the Forth valley. *Trans. Inst. Br. Geogr.*, 55, 161–70.

Carr, A. P. and Baker, R. E. 1968: Orford, Suffolk: evidence for the evolution of the area during the Quaternary. *Trans. Inst. Br. Geogr.*, 45, 107–23.

Carr, A.P. and Blackley, M. W. L. 1973: Investigations bearing on the age and development of Chesil Beach, Dorset. *Trans. Inst. Br. Geogr.*, 58, 99–111.

Carter, J. 1959: Mangrove succession and coastal change in south-west Malaya. *Trans. Inst. Br. Geogr.*, 26, 79–88.

Chowdhury, A. M. 1977: Storms in Bangladesh. In *Space and Atmospheric Research Centre*. Bangladesh Atomic Energy Commission: Dacca, 1–19.

Clark, J. A. 1980: A numerical model of worldwide sea-level changes in a viscoelastic earth. In N.-A. Mörner (ed.), *Earth Rheology, Isostasy and Eustasy*, Chichester: John Wiley and Sons, 525–34.

Clark, J. A., Farrell, W. E. and Peltier, W. R. 1978: Global changes in postglacial sea level: a numerical calculation. *Quat. Res.*, 9, 265–87.

Colquhoun, D. J. (ed.) 1982: *Holocene Sea-level Fluctuations, Magnitude and Causes*. Columbia, SC: University of South Carolina.

Daly, R. A. 1929: Swinging sea level of the ice age. *Bull. Geol. Soc. Am.*, 40, 21–34.

Daly, R. A. 1934: *The Changing World of the Ice Age*. New Haven: Yale University Press.

Devoy, R. J. N. 1979: Flandrian sea-level changes and vegetational history of the lower Thames estuary. *Phil. Trans. R. Soc. Lond.*, B 285, 355–407.

Dunham, K. C. and Gray, D. A. 1972: A discussion on problems associated with the subsidence of south-eastern England. *Phil. Trans. R. Soc. Lond.*, A 272, 79–224.

Embleton, C. 1983: 21 years of British Geomorphology. *Progr. Phys. Geogr.*, 7, 361–83.

Fairbridge, R. W. 1961: Eustatic changes in sea level. in L. H. Ahrens *et al.* (eds), *Physics and Chemistry of the Earth* 4. London: Pergamon Press, 99–185.

Fairbridge, R. W. and Richards, H. G. 1967: The INQUA Shorelines Commission. *Z. Geomorph.*, 11, 205–15.

Faure, H. *et al.* 1980: Scientific report: INQUA mid-congress symposia-meeting. *Striolae*, 1980: 3, 5.

Flemming, N. C. 1979–80: Archaeological indicators of sea level. *Oceanis*, 5, 149–65.

Flemming, N. C. (1982) Multiple regression analysis of earth movements and eustatic sea-level change in the United Kingdom in the past 9000 years. *Proc. Geol. Ass.*, 93, 113–25.

Flierl, G. R. and Robinson, A. R. 1972: Deadly surges in the Bay of Bengal, dynamics and storm tide table. *Nature*, 239, 213–5.

Flint, R. F. 1947: *Glacial geology and the Pleistocene epoch*. New York: John Wiley and Sons, Inc.

Flint, R. F. 1957: *Glacial and Pleistocene geology*. New York: John Wiley and Sons, Inc.

Frank, N. L. and Husain, S. A. 1971: The deadliest tropical cyclone in history? *Bull. Am. Met. Soc.* 52, 438–44.

Fujii, S. *et al.* (eds) 1982: Sea-level changes since the Late Pleistocene in the Japanese Islands and the related problems. *Quat. Res.*, 21, 129–287.

Geddes, A. 1960: The alluvial morphology of the Indo-Gangetic Plain: its mapping and geographical significance. *Trans. Inst. Br. Geogr.*, 28, 253–76.

Gill, E. D. 1967: Criteria for the description of Quaternary shorelines. *Quaternaria*, 9, 237–43.

Gill, E. D. 1971: The Paris symposium on world sea levels of the past 11 000 years. *Quaternaria*, 14, 1–15.

Godwin, H. 1975: *The History of the British Flora: a factual basis for phytogeography*. Cambridge: Cambridge University Press.

Godwin, H. 1978: *Fenland: its ancient past and uncertain future*. Cambridge: Cambridge University Press.

Godwin, H. 1981: *The Archives of the Peat Bogs*. Cambridge: Cambridge University Press.

Godwin, H., Godwin, M. E. and Edmunds, F. H. 1933: Pollen analyses of Fenland peats at St Germans, near King's Lynn. *Geol. Mag.*, 70, 168–80.

Gottschalk, M. K. E. 1971: *Stormvloeden en rivieroverstromingen in Nederland: Deel I – De periode voor 1400*. Assen: van Gorcum.

Gottschalk, M. K. E. 1975: *Stormvloeden en rivieroverstromingen in Nederland: Deel II – De periode 1400–1600*. Assen: van Gorcum.

Gottschalk, M. K. E. 1977: *Stormvloeden en rivieroverstromingen in Nederland: Deel III – De periode 1600–1700*. Assen: van Gorcum.

Grant, D. R. (ed.) 1978: INQUA Commission on Quaternary Shorelines. *Newsletter, 11* (2), 1–8.

Greensmith, J. T. and Tooley, M. J. (eds) 1982: IGCP Project 61. Sea-level movements during the last deglacial hemicycle (about 15 000 years). Final report of the UK Working Group. *Proc. Geol. Ass.* 93, 1–125.

Gregory, S. 1962: The raised beaches of the peninsula area of Sierra Leone. *Trans. Inst. Br. Geogr.*, 31, 15–22.

Gudelis, V. and Königsson, L.-K. (eds) 1979: The Quaternary history of the Baltic. *Acta Univ. Ups. Symp. Univ. Ups. Annum Quingentesimum Celebrantis –* 1. Uppsala.

Hails, J. R. 1968: The Late Quaternary history of part of the mid-north coast, New South Wales, Australia. *Trans. Inst. Br. Geogr.*, 44, 133–49.

Hails, J. R. and Hoyt, J. H. 1969: An appraisal of the evolution of the Lower Atlantic Coastal Plain of Georgia, USA. *Trans. Inst. Br. Geogr.*, 46, 53–68.

Harvey, D. 1969: *Explanation in Geography*. London: Edward Arnold.

Heaps, N. S. 1967: Storm surges. In H. Barnes (ed.), *Oceanography and Marine Biology Annual Review* 5. London: Allen and Unwin, 11–47.

Heaps, N. S. 1983: Storm surges, 1967–1982. *Geophys. J.R. Astr. Soc.*, 74, 331–76.

Hoffman, J. S., Keyes, D. and Titus, J. G. 1983: *Projecting future sea level rise: methodology, estimates to the year 2100, and research needs*.Washington: US Environmental Protection Agency.

Hoover, L. (ed.) 1983: Participation in IGCP Projects (1982). *Geological Correlation*, 11, 54–61.

Hopley, D. (ed.) 1983: Australian sea levels in the last 15 000 years: a review. *James Cook University of North Queensland, Department of Geography, Occasional Paper 3*.

Jardine, W. G. 1982: The INQUA Subcommission on Shorelines of Northwestern Europe, 1977–1982. *Ann. Acad. Sci. Fennicae* AIII, 134, 5–12.

Jelgersma, S. 1961: Holocene sea-level changes in The Netherlands. *Meded. Geol. Sticht.* Serie C, VI, 7, 1–100.

Jelgersma, S., Oele, E. and Wiggers, A. J. 1979: Depositional history and coastal development in the Netherlands and the adjacent North Sea since the Eemian. In E. Oele, R. T. E. Schüttenhelm and A. J. Wiggers (eds). The Quaternary history of the North Sea. *Acta Univ. Ups. Symp. Univ. Ups. Annum Quingentesimum Celebrantis* 2. Uppsala, 115–42.

Jensen, H. A. P. 1953a: Tidal inundations past and present. Part I. *Weather*, 8, 85–9.

Jensen, H. A. P. 1953b: Tidal inundations past and present. Part II. *Weather*, 8, 108–113.

Johns, B., Raw, A. D., Dube, S. K. and Sinha, P. C. 1985: Numerical modelling of the tide-surge interaction in the Bay of Bengal. *Phil. Trans. R. Soc. Lond.*, A. 313, 507–35.

Johnson, D. W. 1933: The correlation of ancient marine levels. *Union Geographique International de Geographie*, Paris 1931. 2:1, 42–54.

Jones, D. K. C. (ed.) 1980: The shaping of Southern England. *Institute of British Geographers Special Publication*, no. 11: x + 1–274. London: Academic Press.

Kidson, C. 1982: Sea-level changes in the Holocene. *Quat. Sci. Rev.*, 1, 121–51.

Kidson, C. and Tooley, M. J. (eds) 1977: *The Quaternary History of the Irish Sea. Geological Journal Special Issue* No. 7. Liverpool: Seel House Press.

Krumbein, W. E. 1985: Applied and economic aspects of sabkha systems – genesis of salt, ore and hydrocarbon deposits and biotechnology. In G. M. Friedman and W. E. Krumbein (eds), *Hypersaline Ecosystems: the Gavish Sabkha*, Berlin: Springer-Verlag, 426–36.

Lamb, H. H. 1980: Climatic fluctuations in historical times and their connection with transgressions of the sea, storm floods and other coastal changes. In A. Verhulst and M. K. E. Gottschalk (eds), Transgressies en occupatie-geschiedenis in de Kustgebieden van Nederland en België, *Belgisches Centrum voor Landelijke Geschiedenis*, Pub. No. 66, 251–84.

Lefevre, M. A. 1960: Niveaux d'erosion. Les faits et leur intrepetation. *Bull. Société Belge d'Etudes Géographiques*, 29, 21–46.

Lougee, R. J. 1955: Commission for the study and correlation of erosion surfaces around the Atlantic. *The IGU Newsletter: Bulletin of the International Geographical Union*, 6, 10–12.

Maddox, J. 1985: Avoiding recurrent catastrophes. *Nature*, 315, 453.

Martinsson, A. (ed.) 1973: Final report of the first session of the IGCP Board. *Geological Correlation*, 1, 17–27.

Martinsson, A. (ed.) 1974: Details of accepted or pending projects. *Geological Correlation*, 2, 19–27.

de Martonne, E. 1950: Brief history of the International Geographical Union. *The IGU Newsletter: Bulletin of the International Geographical Union* 1, 3–5.

Masters, P. M. and Flemming, N. C. (eds) 1983: *Quaternary Coastlines and Marine Archaeology: towards the prehistory of land bridges and continental shelves*. London: Academic Press.

Merriam, D. F. (ed.) 1985: Participation in IGCP Projects: 1983–1984. *Geological Correlation*, 13, 79–89.

Mörner, N.-A. 1969: The Late Quaternary history of the Kattegatt Sea and the Swedish West coast. *Sver. geol. Unders. Afh.* Serie C., 640, 1–487.

Mörner, N.-A. 1971: The Holocene eustatic sea-level problem. *Geol. Mijnbouw*, 50, 699–702.

Mörner, N.-A. 1976: Eustasy and geoid changes. *J. Geol.*, 84, 123–51.

Mörner, N.-A. 1979a: Earth movements in Sweden, 20 000 BP to 20 000 AP. *Geol. För. Stockh. Förh.*, 100, 279–86.

Mörner, N.-A. 1979b: The Fennoscandian uplift and Late Cenozoic geodynamics: geological evidence. *Geojournal*, 3, 287–318.

Mörner, N.-A. 1980: Eustasy and geoid changes as a function of core/mantle changes. In N.-A. Mörner (ed.), *Earth rheology, Isostasy and Eustasy*, Chichester: John Wiley and Sons, 533–53.

Newey, W. 1966: Pollen-analysis of sub-Carse peats of the Forth valley. *Trans. Inst. Br. Geogr.*, 39, 53–9.

Newman, W. S. and Fairbridge, R. W. 1986: The management of sea-level rise. *Nature*, 320, 319–21.

Nivmer 1979–80: Les Indicateurs de Niveaux Marins, *Oceanis*, 5, 145–360.

Nunn, P. D. 1983: The development of the River Thames in Central London during the Flandrian. *Trans. Inst. Br. Geogr.*, 8, 187–213.

Oele, E., Shüttenhelm, R. T. E. and Wiggers, A. J. (eds) 1979: The Quaternary History of the North Sea. *Acta Univ. Ups. Symp. Univ. Ups. Annum Quingentesimum Celebrantis* 2. Uppsala.

Oldfield, F. 1958: Technical data relating to the pollen analysis. In R. K. Gresswell, 1958: The post-glacial raised beach in Furness and Lyth, North Morecambe Bay. *Trans. Inst. Br. Geogr.*, 25, App. 1, 98–102.

Oldfield, F. 1960: Late Quaternary changes in climate, vegetation and sea level in Lowland Lonsdale. *Trans. Inst. Br. Geogr.*, 28, 99–117.

Ollier, C. D. 1979: Evolutionary geomorphology of Australia and Papua–New Guinea. *Trans. Inst. Br. Geogr.*, 4, 516–39.

Ota, Y., Matsushima, Y. and Moriwaki, H. 1981: *Atlas of Holocene Sea-level Records in Japan*. Japanese Working Group ICGP Project 61. Yokohama: Yokohama National University.

Pirazzoli, P. A. 1984: No. 200. Sea-level correlation and applications. *Geological Correlation*, 12, 51.

Pirazzoli, P. A. 1985a: Sea-level Change. *Nature and Resources* 21, 2–9.

Pirazzoli, P. A. 1985b: No. 200. Sea-level correlation and applications. *Geological Correlation*, 13, 51–2.

Pirazzoli, P. A. 1986: Annual Administrative Report. In Shennan I. 1986, 16–21.

Plassche, O. van de 1977: A manual for sample collection and evaluation of sea level data. Amsterdam: Institute for Earth Sciences, Free University, unpublished manuscript.

Plassche, O. van de (ed.) 1986 *Sea-level research: A manual for the collection and evaluation of data*. Norwich: Geo Books.

Plassche, O. van de and Preuss, H. 1978: Explanatory guidelines for completion of the computer form for sample documentation. Amsterdam/Hannover: IGCP 61, Unpublished typescript.

Pons, L. J., Jelgersma, J., Wiggers, A. J. and de Jong, J. D. 1963: Evolution of the Netherlands coastal area during the Holocene. *Verh. K. ned. geol. mijn. Genout.*, 21–2, 197–208.

Preuss, H. 1979: Progress in computer evaluation of sea-level data within the IGCP Project No. 61. In K. Suguio, T. R. Fairchild, L. Martin and J. M. Flexor (eds), *Proc. 1978 International Symposium on Coastal Evolution in the Quaternary*, Brasil: São Paulo, 104–34.

Preuss, H. and Streif, H. 1979: Report on the sea-level investigations in the Federal Republic of Germany. *Sea-level: information bulletin of IGCP Project No. 61*, 1, 15–16.

Psuty, N. P. 1986: The Commission on the coastal environment (1984–1988). *IGU Commission on the Coastal Environment Newsletter*, 20, 3–5.

Reinemund, J. A. and Watson, J. V. 1983: Updated excerpts from 'Achievements of the International Geological Correlation Programme as related to human needs'. In Bally, A. W. and Hoover, L. (eds) 1983, 9–11.

Richmond, G. M. (ed.) 1965: Report of the VII INQUA Congress, Boulder-Denver, Colorado, USA. *Proceedings of the VII INQUA Congress*, 24, 1–98.

Ritchie, W. 1966: The post-glacial rise in sea level and coastal changs in the Uists. *Trans. Inst. Br. Geogr.*, 39, 79–86.

Robin, G. de Q. 1985: Changing the sea level. In *Conference Statement: International Assessment of the Role of Carbon Dioxide and the Greenhouse Gases in Climate Variations and Associated Impacts*, Villach, Austria: UNEP, ICSU, WMO, ch. 7.

Rossiter, J. R. 1962: Long-term variations in sea level. In N. M. Hill (ed.), *The Sea* 1, London: Interscience Publishers, 590–610.

Schou, A. 1954: Commission on coastal sedimentation. *The IGU Newsletter: Bulletin of the International Geographical Union*, 5, 9.

Schou, A. 1967: Commission on coastal geomorphology. *The IGU Newsletter: Le Bulletin de Nouvelles de l'UGI*, 18, 43–5.

Schou, A. 1968: Commission on coastal geomorphology. *The IGU Newsletter: Le Bulletin de Nouvelles de l'UGI*, 19, 48–53.

Schou, A. and Steers, J. A. 1960: Commission on coastal sedimentation. *The IGU Newsletter: Le Bulletin de Nouvelles de l'UGI* 11, 34–7.

Shennan, I. 1983: Flandrian and Late Devensian sea-level changes and crustal movements in England and Wales. In D. E. Smith and A. G. Dawson (eds), Shorelines and Isostasy, *Institute of British Geographers Special Publication*, no. 16, London: Academic Press.

Shennan, I. (ed.) 1986: IGCP Project 200. Late Quaternary sea-level changes: measurement, correlation and future applications. *Newsletter and Annual Report*. Durham: Department of Geography; University of Durham.

Shennan, I. and Pirazzoli, P. A. (eds) 1984: *Directory of Sea-level Research, 1984*. Durham: Department of Geography, University of Durham.

Shennan, I., Tooley, M. J., Davis, M. J. and Haggart, B. A. 1983: Analysis and interpretation of Holocene sea-level data. *Nature*, 302, 404–6.

Sissons, J. B. 1962: A re-interpretation of the literature of Late-glacial shorelines in Scotland with particular reference to the Forth area. *Trans. Edin. Geol. Soc.*, 19, 83–99.

Sissons, J. B. 1963: Scottish raised shoreline heights with particular reference to the Forth valley. *Geografisker Annaler* 45, 180–5.

Sissons, J. B. 1966: Relative sea-level changes between 10 300 and 8 300 BP in part of the Carse of Stirling. *Trans. Inst. Br. Geogr.*, 39, 19–29.

Sissons, J. B. 1969: Drift stratigraphy and buried morphological features in the Grangemouth–Falkirk area, Central Scotland. *Trans. Inst. Br. Geogr.*, 48, 19–50.

Sissons, J. B. 1972: Dislocation and non-uniform uplift of raised shorelines in the western part of the Forth valley. *Trans. Inst. Br. Geogr.*, 55, 145–59.

Sissons, J. B. 1982: The so-called high interglacial rock shoreline of Western Scotland, *Trans. Inst. Br. Geogr.*, 7, 205–16.

Smith, D. E., Cullingford, R. A. and Seymour, W. P. 1982: Flandrian relative sea-level changes in the Philorth Valley, north-east Scotland. *Trans. Inst. Br. Geogr.*, 7, 321–36.

Smith, D. E. and Dawson, A. G. 1983: Shorelines and Isostasy. *Institute of British Geographers Special Publication* no. 16. London: Academic Press.

Steel, R. W. 1961: A review of IBG Publications, 1946–60. *Trans. Inst. Br. Geogr.*, 29, 129–47.

Steel, R. W. 1984: *The IBG: the first 50 years*. London: Institute of British Geographers.

Steers, J. A. 1929: The Queensland coast and the Great Barrier Reefs. *Geogr. J.*, 74, 232–57, 341–67.

Steers, J. A. 1933: Evidences of recent movements of sea level on the Queensland coast: raised benches and the coral reef problem. *Comptes Rendus du Congrès International de Géographie, Paris 1931*, 2, 164–73.

Steers, J. A. (ed.) 1934: *Scolt Head Island: the story of its origin, the plant and animal life of the dunes and marshes*. Cambridge: Heffer and Son.

Steers, J. A. 1939: The nature of coastal changes. *Geogr. J.*, 93, 399–408.

Steers, J. A. 1944: Coastal preservation and planning. *Geogr. J.*, 104, 7–18.

Steers, J. A. 1946: Coastal preservation and planning. *Geogr. J.*, 107, 57–60.

Steers, J. A. 1953: The East Coast floods January 31 – February 1 1953. *Geogr. J.*, 119, 280–95.

Steers, J. A. 1956: The coast as a field for geographical research. *Trans. Inst. Br. Geogr.*, 22, 1–13.

Steers, J. A. 1964: *The Coastline of England and Wales*. Cambridge: Cambridge University Press.

Steers, J. A. 1973: *The Coastline of Scotland*. Cambridge: Cambridge University Press.

Stoddart, D. R. 1965: British Honduras Cays and the low wooded island problem. *Trans. Inst. Br. Geogr.*, 36, 131–47.

Stoddart, D. R. and Gopinadha Pillai, G. S. 1972: Raised reefs of Ramanathapuram South India. *Trans. Inst. Br. Geogr.*, 56, 111–25.

Streif, H. 1985: Field conference 1984 of the INQUA Subcommission on Shorelines of Northwestern Europe, *Eiszeitalter u. Gegenwart*, 35, 1–4.

Suguio, K., Fairchild, T. R., Martin, L. and Flexor, J. M. (eds) 1979: *Proceedings of the 1978 International Symposium on Coastal Evolution in the Quaternary*. São Paulo, Brasil: Universidade de São Paulo, Instituto de Geociencias.

Thiadens, A. A. 1974: *IGCP Project Proposal Form. Sea-level Project*. Paris: IGCP/Unesco.

Tooley, M. J. 1978a: The Unesco-IGCP Project on Sea-level changes. *International Journal of Nautical Archaeology and Underwater Exploration*, 7, 75–7.

Tooley, M. J. 1978b: *Sea-level Changes: North-west England during the Flandrian Stage*. Oxford: Clarendon Press.

Tooley, M. J. 1978c: 61. Sea-level movements during the late deglacial hemicycle. In *United Kingdom contribution to the International Geological Correlation Programme, 1976–1978 Report*, London: The Royal Society, 66–70.

Tooley, M. J. 1982a: Introduction: IGCP Project No. 61 in the UK. *Proc. Geol. Ass.*, 93, 3–6.

Tooley, M. J. 1982b: 61. Sea-level movements during the last deglacial hemicycle. In *United Kingdom Contribution to the International Geological Correlation Programme. 1982 Report*, London: The Royal Society, 21–5.

Tooley, M. J. 1985: Climate, sea-level and coastal changes. In M. J. Tooley and G. M. Sheail (eds), *The Climatic Scene*, London: George Allen and Unwin, 206–34.

Tooley, M. J. 1986: Sea levels. *Progr. Phys. Geogr.*, 10 120–9.

Ufford, H. A. Q. von 1963: The disastrous storm surge of 1 February. *Weather*, 8, 116–20.

Vail, P. R., Mitchum, R. M. and Thompson, S. 1977: Seismic stratigraphy and global changes of sea level, Part 4: Global cycles of relative changes of sea level. In C. E. Payton (ed.), *Seismic stratigraphy – applications to hydrocarbon exploration. Am. Assoc. Petrol. Geol.*, Memoir 26, 83–97.

Walcott, R. I. 1972: Past sea levels, eustasy and deformation of the Earth, *Quat. Res.* 2, 1–14.

West, R. G. 1968: *Pleistocene Geology and Biology, with special reference to the British Isles*. London: Longmans.

Wooldridge, S. W. and Linton, D. 1939: *Structure, surface and drainage in south-east England*. London, Institute of British Geographers. *Transactions and Papers of the Institute of British Geographers, Publications* 9 and 10.

Wright, W. B. 1914: *The Quaternary Ice Age*. London: Macmillan.

Zeuner, F. E. 1959: *The Pleistocene Period: its climate, chronology and faunal successions*. London: Hutchinson.

2

The Holocene Sedimentary History of the Coastal Lagoons of Rio de Janeiro State, Brazil

Stephen Ireland

1.0 INTRODUCTION

The southern coastline of Rio de Janeiro State (figure 2.1) is characterized in the east by numerous lagoons separated by headlands and backed by steeply rising mountains of crystalline rocks, in the form of massifs and inselbergs, and in the west by the bays of Ilha Grande and Sepetiba. The eastern coast, north of Cabo Frio, has few lagoons and is characterized by the delta of the Rio de Paraibá do Sul and by the eastern extremity of the Guanabara Rift.

The crystalline basement, with its north-east to east-north-east trending structures, was completely consolidated early in the Brazilian Cycle (450–700 ma). Later in the same cycle, these structures were obliquely cut by a series of large transcurrent faults which have subsequently been reactivated and which have had an appreciable influence upon the configuration of the present coastline (Almeida 1976). This configuration is unusual because a large part of the coastline, between Ilha Grande Bay and Cabo Frio, has an east-west orientation, the only part of the Brazilian coast south of Cabo de São Roque (Rio Grande do Norte) so oriented.

Ruellan (1944) describing the littoral massifs, distinguished between those to the west of Guanabara Bay, which are relatively high (1024 m) and divided, and the lower, more continuous range which lies to the east. Together they form the elevated southern border of the Guanabara Rift. The rift is between 25 and 30 km wide and extends at least 200 km from Barra de São João in the east to Sepetiba Bay in the south-west and possibly includes Ilha Grande Bay. It probably formed in the Oligocene, but assumed its modern aspect in the Pliocene. The northern border of the rift is formed by the higher Serra do Mar range (2263 m) known

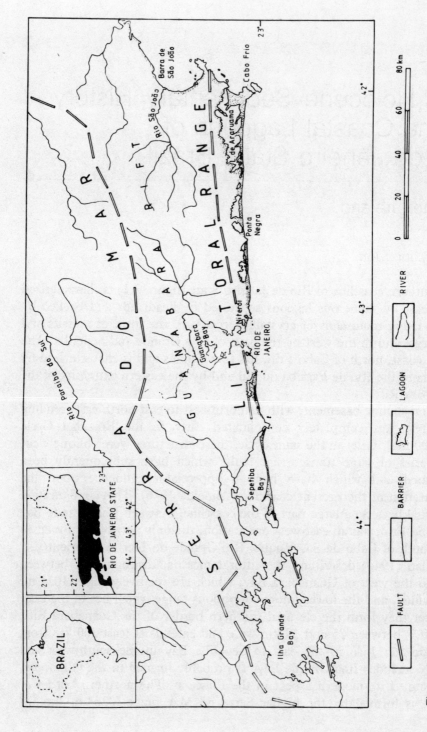

Figure 2.1 A map of the southern part of the State of Rio de Janeiro, Brazil, with inset maps of Brazil and the State of Rio de Janeiro

locally as the Serra dos Orgãos. This range slopes gradually northward into the valley of the Rio de Paraibá do Sul. The southern border of the rift is formed by the Littoral Range.

There are over 20 Holocene lagoons (*lagoas*) along the Rio de Janeiro coast, generally confined on the landward by the Littoral Range and pre-Holocene sedimentary sequences and on the seaward by barriers. In most cases, these barriers isolate the lagoons completely from the Atlantic Ocean, although some have narrow artificial openings. The salinity of the lagoons ranges from alpha mesohaline to metahaline (following Hedgepeth 1953; see table 2.2). There is a wide range of lagoon sizes. The smaller are little over 1 km^2 and have an average depth of $c.0.5$ m, whereas the largest is $c.200$ km^2 and has a mean depth of 3 metres. Such large lagoons are the exception, with only Lagoa de Araruáma and Lagoa Feia of this order. Some lagoons, like those in the Maricá and the Jacarepaguá systems (figure 2.2), are interconnected, forming larger water bodies. In the Maricá system there are five lagoons ranging in size from 1.2 km^2 to 18.4 km^2 with the system as a whole covering 40 km^2 and having a catchment of 270 km^2 (Oliviera *et al.* 1955). This compares with Lagoa de Rodrigo Freitas, a single lagoon, which has a surface area of 2.3 km^2 and a catchment of 20 km^2 (Britto and Lemos 1982).

The barriers (*restingas*) which isolate the lagoons from the sea are composed of quartz sand. There are single barriers, barriers formed by the merging of two, once distinct, barriers, and double barriers which are either separated by a narrow water body or simply divided by a linear depression. In some cases, such as in the Jacarepaguá area, an inner barrier is separated from an external barrier by a considerable distance and each confines a lagoon. There are marked differences in the altitudes of the barriers. Between Niterói and Ponta Negra, the maximum altitudes of the present-day barriers (single and merged) may vary between 4.0 and 10.0 m and the maximum altitudes of fossil barriers range from 7.0 to more than 12.0 m (Muehe 1982).

This coastline differs markedly from the coastlines of São Paulo and Bahia States which have been the subject of intensive sea-level studies. The São Paulo coast has no lagoons at present, but very extensive plains of pre-Holocene and Holocene sediments including lagoonal facies up to 50 m thick (Suguio and Martin 1978). In the north of the state, the Precambrian basement frequently reaches the sea, but south of São Sebastião Island there are extensive sedimentary plains, formed mostly of Quaternary marine and lagoonal deposits, separated by crystalline headlands. These deposits include the 900 km^2 of regressive marine sand designated the Cananéia Formation by Suguio and Petri (1973).

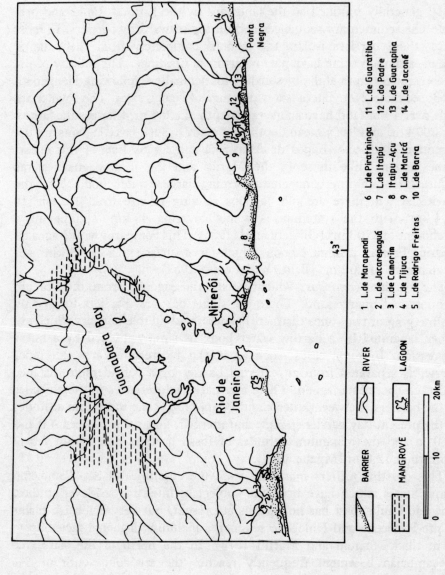

Figure 2.2 A map of the coastal lagoons bordering Guanabara Bay, State of Rio de Janeiro, Brazil

Guanabara Bay

Niterói

Rio de Janeiro

Ponta Negra

43°

| RIVER | | BARRIER |
| LAGOON | | MANGROVE |

1	L. de Marapendi	6	L. de Piratininga	11	L. de Guaratiba
2	L. de Jacarepaguá	7	L. do Itaipú	12	L. do Padre
3	L. de Camorim	8	Itaipu-Açu	13	L. de Guarapina
4	L. de Tijuca	9	L. de Maricá	14	L. de Jaconé
5	L. de Rodrigo Freitas	10	L. de Barra		

0   10   20km

Radiocarbon dating of fossil wood from this sediment (Suguic *et al.*, 1980) gave minimum ages of 30 000 and 35 000 BP.

Along much of Bahia State coast the crystalline basement is also separted from the ocean by sedimentary plains, but these are formed predominantly of Mesozoic and Tertiary sediments. Quaternary deposits occur along much of the coast, but are not continuous (Bittencourt *et al.* 1979): between Todos os Santos Bay and Itacaré, a coastal section characterised by a series of lagoons, islands and small bays, sandy terraces are well developed.

In this chapter, the Holocene sedimentary history of a number of lagoons, found along an homogeneous stretch of coastline between Niterói and Ponta Negra (figure 2.2) is discussed. The lagoons have developed in response to Holocene sea-level rise and have been influenced by fluctuations in sea level during this period. The sedimentary sequences in or around the lagoons thus reflect changes in sea level. These sea-level changes have, however, also influenced the relationship between lagoon level and sea level through their effect on barrier stability. This relationship and the way in which lagoonal sedimentary sequences can be interpreted will be considered.

Sedimentary sequences will be examined together with diatom analytical evidence and radiocarbon dates. This will permit the reconstruction of environmental changes in and around the lagoons. Sea-level movements during the past 7800 years will then be described using these data in conjunction with some of the published Brazilian sea-level index points. The evidence for high interstadial sea levels is also considered.

2.0 RESEARCH METHODOLOGY AND TECHNIQUES

The research methodology applied here is the product of many years of sea-level research in Europe, particularly in Scandinavia, The Netherlands, Britain and West Germany, and employs stratigraphic analyses, micro-palaeontological analyses particularly of pollen and diatoms, plane surveying and radiocarbon dating. It is continually evolving and being refined with notable contributions from Godwin (see Tooley 1986), Florin (1944), Jelgersma (1961), Tooley (1978, 1982), Streif (1979) and Shennan (1980, 1982a,b). The methodology has, however, not previously been applied in the tropics.

It is an inductive methodology, with the site (an area over which a single index point is believed to be representative, Shennan 1982a) forming the basic unit of analysis. Sites consisting of series of boreholes are examined using levelling, stratigraphic analysis and micropalaeon-

Table 2.1 Radiocarbon dates from sediments from the coastal lagoons of the State of Rio de Janeiro

No.	Site/Borehole	Coordinates	Material	Sample thickness (cm)	Altitude [top of sample] (m)	Laboratory code	^{14}C Age±1 σBP [BP=before 1950].
1	Lagoa do Padre 1/32	22°57'03'' S 42°45'22'' W	herbaceous peat	8.0	−2.39	KI-2222.01	6800±110
2	Lagoa do Padre 1/32	22°57'03'' S 42°45'22'' W	herbaceous peat	9.0	−2.61	KI-2222.02	7150±120
3	Lagoa do Padre 2/12	22°56'34'' S 42°46'54'' W	herbaceous peat	8.0	1.42	KI-2223.01	2270±55
4	Lagoa do Padre 2/12	22°56'34'' S 42°46'54'' W	herbaceous peat	9.0	1.04	KI-2223.02	2590±65
5	Lagoa do Padre 2/12	22°56'32'' S 42°46'54'' W	fine detritus mud with clay	6.0	0.39	KI-2373.01	4850±80
6	Lagoa do Padre 2/12	22°56'34'' S 42°46'54'' W	fine detritus mud with clay	8.0	0.04	KI-2373.02	5230±90
7	Itaipu-Açu 1/3	22°57'48'' S 42°54'20'' W	herbaceous peat	8.0	4.9	KI-2224	250±48
8	Itaipu-Açu 2/12	22°57'01'' S 42°59'44'' W	herbaceous peat	7.0	0.47	KI-2225.01	2460±55

9	Itaipu-Açu 2/12	22°57'01''S 42°59'44''W	herbaceous peat	7.0	0.37	KI-2225.02	2700±60
10	Itaipú 1/33	22°57'31''S 43°02'07''W	herbaceous peat	10.0	0.15	KI-2226.01	370±55
11	Itaipú 1/33	22°57'31''S 43°02'07''W	herbaceous peat	9.0	-1.51	KI-2226.02	7110±110
12	Itaipú 1/33	22°57'31''S 43°02'07''W	herbaceous peat	8.0	-1.73	KI-2226.03	7810±75
13	Itaipú 1/33	22°57'31''S 43°02'07''W	herbaceous peat	7.0	-3.51	KI-2226.04	35300 +3400 -2400
14	Itaipú 1/33	22°57'31''S 43°02'07''W	herbaceous peat	6.0	-4.08	KI-2226.05	T min=35400
15	Itaipú 1/33	22°57'31''S 43°02'07''W	herbaceous peat	5.0	-4.34	KI-2226.06	42500 +6000 -3400
16	Itaipú 1/33	22°57'31''S 43°02'07''W	herbaceous peat	17.0	-5.44	KI-2226.07	T min=38200

Table 2.2 Halobeous classification systems for diatoms (Adapted from Ehrlich 1975)

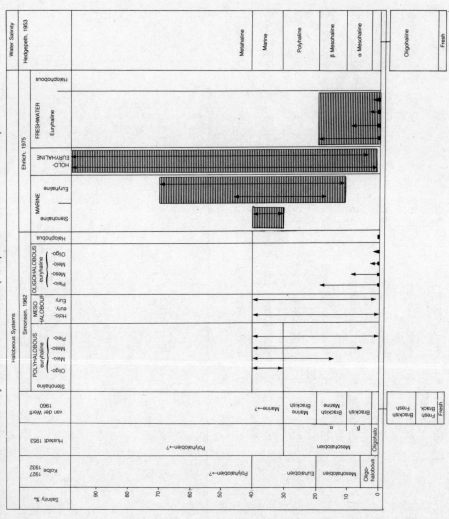

tological analyses in order to identify sea level index points and to determine tendencies of sea-level change. These are then compared between sites, areas (approximately the size of the present study area) and regions (approximately the size of Rio de Janeiro State) in an attempt to identify regionally significant sea-level changes.

The use of the terms regressive overlap and transgressive overlap follows Tooley (1982) and Shennan (1982a), indicative meaning follows van de Plassche (1977) and the concept of tendencies of sea-level movement follows Strief (1979) and Shennan (1980, 1982a).

The sites studied were selected following an extensive reconnaissance survey between Niterói and Ponta Negra. Sites of potential value were selected using engineering borehole records, aerial photographs and 1:50 000 scale topographic maps. Each site was then assessed using trial boreholes. The most promising sites were subsequently studied in detail.

The stratigraphy of the selected sites was analysed using a modified Eijkelkamp hand operated *puls* auger set. The sampling technique employed minimised sample contamination and extension rod curvature. Troels-Smith's (1955) scheme, modified according to Shennan (1980) and the author, was used to describe the sediment, but was not employed in the stratigraphic diagrams. On the completion of this analysis, representative cores were taken for use in laboratory analysis. All sites have been levelled to mean sea level at Imbituba, Santa Caterina which is the national altitudinal datum for Brazil.

The particle size distribution for one core from each site was determined and 25 samples of organic material were dated (table 2.1) at the Christian-Albrechts-Universität, Keil. Diatom analyses were carried out on at least one core from each site. The relative method, described by Berglund (1979), was used. Diatom nomenclature follows Cleve-Euler (1951–1955).

The allocation of species and varieties to salinity groups is central to the use of diatom analysis in the study and requires more detailed consideration. Field investigations have led to the production of several halobeous classification systems (table 2.2). The differences partly reflect the different study areas: van der Werff (1960) working in the Eems-Dollard Estuary (Dutch-German Waddensea), Simonsen (1962) working in the western Baltic and Ehrlich (1975) studying the Bardawil Lagoon (Northern Sinai). In addition, a few laboratory experiments, utilizing rate of photosynthesis and cell division rate as indicators of sensitivity to salinity variation, have been carried out over wide salinity ranges. Unfortunately, very few species have been studied (Williams (1964) used 14 species and Admiraal (1977) examined only six). The experimental results suggest broader ranges of salinity tolerance than those proposed by Kolbe (1927, 1932), Hustedt (1953) and van der Werff (1960).

The classifications of Simonsen (1962) and Ehrlich (1975) reflect both field investigation and theories developed largely as a consequence of laboratory experimentation. They remain, however, largely theoretical because only a small number of species has been classified according to these schemes. In contrast, many diatoms have been classified according to the systems of Hustedt (1953) and van der Werff (1960) and, as table 2.3 indicates, it is not simply a matter of redefining boundaries. Nevertheless, it is possible, as will be illustrated later, to use the schemes of Simonsen (1962) and Ehrlich (1975) to aid interpretation when another classification is used.

Van der Werff's (1960) classification has not been as widely adopted as the Hustedt system (although the 1953 system has not been used consistently), but it is applied here for two reasons of comparability, (a) because van der Werff's classification further subdivides the Hustedt (1953) system allowing summary diagrams to be produced for both classifications. This is important because sea-level studies have employed both systems; (b) because Oliviera *et al.* (1955) used Hedgepeth's (1953) classification for saline water in their study of the Maricá lagoon complex and van der Werff's (1960) classification relates closely to this (table 2.3).

When a species is only classified according to Hustedt (1953), it is attributed to the least saline class of the corresponding group in the van der Werff (1960) classification.

This is not an ideal classification and more work is required to permit the widespread adoption of a system similar to that of Ehrlich (1975), but incorporating freshwater species. It has not been shown categorically that the zonation observed by van der Werff (1960) in the Eems-Dollard Estuary is the result of the salinity gradient. Admiraal (1977) believes that other factors may govern the distribution and quotes Bakker and De Pauw (1974) who suggest turbulence is a major factor.

In Europe, pollen analysis has been used more frequently than diatom analysis in the application of this research methodology. Pollen analysis is used to indicate vegetational changes consequent upon water level and climatic changes and, most importantly, to provide an independent relative age determination. It is not clear whether pollen analysis can be used in a similar way in the lowland tropics.

Vegetation changes of coarse resolution, which are consequent upon sea-level changes have been identified from pollen analysis in South American coastal areas dominated by mangroves (van der Hammen 1963, 1974; Roeleveld 1969). Such changes have, however, yet to be identified

van der Werff (1960)	Ehrlich (1975)			
	Freshwater	Holoeuryhaline	Marine euryhaline	Marine stenohaline
FB	Coconeis placentula Fragilaria pinnata Gomphonema parvulum Melosira granulata Navicula cincta Pinnularia borealis	Nitzschia sigmoidea		
B	Cyclotella meneghiniana Navicula mutica	Nitzschia frustulum Nitzschia sigma	Nitzschia tribionella	
B		Amphora coffaeiformis Mastogloia braunii Mastogloia elliptica Rhopalodia gibberula	Achnanthes hauckiana Amphora holsatica Rhopalodia musculus	
BM			Achnanthes brevipes Nitzschia punctata Synedra tabulata	
MB			Amphiprora alata	
M			Amphora proteus Nitzschia granulata Opephora parva	Coscinodiscus lineatus Dimerogramma marinum Paralia sulcata Navicula lyra Navicula palpebralis

The diatoms used in this table are all found amongst the fossil assemblages examined in this study.

Table 2.3 A comparison of the classification of several species according to van der Werff (1960) and Ehrlich (1975)

in areas which lack mangrove swamp, but Tooley (1985) believes that the coastal vegetation succession in São Paulo and Rio de Janeiro States offers similar potential. In the tidal flat and lagoonal zone of the present study area, it is unclear what type of pollen succession would result from sea-level changes, because at present many of the lagoons are backed by cliffs or by inselbergs vegetated by rainforest, the marsh areas are relatively restricted with mangroves rarely present, and there is well developed barrier vegetation. Some preliminary work has been carried out by the author, but much remains to be done on the pollen taxonomy of coastal plant taxa and on pollen taphonomy.

A disadvantage of employing pollen analysis at present is that a chronology of regionally synchronous vegetation changes has not been established in Brazil. In order to provide such an independent age determination for Holocene sea-level movements, synchronous regional changes in the forest canopy must have occurred, at relatively frequent intervals during the present interglacial. Assuming that such changes have occurred, it may not be possible to identify them using pollen analysis because of problems of recognising the regional component of tropical pollen assemblages. Muller (1965) and Flenley (1973) found that lateral movement of pollen was restricted and that the assemblage was dominated by local trees. This factor coupled with relatively low pollen productivity and the fact that grains can frequently only be identified to family or generic level, suggests that the use of pollen analytical results to provide relative age determinations will not be possible.

The applicability of pollen analysis to tropical sea-level studies contrasts strongly with that of diatom analysis, which has proved to be extremely valuable. The only potential problem was the identification of valves to species level, especially in the case of freshwater forms. This, however, proved not to be problematical as many species are also found in temperate regions and, unlike pollen, tropical diatoms, including those of Brazil, have been relatively well studied.

3.0 HOLOCENE SEDIMENTARY HISTORY

The results of the stratigraphic, diatom and radiocarbon analyses in three coastal lagoons, Lagoa do Padre, Itaipu-Açu and Lagoa de Itaipú are described. The unconsolidated sediments along this coast have been considered to be entirely Holocene sequences. Muehe (1982) has suggested that 9 metres of sediment have been deposited in Lagoa de Itaipú since 5100 BP and that the sedimentary sequences at Itaipu-Açu were also entirely Holocene in age (Muehe, pers. comm.). However there is now clear evidence that pre-Holocene sedimentation has occurred in the areas now occupied by Holocene lagoons. This evidence will only be discussed in detail at Lagoa de Itaipú but will be considered generally as it provides a context for the onset of Holocene sedimentation.

3.1 Lagoa do Padre

Lagoa do Padre, a small lagoon of 1.2 km², is part of the large Maricá lagoonal system, which covers 40 km². Two sites were examined at this lagoon. Site 1 is located on marshland at the seaward side of the lagoon, immediately behind the coastal barrier. Thirty-two borings were put down here and showed that the sediments were the most heterogeneous of all the sites studied. Over most of the site sedimentation was predominantly inorganic, with organic deposits confined to within 1.5 m of the surface. There is, however, a small area of marsh in the south-east corner of the site, in which organic deposits are found at much greater depth.

The stratigraphy of a north-south transect across the widest part of the marsh, with boreholes at 80 m intervals (figure 2.3), shows that below −1.0 m altitude the strata range from predominantly clay to predominantly medium and coarse sand with fine and medium gravel. There are only traces of fine detritus mud, and in the case of LP-1/6, *Anomalocardia brasiliana* (Gmelin) shell fragments are present. Above −1.0 m altitude, organic deposits, either in the form of fine detritus mud or herbaceous peat dominate the sedimentary sequence. In some cases there is one peat stratum and in others there are two such strata. The boreholes with two peat strata (LP-1/3, 1/4 and 1/6) are located in the centre of the marsh. The predominantly organic strata are intercalated with fine grained inorganic deposits. Close to the barrier (LP-1/11 and 1/12) fine and medium sand dominate much of the stratigraphic column.

Borehole LP-1/10 is an exception, with fine detrital mud extending to −4.5 m altitude with *Anomalocardia brasiliana* (Gmelin) fragments to −3.7 m altitude. This is considered to be consequent upon its proximity to the Canal de Ligação which is dredged periodically.

In the southeast of the site, where a 20-metre sampling grid was employed, strata could be traced between six boreholes. On figure 2.4 the stratigraphic record from six boreholes, LP-1/23 to LP-1/28, running north-south and normal to the trend of the coastline, is shown. The area in which the stratigraphic record was taken is characterised by a small body of peat (2,280 m²), which has a mean recorded thickness of 17.6 cm

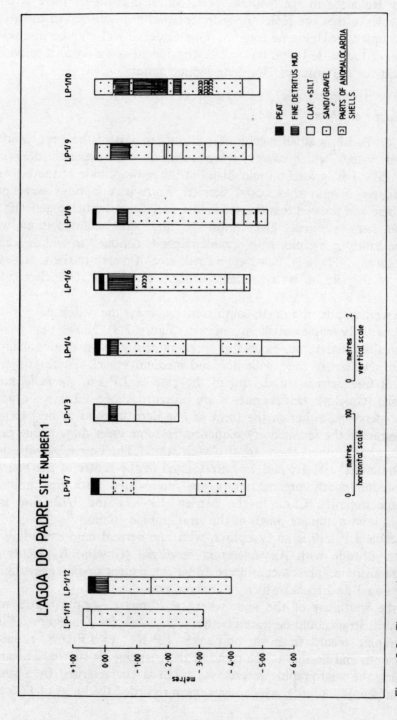

Figure 2.3 The stratigraphy on a north (LP-1/10) to south (LP-1/11) transect at site 1 in the south-east quadrant of Lagoa do Padre

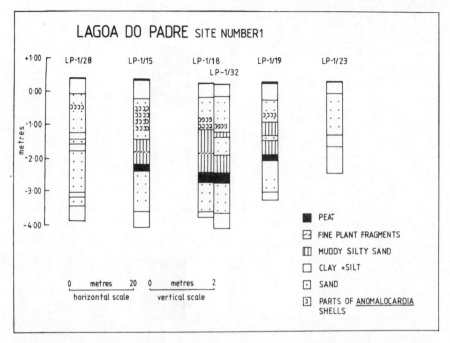

Figure 2.4 The stratigraphy on a north (LP-1/23) to south (LP-1/28) transect at site 1 in Lagoa do Padre, 300 m east of the line shown in figure 2.3

and a maximum recorded thickness of 30.0 cm. Initially, from an altitude of −1.77 m, it dips southwards towards the sea at an angle of one degree then flattens. The peat is predominantly herbaceous with some woody roots and woody detritus. Shell fragments of *Anomalocardia brasiliana* (Gmelin) in the overlying sand, at altitudes between −0.2 and −1.32 m cover a larger area than the peat body.

Diatom analyses (figure 2.5) were carried out on samples from two cores, LP-1/32 and LP-1/31, 10 m apart. The lowermost levels represent a fresh-brackish phase which marks the end of an impoverished zone. The succession of assemblages then fluctuates between fresh and fresh-brackish phases, with one fresh-marine phase, until there is a sharp transition into a marine phase, at *c*.2 m depth in both cores. Following a second impoverished zone (*c*.1.8 to 1.4 m depth) the assemblages contain many more freshwater forms, but also brackish and marine diatoms. Holocene sedimentation probably began with the deposition of a clayey sand stratum which overlies the highly compacted clay at *c*.3.8 m depth (figure 2.4). Close to the surface of the clay, well-humified herbaceous roots are present. This clay, because of its highly compacted nature, is considered to have been deposited in the pre-Holocene period, and

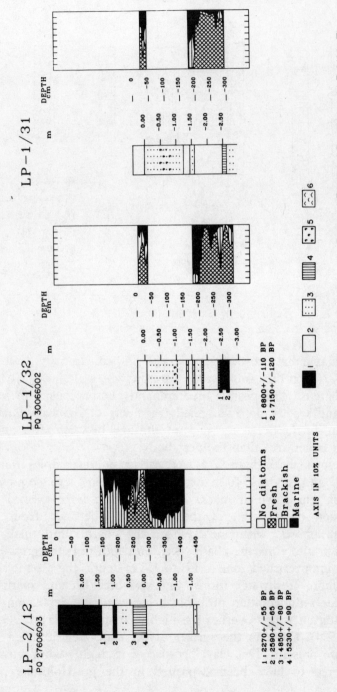

Figure 2.5 Diatom summary diagrams from three sampling sites in Lagoa do Padre: LP-1/31, LP-1/32 and LP-2/12. The stratigraphic symbols comprise: 1, peat; 2, clay and/or silt; 3, sand; 4, detrital mud; 5, shells; 6, charcoal

subsequently exposed, forming an early Holocene vegetated surface. The clayey sand was deposited in a high-energy marine environment, indicated by the presence of marine diatoms in declining frequency immediately below the overlying peat. The impoverished diatom zone below this is similar to that above 1.7 m depth and is thought to be the consequence of frustules being fractured and abraded, then dissolved in marine coastal waters. The decline in marine diatoms beneath the peat stratum is indicative of a regressive overlap that must have commenced before 7 150±120 BP, the age of the base of the peat (LP-1/32 on figure 2.5).

This peat was overlaid by fresh to fresh-brackish sediments at 6800±110 BP, which was later overlaid by marine sediment. The sediment is fine grained and indicative of a very low energy environment. The maximal age for the onset of this transgressive overlap is 6800±110 BP.

This depositional succession from regressive to transgressive overlap is interpreted as the first Holocene lagoonal sedimentation. Evidence for the hypothesis is provided by remnants of fossil barriers along this part of the coast, many of which were identified by Muehe (1982), although he attributed a much younger age to the features, based upon the sea-level evidence of Suguio and Martin (1981). The sedimentary sequence and diatom assemblage recorded at Lagoa do Padre are also consistent with this hypothesis. Fresh to fresh-brackish sediment accumulated to a depth of almost one metre following the decline of marine influence. This sequence indicates that drainage was obstructed between the site and the ocean and that the water-level rose. The formation of the first Holocene barrier chain must therefore predate 7150±120 BP.

In order to interpret the evidence of sea-level change accurately, it is necessary to establish whether the lagoon was completely isolated from the influence of the sea and to determine the relationship between sea level and lagoon level under open and closed lagoonal conditions. Sedimentary and diatom analytical evidence are two forms of evidence which help to determine whether tidal inlets existed. The sedimentary evidence is likely to be inconclusive because the high energy environment of the inlet falls off rapidly in the shallow waters of the lagoon. It is only likely to provide valuable evidence in the case of an extremely large inlet. Diatom analytical data, on the other hand, provide evidence throughout the lagoonal system. Nevertheless, it may not be possible, for instance, to distinguish between a lagoon with a narrow inlet and a completely closed lagoon. Evaporation in a closed lagoon may produce a similar salinity regime to that of a lagoon with a narrow inlet.

In this case, the sedimentary evidence indicates that if an inlet existed it was not in the south-east of the site, but one can be no more specific. Using the diatom salinity classification employed here (van der Werff 1960), it is possible to detect increasing or decreasing salinity, but it is not possible to be confident about the relationship of the diatom classification to the salinity of the water body.

In order to clarify this situation, modern-day studies were carried out at Lagoa de Itaipú and Lagoa do Padre. Bottom samples were taken from each lagoon along the 50 cm isobath and along a transect of increasing water depth; the resulting assemblages are summarised in table 2.4. For both lagoons, the intra-lagoonal variation in the salinity characteristics of the assemblages is small, but the inter-lagoonal characteristics are significantly different, reflecting the open nature of Lagoa de Itaipú and the fact that the only inlet in the Maricá Lagoonal System is at Ponta Negra, a considerable distance from Lagoa do Padre.

Table 2.4   Fresh/brackish/marine percentages for contemporary diatom assemblages taken from Lagoa do Padre and Itaipú[a]

	Mean (%)	Standard deviation	Minimum (%)	Maximum (%)
Lagoa do Padre				
Fresh	71	14	42	89
Brackish	25	13	7	50
Marine	4	2	1	8
Itaipú				
Fresh	12	17	0	55
Brackish	72	16	38	90
Marine	16	7	8	34

[a]Thirteen samples were taken from the 50 cm isobath of each lagoon and the data are expressed as percentage total valves counted in each sample.

It is difficult to relate the assemblages to a particular salinity because species of a wide range of salinities are found in each. At Lagoa do Padre, the assemblage is dominated by fresh (fresh to fresh-brackish) and brackish (brackish-fresh to brackish-marine) diatoms, with the fresh making up about 70 per cent of the assemblage. At Lagoa de Itaipú, the assemblage is dominated by brackish (brackish-fresh to brackish-marine) and marine (marine-brackish to marine) diatoms, brackish diatoms constituting about 80 per cent of the assemblage.

The samples of bottom sediment for use in this analysis were collected in small phials. Attempts to measure the salinity of water contained in these phials proved unsuccessful, presumably because chloride was concentrated in the bottom mud and increased the concentration in the water. The readings were all excessively saline.

In 1955, however, Oliveira *et al.* (1955) measured the salinity of water in various parts of the Maricá Lagoonal System. Salinities ranged from 6.7 to 8.4 ‰ with a reading of 8.4 in Lagoa do Padre. This is alpha mesohaline (Hedgepeth 1953) and (table 2.2) is consistent with the recorded assemblage according to the more realistic classifications of Simonsen (1962) and Ehrlich (1975).

Lagoa de Itaipú has been artificially opened since Oliveira (1948) studied the lagoon, so the salinity readings are no longer valid. Its present open nature, plus the freshwater input of several streams and the canal from the closed Lagoa de Piratininga, should make the water polyhaline. Again, the diatom assemblage is consistent with the classifications of Simonsen (1962) and Ehrlich (1975). Thus, while we cannot classify the assemblages according to Simonsen and Ehrlich, it is essential that their scheme is used in the interpretation of the salinity regime.

The fossil assemblage between *c.*3.0 and 2.0 m depth at Lagoa do Padre site 1 is dominated in most levels by approximately 90 per cent fresh with about 5 per cent each of brackish and marine species. Using the scheme of Simonsen (1962), this assemblage is oligohaline to alpha mesohaline. It is not possible from these data to ascertain whether an inlet existed, but if it did, it was probably small and at a considerable distance from Lagoa do Padre. Equally, there could have been no permanent inlet, the marine diatoms entering the lagoon during high tides when low points in the barrier were overwashed, or when freshwater built up in the lagoon to a similar level and discharged to the ocean through a short-lived inlet (Oliveira *et al.* 1955).

Therefore, in order to interpret this evidence accurately in relation to sea-level change, the relationship between sea level and lagoon level must be established in open and closed lagoonal situations. Only if there is no significant difference can the data be accurately interpreted.

Three lagoons, one closed, one a long distance from an opening and one with a narrow artificial opening (Lagoa de Jaconé, Guaratiba and Guarapina respectively) provide suitable case studies (figure 2.2). The water level data, covering a three-year period (1980–82), were recorded continuously with tide gauges.

The average maximum annual range of lagoon level was 71 cm for Jaconé, 75 cm for Guaratiba and 73 cm for Guarapina, while the maximum range over three years was 91 cm, 91 cm and 109 cm respectively. Not only are the ranges very similar, but the water levels, which are all related to the national datum, are also similar in altitude. Taking the extreme values over three years for the open and closed lagoons, Jaconé is 1.31 m and Guarapina is 1.24 m which is a difference of 0.07 m. The greatest altitudinal difference between water levels in different lagoons is 0.43 m. Within the limits of accuracy of the methodology, these differences are not significant.

In addition, historical studies by Oliveira (1948) and Oliveira *et al.* (1955) suggest that the low points or *lidos* (Oliveira 1948) of the barriers enclosing closed lagoons are lower that the altitude of the highest local tides. Therefore, the lagoon level cannot exceed the level of the highest local tide. Thus, in terms of sea-level change, the rising freshwater level in the lagoon can be interpreted as reflecting a positive tendency of sea-level movement. As sea-level continued to rise, the Lagoa do Padre barrier was breached, leaving only 1.3 km at the east of the lagoon intact. Unfortunately, the date of the breach has not been determined because the quantity of coarse plant fragments recovered at this level was not sufficient to permit ^{14}C dating. The breach is marked, in the sedimentary sequence, by coarser sediment – gravelly sand dominating at 1.92 to 1.96 m depth in LP-1/32 – and by a marine diatom assemblage dominated firstly by *Cyclotella striata americana* then by *Paralia sulcata biseriata*, the latter indicating marine (Hedgepeth 1953) water. It seems likely that the Guaratiba and Maricá barriers would also have been breached at this time.

Diatom evidence is then lacking until 50 cm of the surface, but there is sand dominated sediment with concentrations of *Anomalocardia brasiliana* (Gmelin) shell fragments. This species inhabits open silty or sandy floored lagoons whose salinity is somewhat freshened by runoff (Fairbridge 1976). Thus open lagoonal conditions appear to continue.

Lagoa do Padre site 2 is situated in a narrow, sediment-filled bay on the landward site of the lagoon, and is separated from it by a sand barrier. At this site, which is at higher altitude than site 1, the sampling interval varies between 80 m and 5 m depending on the complexity of the stratigraphy (figure 2.6). At depth, a sandy stratum dips 1.8 degrees southwards towards the sea and is covered by silty clay. Further south the stratigraphic column is then almost entirely composed of the sand of the barrier, while northwards towards the land a more complex sequence exists of silty, fine detrital mud, silty clay and peat.

Diatom and radiocarbon analyses were carried out on core LP-2/12 and the results are summarised in figure 2.5. The basal assemblages, in the silty clay layer, are dominated by marine, benthic and planktonic diatoms. This is followed by fresh and fresh-brackish phases. The subsequent brackish-marine and marine-brackish phases are separated by a fresh

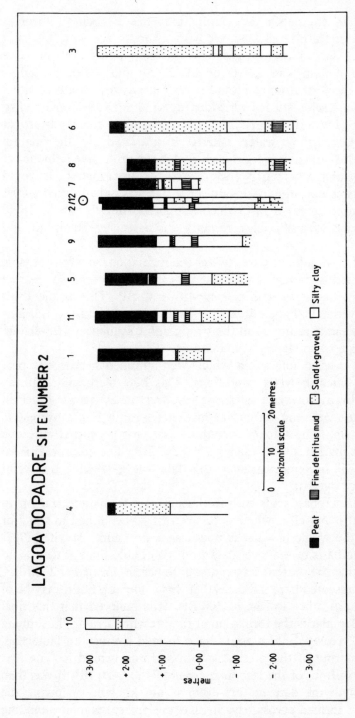

Figure 2.6 The stratigraphy on a north-west (10) to south-east (3) transect at Lagoa do Padre, Site 2. This site lies south-east of a low col, less than 5 metres above mean sea level, that separates Lagoa do Padre from Lagoa de Guaratiba

phase. Above 200 cm depth the marine influence is reduced through brackish-marine to fresh-brackish at the base of the surface peat. The silty clay with marine diatom assemblages below the zero datum is at the same altitude as the diatom-poor sands of site 1. Marine sedimentation is interrupted by the formation of a sand barrier across the mouth of site 2 bay. The marine, clayey silt is overridden by sand at the seaward end of the site and freshwater sedimentation commences on the landward at 5230±90 BP. Oligohaline water salinity is indicated by the diatom assemblage. This regressive overlap results from the protective influence of the barrier, but as the barrier is characteristic of progradation, it would seem that this was not an extra-local event. Barriers have formed across many back-barrier embayments, which supports Gilbert's (1885, 1890) theory of barrier over-stepping, recently discussed by Rampino and Sanders (1982).

The phase of predominantly freshwater sedimentation, in which organic rich, fine grained sediment accumulated, came to an end as marine conditions again began to dominate at 4850±80 BP. This is the third transgressive overlap at Lagoa do Padre. Full marine-brackish conditions are heralded by sandy sediment in the stratigraphic sequence. The diatom assemblage suggests polyhaline water salinity.

A regressive overlap follows in which well-humified herbaceous peat formed under brackish water conditions. This beta mesohaline salinity phase is short-lived, however, as the peat is overlaid by marine-brackish clayey silt which marks the last marine incursion and the last transgressive overlap at this site. The thickness of this basal peat permitted only one ^{14}C age determination to be made: 2590±65 BP. For interpretational reasons which will become clear later, this date will be taken as the age of the transgressive overlap.

The final marine phase ends with freshwater peat formation, starting at 2270±55 BP. It is not clear whether this retreat was confined to site 2 or occurred over the whole of what is now Lagoa do Padre. Muehe (1982) believed, on the basis of sea-level data from São Paulo State (Suguio and Martin 1981), that the present Lagoa do Padre barrier formed at 2700 BP. The evidence presented here indicates that this is too old, but it may be of the right order, in other words, c.2300 BP. It is believed that this final regressive overlap marks the formation of the present barrier. Thus, along this part of the coast, three barriers have formed during the Holocene. Two formed in front of the present lagoon and one behind it. The first barrier formed in front of the lagoon at around 7150±120 BP. It was then breached although the date of this event is not known. Following the breach, barriers formed across bays behind the present lagoon including the site 2 bay. These barriers formed in two stages with an intervening breach. The first stage of formation has been dated at 5230±90 BP and the present barrier is believed to have formed at approximately 2700 BP. At Lagoa do Padre, four transgressive and four regressive overlaps have been identified.

3.2 Itaipu-Açu

At Itaipu-Açu there are two barriers, an inner, fossil barrier and an outer, present-day barrier. The crest of the former is 4.8 m higher that the crest of the present barrier, which has an altitude of 7.4 m (Muehe 1982). These barriers are separated by the Canal do Costa, a channel which is now dredged periodically. There is no lagoon behind the fossil barrier, but there are some marshy areas. The quartz sand which forms the beach at Itaipu-Açu is coarser than beach sand elsewhere along this part of the Rio de Janeiro coast (Muehe 1979). Two sites were examined. The first lies between the higher barrier and Morro de Céu and the second between the two barriers, close to the Rio Itocaia. At site 1 the stratigraphic sequence is dominated by well rounded quartz sand with fine gravel to a depth of over seven metres. Locally organic rich strata, usually peats, are present close to the surface.

Countable concentrations of diatoms occurred only between 4.84 and 4.95 m altitude at one sampling point. The assemblages are dominated by freshwater taxa such as *Pinnularia stauroptera* with *Eunotia veneris* and *Eunotia tenella*. At a second site, *c.*2.8 km to the south-west and between the fossil and present-day barriers, the stratigraphy in 12 boreholes revealed a different record. The base of the sequence was dominated by gravelly sand, which is predominantly quartz, but includes feldspar at depth (maximum 5.94 m) and *Anomalocardia brasiliana* (Gmelin) fragments near its surface. This sand body dips seaward at an angle of 1.5 degrees from an altitude of +1.37 m at the most landward borehole. It is overlaid by a wedge of finer grained material with up to 50 per cent organic matter, the grain size varying between silty clay and silty sand. This is covered by a peat stratum which slopes seaward at an angle of 0.4 degrees and varies in thickness between 4 and 17 cm. Organic clayey silt then (over most of the site) sand overlies the peat.

Diatom analyses showed (figure 2.7) that at the top of the sand body the succesion is marine, dominated by *Cyclotella striata americana* or *Opephora parva*, but rapidly becomes fresh-brackish. The salinity then fluctuates between fresh and fresh-brackish, with brackish and marine diatoms always present. Immediately below the peat it becomes brackish,

ITAIPU−ACU−2/12

PQ 05455884

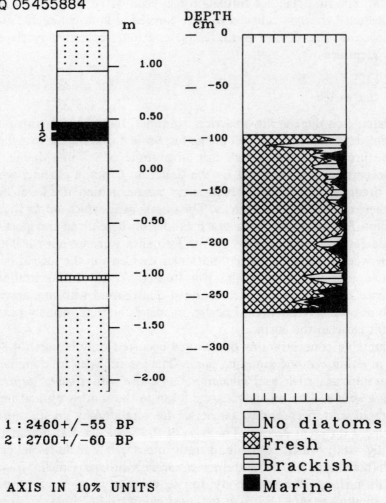

1 : 2460+/−55 BP
2 : 2700+/−60 BP

AXIS IN 10% UNITS

☐ No diatoms
▨ Fresh
🮯 Brackish
■ Marine

Figure 2.7 A diatom summary diagram from Itaipu-Açu. The stratigraphic symbols are the same as for figure 2.5

dominated by *Campylodiscus clypeus*. The peat base is fresh. Above the peat no diatoms were found. Muehe (1982) believed that the fossil barrier at Itaipu-Açu formed at 5100 BP and that the present barrier formed at 2700 BP. These age estimates are again based upon the sea-level data of Suguio and Martin (1981). Muehe (1982) suggested that the fossil barrier had enclosed a lagoon similar in character to that at Maricá which has filled with lagoonal sediment during the late Holocene. The sedimentary, diatom and radiocarbon evidence contradict this view.

The sedimentary sequence at site 1, with well-rounded quartz sand and gravel similar to that composing the present Itaipu-Açu beach, is indicative of marine sedimentation. Freshwater peat and clay have formed over the marine laid sediment, and the radiocarbon date on the peat of 250±48 BP indicates that this is a very recent phenomenon.

On the seaward side of the fossil barrier at site 2, the basal sand is characteristic of marine deposition, although at depth, the mineral composition and presence of coarse gravel suggests fluvial influences. At the top of the basal sand are concentrations of *Anomalocardia brasiliana* (Gmelin) shells suggesting that open sea conditions are changing to open lagoonal conditions, and that a barrier is forming. This is supported by the rapid decline of marine diatoms at the point where fine grained material over-lies the basal sand and by the deposition of this fine grained material. This transition represents the first regressive overlap at this site, which has not been dated because of the lack of *in situ* organic matter at this depth.

Sedimentation of fine grained material in freshwater seems to have persisted for some time as over 2.5 m of sediment were deposited under these conditions. This is similar to the depth of sediment deposited at Lagoa do Padre and, as will be seen, at Lagoa do Itaipú since about 7000 BP. The proximity of the sea to the site during this period is indicated by the continued presence of small numbers of marine and brackish diatoms. The diatom assemblage indicates alternating phases of fresh or oligohaline (Hedgepeth 1953) water conditions with increasingly frequent fluctuations towards the surface.

The period of fresh-oligohaline sedimentation came to an end when a brackish diatom assemblage (figure 2.7), dominated by *Campylodiscus clypeus*, replaced the freshwater assemblage. Following this beta meso-haline water salinity phase, peat formation began at 2700±60 BP, the date at which Muehe (1982) suggested the present barrier formed. This regressive overlap seems likely to be the consequence of sediment accumulation. Peat growth terminated at 2460±55 BP, when it was overlaid by silty clay, marking a transgressive overlap.

It is thus clear that the present barrier is older than 2700 BP. The age estimates used in the following section are speculative, but seem the most probable when all the evidence from this and other sites is considered. It is suggested that the fossil barrier and the sedimentary sequences behind it are Pleistocene in age, with only the surface sediments in the area behind the barrier and sediment on the face of the barrier being reworked during the Holocene. This formation is considered to be related to the

Cananéia Formation which has been described in São Paulo State (Suguio and Petri 1973, Petri and Suguio 1973).

The present barrier is believed to have formed at about 7150 BP at the same time as the first barrier at Lagoa do Padre. However, unlike the barriers of the Maricá System, this barrier was not subsequently breached; freshwater sedimentation prevailed until 2460±55 BP when the barrier was breached or overtopped.

It has not been possible to identify a transgressive overlap within the basal sand, although such an overlap must have occurred. Two regressive overlaps (one of which is dated) and one transgressive overlap have been described at Itaipu-Açu. The transgressive overlap at 2460±55 BP is almost identical in age to the fourth overlap at Lagoa do Padre.

3.3 Lagoa de Itaipú

Lagoa de Itaipú is a small lagoon (figure 2.2) covering 1.5 km² and protected by a single merged barrier (Muehe 1982). Five small streams flow into the lagoon (figure 2.8). Two sites on the east and west margins of the lagoons were examined, and the results from the eastern site are described here.

The stratigraphic succession in 17 of the 33 boreholes is shown in figure 2.9. Clay and silt with varying proportions of organic matter intercalate four peat strata. Beneath the basal peat is silt and fine detrital mud and a trace of sand, which was proved in borehole 6 to extend to an altitude of −8.74 m. The basal peat is a dark reddish brown, well humified, woody, herbaceous peat of variable thickness (0.45 – 1.85 m) and altitudinal range. It displays no clear altitudinal or spatial pattern. Over most of the site, the top of the basal peat is marked by a thin layer of charcoal. The basal peat is separated from the overlying peat by organic silty clay. This peat, which is also of variable thickness (0.10 – 0.75 m), is intermittent and also shows no altitudinal or spatial pattern. It is overlaid, in turn, by organic clay and a third peat stratum. This very dark brown, well-humified, woody, herbaceous peat shows a clear altitudinal and spatial pattern, covering the whole site and dipping seaward. It is separated from the surface herbaceous peat by muddy, silty clay.

The radiocarbon dates (figure 2.10) from the lower two peat beds indicate that the lower sequence formed during a period of time equivalent to interstadial conditions during the last full glacial age in north-west Europe and North America. The peat beds intercalating clastic sediments may indicate either water-level fluctuations in the lagoons consequent upon changes in a high interstadial sea level, or water-level

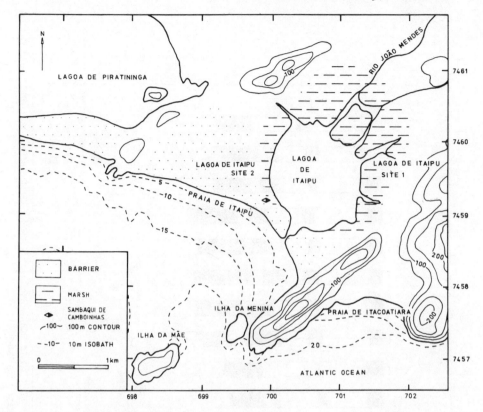

Figure 2.8 A map of Lagoa de Itaipú showing the location of the sampling sites

fluctuations resulting from climatic oscillations.

A high interstadial sea-level is indicated by the presence, in a single layer within the basal peat, of marine diatom taxa, which have been described by Ehrlich (1975) in hypersaline environments associated with tidal inlets. Milliman and Barretto (1975) have also described hypersaline coastal lagoon environments of pleniglacial age from the Amazon-Amapa outershelf based on sedimentary evidence. In support of a high interstadial sea level, Thom (1973) marshalled evidence from around the world that pointed to a climatic amelioration around 35 000±10 000 BP and sea levels attaining altitudes of 30 m below present day sea level and perhaps higher locally. (See also the discussions on interstadial sea levels in chapters 5, 6, 7, 8 and 10). From the Brazilian continental shelf, Kowsmann *et al.* (1977) and Kowsmann and Costa (1979) presented evidence for a rapid fall of sea level between 23 050±550 and 19 910±330 from a minimum present day water depth of 28 m to 115 m: the evidence

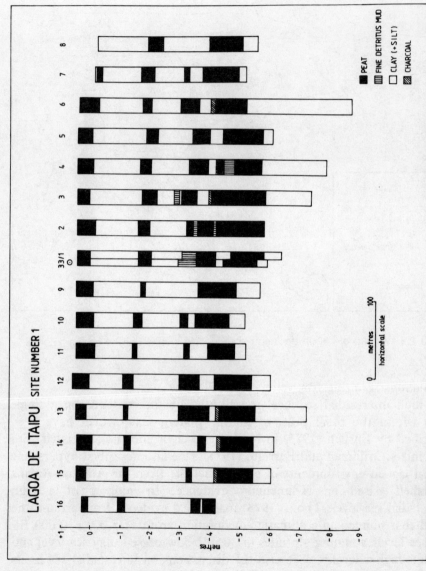

Figure 2.9 The stratigraphy on a north-east (16) to south-west (8) transect over partly reclaimed marshes at site 1 on the eastern side of Lagoa de Itaipú

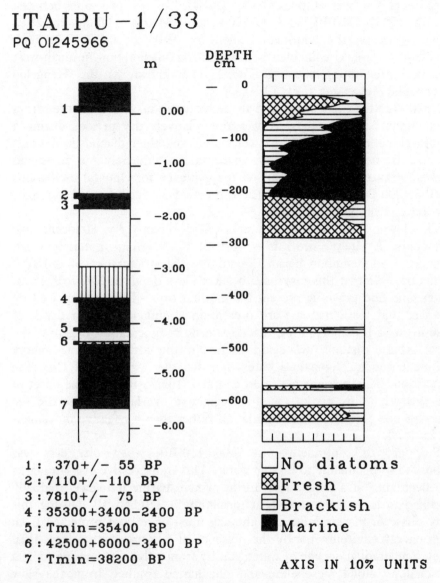

ITAIPU–1/33
PQ 01245966

m

DEPTH
cm

1   0.00

—   0

— -100

-1.00

2   -2.00
3

— -200

-2.00

— -300

-3.00

— -400

4   -4.00

5   -4.00
6   -5.00

— -500

-5.00

7   -600

— -600

-6.00

1 : 370+/- 55 BP
2 : 7110+/-110 BP
3 : 7810+/- 75 BP
4 : 35300+3400-2400 BP
5 : Tmin=35400 BP
6 : 42500+6000-3400 BP
7 : Tmin=38200 BP

☐ No diatoms
☒ Fresh
⊟ Brackish
■ Marine

AXIS IN 10% UNITS

Figure 2.10 A diatom summary diagram from Itaipú – 1/33. The stratigraphic symbols are the same as for figure 2.5

from Lagao de Itaipú and Itaipu-Açu may indicate a maximum high interstadial sea-level at present day altitudes of −4 to −6 m between 30 500+1500/−1200 BP and 42 500+6000/−3400 BP falling to 28 m water depth on the continental shelf by 23 050±550 BP. The high interstadial sea-level coincided with a climatic amelioration in north-west Europe, interrupting the pleniglacial, and known as the Hengeloo Interstadial (Jelgersma *et al*. 1979).

An alternative explanation is that the sequence may have resulted from fluctuations between relatively wet and relatively dry periods during a humid climatic phase. Brackish conditions and their diagnostic diatoms resulted from evaporation in an environment comparable to an inland *sabkha*. Prance (1978) summarised the evidence for climatic oscillations after 36 000 BP in Amazonia that comprised a succession of wet-cold, dry-hot and dry-cold conditions.

The lower two peat beds are overlaid directly by Holocene age sediments. At Itaipú site 1 it is difficult to determine precisely when Holocene sedimentation began. Examining the stratigraphy of It-1/1, it seems possible that this may have occurred at a depth of 2.47 to 3.35 m, when sand and gravel is present for the first time. This is supported by the fact that fossil diatoms are present in abundance from a depth of 2.86 m in It-1/33. Assuming that Holocene sedimentation began at the point where diatoms are again found in the sediment, low energy sedimentation in oligohaline water signalled the beginning of Holocene deposition. This phase came to an end at 7810±75 BP with the onset of peat growth. This marks the first regressive overlap, but may be the consequence of sediment accumulation rather than a negative movement of sea level.

Peat growth continued until 7100±110 BP, when silty clay was deposited in polyhaline to marine water. This transgressive overlap marks the beginning of a long phase during which marine influence gradually declined to leave freshwater peat formation at 370±55 BP. During this long phase of marine influence, the site must have been protected from high energy environments by the presence of a barrier with a large tidal inlet. The gradual decline of water salinity from polyhaline/marine to beta mesohaline, alpha mesohaline and oligohaline resulted from the slow closure of the inlet.

Independent evidence for the existence of a barrier from *c*.6000 BP is provided by the study of the Sambaqui de Camboinhas (figure 2.8), by Kneip *et al*. (1981). The midden, or *sambaqui*, which was built by prehistoric tool-making man (excavation of the site yielding 1062 artefacts) was found in a fossil dune 7–8 m above mean sea level. Five samples of mollusc shells from several levels in the midden were dated: the two oldest dates are 7958±224 BP and 4475±160 BP. Muehe (1982) considered the oldest date to be in error, but the evidence presented here suggests that this conclusion should be re-evaluated. It is almost certain that the mollusc shells gave ^{14}C ages which were older than the true ^{14}C ages, not least because of the delay in the transmission of carbon dioxide to oceanic water (Tooley 1981), but the error would not be of the magnitude envisaged by Muehe. It seems reasonable that, within two standard errors, the sample should have a ^{14}C age of at least 7500 BP. Thus it may be the case that this barrier formed at a similar time to the first Lagoa do Padre barrier, in other words, before 7100 BP. This would be consistent with the stratigraphic and archaeological evidence.

At Itaipú, one transgressive overlap has been identified at 7100±100 BP. This is similar in age and altitude to the first overlap identified at Lagoa do Padre. In addition, two regressive overlaps have been identified and dated at 7810±75 and 370±55 BP.

4.0 SEA LEVEL CHANGE ALONG THE RIO DE JANEIRO STATE COAST

Brazilian sea-level studies have a relatively long history, with evidence of sea-level change first being described in the nineteenth century. Studies have followed one of three basic approaches: geomorphological; fossil based; or geomorphological and fossil based.

A geomorphological approach to sea-level studies has frequently been adopted. From the late nineteenth century to the present, several coastal morphological features such as exposed sandstone reefs, wave-built terraces and coastal barriers have been interpreted as being indicative of higher sea-level stands (Hartt 1870, Branner 1904, Tricart 1959, Mabesoone 1964, Bigarella and Andrade 1965, Jost and Godolphim 1975, Cunha and Andrade 1977, Muehe 1982). Although these features have generally not been dated, most authors have presented tentative age estimates.

Van Andel and Laborel (1964), using fossil and ecological evidence, were the first to publish radiocarbon dated sea-level index points of Holocene age for Brazil. Former sea levels were reconstructed by comparing the position and altitude of living and fossil Vermetidae limestone from Gaibu, Pernambuco. The living Vermetidae in this area, dominated by *Petaloconchus (Macrophragma)* Carpenter, have a limited altitudinal range from 0.30 to 0.80 m above mean low water in a well defined ecological position. This permitted, by extrapolation, the sea level at the time of formation of the fossil limestone to be defined with an altitudinal error of 0.50 m, and becasuse Vermetids live on rocky outcrops this altitude is not affected by compaction. Changes in sea level were then calculated as the difference between the dated fossil Vermetid remains and the living Vermetids close to the site (Laborel 1979). On the Brazilian coast, this relationship can only be established as far south as Cabo Frio. Further south living Vermetids are not recorded and fossil Vermetid remains have to be related to some other stenovalent organism such as the barnacle, *Tetraclita* sp. (Laborel 1979). This type of research was extended both geographically (figure 2.11(a)) and in the types of fossil dated by Delibrias and Laborel (1971). The range was extended to over 3000 kilometres from Recife to Santo Amoro and corals, *in situ* oysters and shells from beach rock were included. The greater altitudinal uncertainty which arises from the use of this material is indicated on the time/altitude diagram shown on figure 2.11(b).

Distinctive sea-level curves (figure 2.13) have been published for the Brazilian coast (Martin *et al*. 1979–80, Martin and Suguio 1975) employing a variety of evidence, both fossil-based and geomorphological. The radiocarbon age and altitude of *in situ* fossils such as the shells of *Ostrea* and encrusting tubes of the gastropod Vermetids, have been complemented with dates from allochthonous and *in situ* wood, embedded in marine sediments, the altitudes of morphological features, such as marine terraces, and the dates from shells taken from the base of *sambaquis* (shell middens). Surprisingly little data have derived from the kind of lagoonal sediments described in this chapter and employed as index points on Brazilian sea-level graphs or used to establish periods of transgressive and regressive overlap. The consideration that has been given to the number, pattern and age of transgressive and regressive overlaps that have affected the Brazilian coast is contradictory. Fairbridge (1976) has argued that the *sambaquis* on the coast of south-east Brazil contain a record of occupation and abandonment of the coast by shellfish-eating Indians, explained by rises and falls of sea level, and associated periods of submergence and emergence. He argues for three periods of submergence during the Holocene – the Alexandro Submergence, the Cananéia Submergence and the Paranagua Submergence. In contradistinction, Suguio and Martin (1978) recognise only two periods of submergence or transgression: the first, known as the Cananéia transgression occurred during a time equivalent to an interglacial age, *c*.100 000 to 120 000 BP, whereas the second, known as the Santos transgression, reached a maximum altitude *c*.5000 BP. Subsequently, Bittencourt *et al*. (1979) identified a third, unnamed transgression which attained a

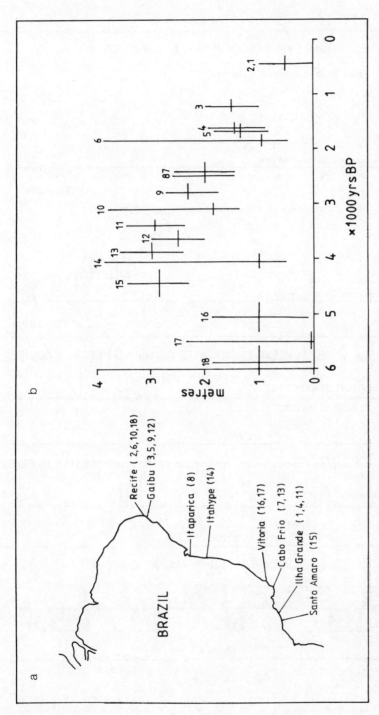

Figure 2.11 Sea-level index points identified in eastern Brazil by Delibrias and Laborel (1971): a. A map to show the location of sites 1–18; b. A time/altitude graph on which each index point is plotted with a single standard error for each radiocarbon date and an altitudinal range in metres given

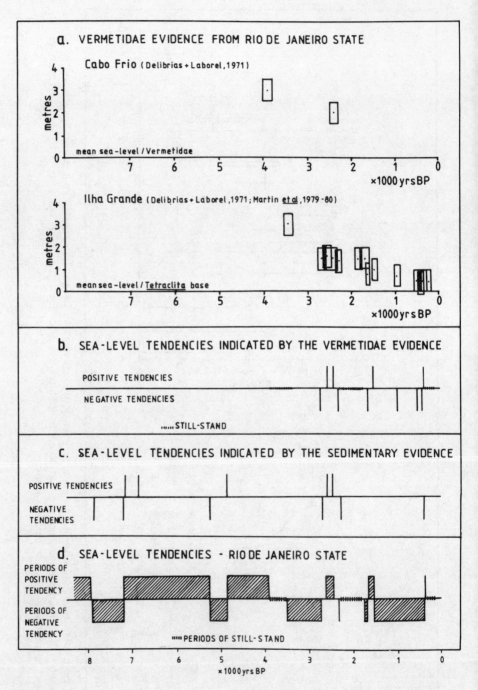

Figure 2.12 Sea-level changes in the State of Rio de Janeiro using stratigraphic and biological evidence, and showing a partial chronology of sea-level tendencies

maximum altitude *c.*3500 BP. In order to attempt to resolve these contradictions for part of the coast of the State of Rio de Janeiro, the exploratory approach to the analysis and interpretation of Holocene sea-level data, proposed by Shennan *et al.* (1983) and effectively employed in the United Kingdom, has been applied to the data from the coastal lagoons described here. On figure 2.12(c), the distribution of eleven radiocarbon dates from three lagoon sites, Lagoa do Padre, Itaipu-Açu and Lagoa de Itaipú is shown in combination and an interpretation of their relationship to a positive or negative tendency of sea-level movement is given.

A comparison can be made with the tendency of sea-level movements inferred from the Vermetid data from Cabo Frio and Ilha Grande Bay (figure 2.12(a) and (b)). The age and altitude of adjacent Vermetid samples are considered, sequentially from oldest to youngest: if the adjacent sample is at a higher altitude, a positive tendency is indicated, if at a lower altitude a negative tendency is indicated and if at the same altitude a still-stand is indicated. Where sedimentary and Vermetid evidence coincide temporally, the same sea-level tendencies are indicated: the Vermetid evidence then reinforces and contributes to the partial chronology tendencies of sea-level movement (figure 2.12(d)). The stillstands from the Vermetid evidence may represent periods of weak positive or negative tendency which are masked by inherent dating and altitudinal measurement problems. The existence of true periods of still-stand requires verification, but, at present, the Vermetid evidence provides the most altitudinally sensitive index points and it is unlikely that sedimentary sequences will provide the same quality of altitudinal resolution.

The model, devised by Mörner (1969) and developed at Durham (Shennan 1982b, Shennan *et al.* 1983), indicates that in areas undergoing uplift positive tendencies of sea-level movement are likely to be regionally significant and that in subsiding areas negative tendencies are likely to be significant. Both theoretical and empirical results show that the Brazilian coast is emergent, which suggests that positive tendencies of sea-level will assume greater importance in regional comparisons. The theoretical evidence is provided by Clark and Bloom (1979) using a spherical earth model to predict the results of meltwater loading of the South Atlantic Ocean upon the continental shelf regions of South America, and particularly Brazil, and yielding a two to four-metre emergence since 5000 BP. This prediction is supported by the available Vermetid evidence from different areas of Brazil and by the lagoonal evidence from the coast of Rio de Janeiro State.

A consideration of the tendencies displayed by the sea-level index points from the sediments of the Holocene lagoons in the State of Rio de Janeiro, compared with the sea-level curves from the Itanhaém-Santos unit of the State of Sao Paulo (Suguio *et al.* 1980) and from the Porto da Barra-Arembepe unit of the State of Bahia (Bittencourt *et al.* 1979) reveals fundamental differences in the three data sets (figure 2.13). Prior to 7100 BP the evidence from both Lagoa do Padre and Lagoa de Itaipú indicates negative sea-level tendencies (table 2.1, nos. 2 and 12) and positive tendencies begin only after 7110±110 BP (table 2.1, no. 11), corroborating the direction of sea-level tendency shown in both curves from the coasts of Bahia and São Paulo States.

An important diagnostic characteristic of the Brazilian sea-level curves is the period of high sea-level *c.*5000 BP when sea level reached a maximum altitude of +3.5 to 4.7 m above present mean sea level in the States of São Paulo and Bahia. The evidence from the Lagoa do Padre (figure 2.5 and table 2.1, nos. 6 and 5) indicates a period of fresh water influx into the lagoon and a marked negative sea-level tendency between 5230±90 and 4850±80 BP.

After 3600 BP, the sedimentary evidence from the Holocene lagoons supports the fall in sea-level recorded by Bittencourt *et al.* (1979) from the State of Bahia between 2600 and 2700 BP, but the sea-level tendencies recorded during the period from 2700 BP to 2270 BP indicate a more complex pattern of water level changes. It is perhaps surprising that there is a greater similarity in sea-level changes at this period between the States of Bahia and Rio de Janeiro than the adjacent States of Rio de Janeiro and São Paulo.

It is clearly important to subject all index points to scrutiny, establishing their indicative meaning, that is the relationship of a dated sample to its contemporary tidal level, and their sea-level tendency. This procedure is facilitated by the use of an homogeneous data set, such as the set originating from the lagoons of the coast of the State of Rio de Janeiro. Until this is done, any conclusions about the migration of the geoid since the mid-Holocene, and the verification of theoretical models of emergence and submergence are liable to question.

ACKNOWLEDGEMENTS

The rescarch described here was carried out while the author was in receipt of an NERC studentship. Additional funds were provided by the British Council and the Brazilian CNPq. I am pleased to acknowledge the

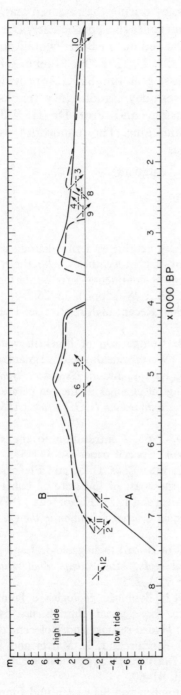

Figure 2.13 Sea-level index points from Rio de Janeiro State and sea-level curves from (A) São Paulo State (Suguio et al. 1980) and (B) the State of Bahia (Bittencourt et al. 1979). Each index point is a radiocarbon dated sample and shown with one standard deviation. An arrow pointing upwards indicates a transgressive overlap and one pointing downwards a regressive overlap. The altitude of each index point is related to Mean Sea Level at Imbituba whereas the altitudes of the curves are related to local water levels. The altitudes of high and low tide are taken from figure 4B of Suguio et al. (1980). The altitudinal relationships of the data sets remain to be established

help and advice of Dr. M. J. Tooley during the research and the support and advice provided by my Durham colleagues, particularly Dr. I. Shennan and Mr. J. B. Innes. The work carried out in Brazil would not have been possible without the assistance of Dr. D. C. E. H. Muehe, UFRJ and the Speer family, to whom I am most grateful. SERLA provided lagoonal level data for several of the present-day lagoons. My thanks also go to Prof. Dr. O. Fränzle for organising, and Prof. Dr. H. Willkomm for carrying out, the ^{14}C age determinations. The manuscript was typed by Miss N. Rogers and Mrs V. Innes.

Revised typescript received 1986, August.

REFERENCES

Admiraal, W. 1977: Salinity tolerance of benthic estuarine diatoms as tested with a rapid polarographic measurement of photosynthesis. *Mar.Biol.*, 39, 11–18.

Almeida, F. F. M. 1976: The system of continental rifts bordering the Santos Basin, Brazil. *Anais.Acad. Bras. Cienc.*, 48 (suppl.), 15–26.

Andel, T. H. van and Laborel, J. 1964: Recent high relative sea-level stand near Recife Brazil. *Science*, 145, 580–1.

Bakker, C. and de Pauw, N. 1974: Comparison of brackish water plankton assemblages in an estuarine tidal (Westerschelde) and stagnant (Lake Vere) environment (S.W. Netherlands) I. Phytoplankton. *Hydrobiol. Bull.*, 8 197–89.

Berglund, B. E. 1979: Palaeohydrological changes in the temperate zone in the last 15 000 years. *Lake and Mire Environments IGCP Project 158 publication: Specific Methods*, Vol. 2, 1–340.

Bigarella, J. J. and Andrade, G. O. 1965: Contribution to the study of the Brazilian Quaternary. *Geol. Soc. Am.* Special paper 84, 433–51.

Bittencourt, A. C. S. P., Martin, L., Vilas Boas, G. S. and Flexor, J.-M. 1979: Quaternary marine formations of the coast of the state of Bahia (Brazil). In K. Suguio, T. R. Fairchild, L. Martin and J.-M. Flexor (eds.) 1979 *Proceedings of the 1978 International Symposium on Coastal Evolution in the Quaternary.* São Paulo, Brasil, 232–53.

Branner, J. C. 1904: The stone reefs of Brazil; their geological and geographical relations, with a chapter on coral reefs. *Mus. Comp. Zool. Bull., Harvard College*, Cambridge, 41 (geol. Ser. 7) 1–285.

Brito, I. M. and Lemos, E. E. 1982: Evolução geológica e fauna da Lagoa Rodrigo de Freitas, Rio de Janeiro. *Anais. Acad. Bras. Cienc.*, 54, 143–64.

Clark, J. A. and Bloom, A. L. 1979: Hydro-isostasy and Holocene emergence of South America. In K. Suguio, T. R. Fairchild, L. Martin and J.-M. Flexor (eds) 1979. *Proceedings of the 1978 International Symposium on Coastal Evolution in the Quaternary.* São Paulo Brasil, 41–60.

Cleve-Euler, A. 1951–1955: Die Diatomëen von Schweden und Finnland. *Kungl*

Svenska Vetensk. Akad. Handl. Ser. 4: 2(1), 1–163; 3(3), 1–153; 4(1), 1–158; 4(5), 1–255; 5(4), 1–232.

Cunha, F. L. S. and Andrade, A. B. 1977: Evidência glácio-eustática no littoral de Niterói, R. J. *Bolm. geogr., Rio de J.* 35, 152–64.

Delibrias, C. and Laborel, J. 1971: Recent variations of the sea level along the Brazilian coast. *Quaternaria*, 14, 45–9.

Ehrlich, A. 1975: The diatoms from the surface sediments of the Bardawil Lagoon (northern Sinai) – palaeo-ecological significance. In R. Simonsen (ed.) 1975: Proceedings of the 3rd Symposium on recent and fossil Marine Diatoms. Keil, 9–13 September 1974. *Nova Hedwigia*, 53, 253–80.

Fairbridge, R. W. 1976: Shellfish-eating preceramic indians in coastal Brazil. *Science*, 191, 353–9.

Flenley, J. R. 1973: The use of modern pollen rain samples in the study of the vegetational history of tropical regions. In H. J. B. Birks and R. G. West (eds) 1973: *Quaternary plant ecology. The 14th symposium of the British Ecological Society, March 1972.* Oxford: Basil Blackwell, 131–41.

Florin, M.-B. 1944: En sensubarktisk transgression; trakten av södra Kilsbergen enligt diatomacésuccessionen i områdets högre belägna fornsjölager följder. *Geol. For.Stockh. Forh.*, 66, 417–48.

Gilbert, G. K. 1885: The topographic features of lake shores, *US Geological Survey. Fifth Annual Report*, pp. 69–123.

Gilbert, G. K. 1890: Lake Bonneville. *US Geological Survey, Monograph* 1, 1–438.

Hammen, A. van der. 1963: A palynological study on the Quaternary of British Guiana. *Lied. Geol. Meded.*, 29. 125–80.

Hammen, A. van der. 1974: The Pleistocene changes of vegetation and climate in tropical South America. *J. Biogeogr.*, 1, 3–26.

Hartt, C. F. 1870: *Geology and physical geography of Brazil.* Boston: Field Osgood and Co.

Hedgepeth, J. W. 1953: An introduction to the zoogeography of the N. W. Gulf of Mexico. *Publ. Inst. Mar. Sci.*, 3, 111–224.

Hustedt, F. 1953: Die systematik der Diatomeen in ihren Beziehungen zur Geologie und Ökologie nebst einer Revision des Holobien-Systems. *Svensk Bot. Tidskr.*, 47, 509–19.

Jelgersma, S. 1961: Holocene sea-level changes in the Netherlands. *Meded. Geol. Sticht.* Serie C, v. 17, 1–100.

Jelgersma, S., Oele, E. and Wiggers, A. J. 1979: Depositional history and coastal development in the Netherlands and the adjacent North Sea since the Eemian. In E. Oele, R. T. E. Schüttenhelm and A. J. Wiggers (eds), The Quaternary history of the North Sea. *Acta Univ. Ups. Symp. Univ. Ups. Annum Quingentesimum Celebrantis* 2. Uppsala, 115–42.

Jost, H and Godolphim, M. 1975: Holocene sea-level fluctuations in the Rio de Grande do Sul coastal province (abstract) *Bolm. parana. Geocienc.* 33, 55.

Kneip, L. M., Pallestrini, L. and Cunha, F. L. S. (eds) 1981: *Pesquisas arqueologicas no litoral de Itaipú, Niterói, R.J.* Rio de Janeiro: Cia. de Desenvolvimento Territorial, 174.

Kolbe, R. W. 1927: Zur Ökologie, Morphologie und Systematik der Brackwasserdiatomeen. Die Kieselalgen des Sperenberger Salzgebietes. *Pflanzenforschung*, 7, 1–146.

Kolbe, R. W. 1932: Grundlinien einer allgemeinen Ökologie der Diatomeen. *Ergebn. Biol.*, 8, 221–348.

Kowsmann, R. O. and Costa, M. P. A. 1979: Evidence of late Quaternary sea-level stillstands on the upper Brazilian continental margin: a synthesis. In K. Suguio, T. R. Fairchild, L. Martin and J.-M. Flexor (eds), 1979: *Proceedings of the 1978 International Symposium on Coastal Evolution in the Quaternary*, São Paulo, Brasil, 170–92.

Kowsmann, R. O., Costa, M. P. A., Vicalvi, M. A., Coutinho, M. G. N. and Gamboa, L. A. P. 1977: Modelo da sedimentação holocênica na plataforma sul brasileira. In *PROJECT REMAC – Evolucado sedimentar holocênica da plataforma continental e do talude do sul do Brasil*. Rio de Janeiro: Petrobras, Cenpes/Dintep Serie Projecto REMAC, 2, 7–26.

Laborel, J. 1979: Fixed marine organisms as biological indicators for the study of recent sea-level and climatic variations along the Brazilian Tropical coast. In K. Suguio, T. R. Fairchild, L. Martin and J.-M. Flexor (eds), 1979: *Proceedings of the 1978 International Symposium on Coastal Evolution in the Quaternary*, São Paulo, Brasil, 193–211.

Mabesoone, J. M. 1964: Origin and age of the sandstone reefs of Pernambuco (northeast Brazil). *J. Sedim. Petrol.*, 34, 715–26.

Martin, L. and Suguio, K. 1975: The state of Sao Paulo coastal marine Quaternary geology – the ancient standlines. *Anais Acad. Bras. Cienc.*, 47 (suppl.), 249–63.

Martin, L., Suguio, K., Flexor, J.-M., Bittencourt, A. and Vilas Boas G. 1979–80: Le Quaternaire marin bresilien (littoral pauliste, sud fluminense et bahianais). *Cah. O.R.S.T.O.M.*, ser. Geol. XI, 95–124.

Milliman, J. D. and Barretto, H. T. 1975: Relict magnesian calcite oolite and subsidence of the Amazon shelf. *Sedimentology*, 22, 137–45.

Mörner, N.-A. 1969: The Late Quaternary history of the Kattegatt Sea and the Swedish west coast. *Sver. geol. Unders.*, serie 6, 640, 1–487.

Muehe, D. 1979: Sedimentology and topography of a high energy coastal environment between Rio de Janeiro and Cabo Frio – Brazil. *Anais. Acad. Bras. Cienc.*, 51, 473–81.

Muehe, D. 1982: Küstentwicklung und Sedimentation im Bereich der Brasilianischen Randtropen – Untersuchungen zwischen Rio de Janeiro und Ponta Negra. Doctoral Thesis, Univ. Kiel.

Muller, J. 1965: Palynological study of Holocene peat in Sarawak. *Proceedings of the Symposium on ecological research in humid tropics*. Kuching, Sarawak: July 1963. 147–56.

Oliveira, L. 1948: Estudo hibrobiológico das lagôas de Piratininga e Itaipú.

Mems. Inst. Oswaldo Cruz, 46, 673–718.

Oliveira, L., Nascimento, R., Krau, L. and Miranda, A. 1955: Biogeographic and hydrobiologic observations on the lake of Maricá. *Mems. Inst. Oswaldo Cruz*, 53, 228–62.

Petri, S. and Suguio, K. 1973: Stratigraphy of the Iguape-Cananéia lagoonal region sedimentary deposits, São Paulo State – Brazil. Part II: heavy mineral studies, micro-organism inventories and statigraphic interpretations. *Bolm. IG Inst. Geocienc. USP*, 4, 71–85.

Plassche, O. van de 1977: A manual for sample collection and evaluation of sea level data (draft). Amsterdam: Free University.

Prance, G. T. 1978: The origin and evolution of the Amazon flora. *Interciencia*, 3, 207–22.

Rampino, M. R. and Sanders, J. E. 1982: Holocene transgression in south-central Long Island, New York – reply. *J. Sedim. Petrol.*, 52, 1020–5.

Roeleveld, W. 1969: Pollen analysis of two sections in the young coastal plain of Surinam. *Geol. Mijnbouw*, 48, 215–24.

Ruellan, F. 1944: A evolução geomorphologica da Baia de Guanabara et das regiões vizinhas. *Revta. bras. Geogr.*, VI, 443–508.

Shennan, I. 1980: Flandrian Sea-level Changes in the Fenland. Unpub. PhD Thesis, Univ. Durham.

Shennan, I. 1982a: Interpretation of Flandrian sea-level data from the Fenland, England. *Proc. Geol. Ass.*, 93, 53–63.

Shennan, I. 1982b: Problems of correlating Flandrian sea-level changes and climate. In A. Harding (ed.), *Climatic Change in Later Prehistory*, Edinburgh: Edinburgh University Press, 52–87.

Shennan, I., Tooley, M. J., Davis, M. J. and Haggart, B. A. 1983: Analysis and interpretation of Holocene sea-level data, *Nature*, 302, 404–6.

Simonsen, R. 1962: Untersuchungen zur Systematik und Ökologie der Bodendiatomeen der westlichen Ostsee. *Syst. Beih. Intern. Rev. Gesamt. Hydrobiol.*, 1, 1–144.

Streif, H. 1979: Cyclic formation of coastal deposits and their indications of vertical sea-level changes. *Oceanis*, 5, 303–6.

Suguio, K. and Martin, L. 1978: Quaternary marine formations of the State of São Paulo and Southern Rio de Janeiro. *1978 International Symposium on coastal evolution of the Quaternary. Special Publication no. 1.* Brazilian National Working Group for IGCP-Project 61, São Paulo, Brasil.

Suguio, K. and Martin, L. 1981: Progress in research on Quaternary sea-level changes and coastal evolution in Brazil. In *Variations in Sea Level in the Last 15 000 years, magnitude and causes.* Wade Hampton Conference Center, Univ. of S. Carolina, Columbia, USA April 6–10, 1981, 166–81.

Suguio, K., Martin, L. and Flexor, J.-M. 1980: Sea-level fluctuations during the past 6000 yers along the coast of the state of São Paulo, Brazil. In N.-A. Mörner (ed.) 1980, *Earth Rheology, Isostasy and Eustasy*. Chichester: John Wiley and Sons, 471–86.

Suguio, K. and Petri, S. 1973: Stratigraphy of the Iguape-Cananéia lagoonal region sedimentary deposits, Sao Paulo State, Brazil. Part 1: field observations and grain size analysis. *Bolm. IG. Inst. Geocienc.*, *U.S.P.* 4: 1–20.

Thom, B. G. 1973: The dilemma of high interstadial sea levels during the last glaciation. *Prog. Phys. Geogr.*, 6, 233–59.

Tooley, M. J. 1978: *Sea-level changes in North-west England during the Flandrian stage*. Oxford: Clarendon Press.

Tooley, M. J. 1981: Methods of reconstruction. In I. G. Simmons and M. J. Tooley (eds), *The Environment in British Prehistory*, London: Gerald Duckworth and Co. Ltd, 1–48.

Tooley, M. J. 1982: Sea-level changes in northern England. *Proc. Geol. Ass.*, 93, 43–51.

Tooley, M. J. 1986: Sea levels. *Prog. Phys. Geogr.*, 10, 120–9.

Tricart, J. 1959: Problemes geomorphologiques du littoral oriental du Brésil. *Cah. Océanogr.*, 11, 276–308.

Troels-Smith, J. 1955: Karakteriserig af løse jordarter. *Danm. geol. Unders*, *IV*, 3, 1–73.

Werff, A. van der 1960: Die Diatomeen des Dollart-Emsgebietes. *Verh. K. Ned. Geol. mijnbouw Genoot.* (Geol. Ser.) 19, 153–201.

Williams, R. B. 1964: Division rates of salt-marsh diatoms in relation to salinity and cell size. *Ecology*, 45, 877–86.

3

Relative Sea-level Changes in the Moray Firth area, Scotland

B. Andrew Haggart

1.0 INTRODUCTION

The most detailed evidence for relative sea-level change in Scotland since deglaciation is from the Forth and Tay valleys (reviewed in Sissons 1983, Sutherland 1984). In these areas detailed morphological mapping, stratigraphic survey, levelling and radiocarbon dating have led to the establishment of a shoreline sequence which has become an informal model for comparison with relative sea-level changes in other parts of Scotland. At present there is no comparable shoreline sequence for the other major estuaries of eastern Scotland. In the absence of such a scheme, positive and negative movements in relative sea level have to be assessed from lithostratigraphic and biostratigraphic indicators at each site of investigation.

This paper provides a description and assessment of sea-level indicators from Moniack (NH 54 43), a site located at the head of the Beauly Firth 12 km west of Inverness (figure 3.1). The description is preceded by a review of the published literature relevant to relative sea-level changes since deglaciation of the inner Moray Firth estuaries. In the sections which follow an assessment is made of the extent to which the Moniack data reflect regional sea-level tendencies as opposed to site-specific changes in the sedimentary environment. This is achieved by comparison with radiocarbon-dated stratigraphies from neighbouring sites which constitute part of a more comprehensive stratigraphic survey of the area (Haggart 1982, 1986). Finally the evidence from the Moray Firth area is compared with that from other areas of Scotland.

The methodology adopted follows that of Shennan (1983a,b) in using lithostratigraphic and biostratigraphic evidence and radiocarbon dating to assess the geographical scale, direction and timing of the sea-level

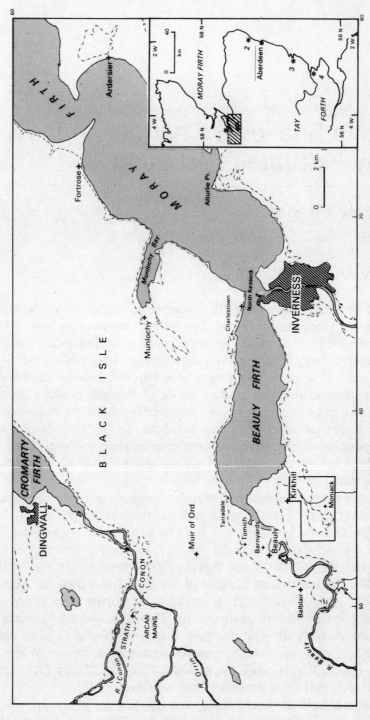

Figure 3.1 A map showing the locations of sites mentioned in the text, with an inset map of eastern Scotland: 1, Cromarty Firth C2 borehole; 2, Ythan estuary; 3, Montrose Basin; 4, St. Michael's Wood, East Fife

tendencies represented by each index point. Once all relevant data have been assessed the dominant tendency through time can be determined and relative sea-level movements inferred.

2.0 RELATIVE SEA-LEVEL CHANGES IN THE INNER MORAY FIRTH ESTUARIES

Fine-grained marine sedimentary units deposited during ice-sheet deglaciation are preserved at a range of altitudes both on land near the coast of Scotland and offshore on adjacent shelf areas. Though displaying considerable lateral and vertical variation these deposits have been subdivided into two informal lithostratigraphic units, based largely on their macro- and microfossil content, termed Errol beds and Clyde beds (Peacock 1975, 1981). The Errol beds are found mainly on the east coast of Scotland in the Forth and Tay valleys and offshore from the Forth Approaches to the Aberdeen area (figure 3.1). They contain a low-diversity arctic fauna and were deposited between *c.*18000 BP and *c.*13500 BP (Peacock 1981). The Clyde beds occur mainly in the Clyde estuary, in neighbouring areas on the west coast of Scotland and in the western Forth valley. The transition from Errol beds to Clyde beds is considered to represent a general warming of Scottish nearshore waters between *c.*13500 BP and *c.*13000 BP (Peacock 1981). In the Cromarty Firth area, Peacock *et al.* (1980) showed that the lowermost deposits encountered in estuarine sediments *c.*5 km north-east of Dingwall (figure 3.1, inset) contained a cold water macro- and microfauna which they considered equivalent in character to Clyde beds faunas. No deposits similar to the older Errol beds were discovered which implies that the inner Cromarty Firth area, and by extension the Beauly Firth area, were probably under ice until *c.*13500–13000 BP.

As ice-sheet deglaciation proceeded westward to the heads of the inner Moray Firth estuaries it was accompanied by a high relative sea level which flooded into the newly deglaciated areas. The field evidence for the period between ice-sheet deglaciation and the Loch Lomond Stadial is fragmentary around the shores of the inner Moray and Beauly Firths and includes deposits of beach gravel, beach ridges, deltas and fluvioglacial terraces graded to former sea level at altitudes between *c.*40 m and *c.*26 m OD (Synge 1977, Synge and Smith 1980). At Englishton (NH 60 40, figure 3.2), for example, a flat-topped delta graded to a sea level of *c.*30 m OD was fed from the south by a large meltwater channel. An exposure showing foreset bedding capped by topset bedding provides strong evidence for the contemporaneity of retreating ice and high relative sea level (Synge and Smith 1980). Nearby, at Barnyards (NH 52 47, figure 3.1), *c*.70 cm of fine-grained grey marine silts and clays overlie a pink sandy till at *c*.0.6 m OD and constitute additional evidence of marine sedimentation accompanying deglaciation (Haggart 1986). At Balblair (NH 50 45, figure 3.2) a large delta graded to a sea level of *c*.26–30 m OD, backed by an ice contact slope, suggests that by the time sea level had reached this altitude the ice front position lay to landward of the present shore of the Beauly Firth in the lower Beauly valley.

By the start of the Loch Lomond Stadial relative sea level had fallen to below that of the present. Sissons (1981) has described a buried gravel layer and shoreline beneath the Kirkhill carse (NH 56 45) which he considers to be the equivalent of the buried gravel layer and Main Lateglacial Shoreline of south-east Scotland. The layer is extensive at Kirkhill and normally truncates finer Late Devensian marine silts and clays. It rises to landward from *c*.−1 m OD to a shoreline at *c*.2 m OD and further to landward it rises more steeply to form a surface of marine erosion which reaches *c*.6.6 m OD. Sissons suggested that the shoreline was formed during the severe climatic regime of the Loch Lomond Stadial at the culmination of a period of slowly rising relative sea level and before a more rapid rise which led to the formation of the steeper erosion surface. A similar coarser layer composed of silt, sand and gravel attaining an altitude of *c*.10 m OD has been described from Barnyards (Haggart 1986) where it also truncates finer Late Devensian marine deposits. The layer at Barnyards is considered to be the correlative of the gravel layer at Kirkhill and supports the interpretation of a widespread erosional event during the Loch Lomond Stadial in the Beauly Firth area.

At Barnyards a widespread deposit of grey silts and clays, the upper section of which contains a marine and brackish diatom flora, overlies the coarser silt, sand and gravel and reaches an altitude of 6.6 m OD. A radiocarbon date of 9610±130 BP (Birm 1123) on peat above the silts and clays near to their landward limit and another of 9200±100 BP (Hv 10010) close to the seaward extent of peat deposition at *c*.2 m OD suggest that relative sea level fell during this period (Haggart 1986). This evidence implies that if Sissons' interpretation of the direction of relative sea level during the Loch Lomond Stadial is accepted, relative sea level fell during the Late Devensian/Flandrian transition at Barnyards. This was followed by a period of stillstand or minor rise during which the grey silts and clays were deposited up to 6.6 m OD and then by a major fall commencing before *c*.9600 BP which enabled peat to develop on the former estuarine surface. This period of low relative sea level may be reflected by a series of deeply incised gullies cut to a level below that of the Main Postglacial Shoreline in the area which occur on the south side of the Cromarty Firth between Jemimaville and Cromarty (Smith, J. S. 1963 and figure 3.2) and also by the many records of peat exposed below present MHWST around the shores of the Moray Firth (Haggart 1982).

Renewed deposition of marine-estuarine silts and clays over peat and representing the main Flandrian rise in sea level began at Barnyards after *c*.8800 BP and continued until after *c*.7300 BP (Haggart 1986). Prior to the end of this rise a thin layer of grey micaceous silty sand was laid down during a higher energy episode at Barnyards. The correlation of this with similar deposits from a number of sites around the coasts of eastern Scotland has led to the suggestion that it may have resulted from a North Sea storm surge event (Smith, D. E. *et al.* 1985).

The end of the main Flandrian rise in relative sea level coincides with the formation of the Main Postglacial Shoreline in the area. It is surprising that even though this and other Flandrian shorelines are continuous for many kilometres around the shores of the Moray Firth and have been described by many researchers (Peach 1912, Horne and Hinxman 1914, Ogilvie 1914, 1923, Read *et al.* 1925, 1926, Steers 1937), little accurate altitudinal information is available. However Smith (1966) surveyed the Main Postglacial Shoreline in the Beauly Firth area and demonstrated a rise to westward of 0.09 m/km between Kessock (8.2 m OD) and Tarradale (9.1 m OD, figure 3.2). This latter altitude is in accord with the highest level reached by the marine-estuarine silts and clays at Barnyards (8.6 m OD) and Arcan Mains (9 m OD). Two radiocarbon dates of 5510 ± 80 BP (Birm 1122) and 5775 ± 75 BP (Hv 10012), both supported by pollen and diatom stratigraphies, give a minimum age for the formation of the Main Postglacial Shoreline in the area. Relative sea level has continued to fall to the present with perhaps several periods of stillstand or minor rise during which up to five lower beaches were formed (Smith 1966, Firth 1984).

3.0 TECHNIQUES

All boreholes were instrumentally levelled to Ordnance Datum (Newlyn) and all traverses were closed. The total closing error for traverses ranged from 0.23 m to 0.03 m with a mean of 0.1 m and a median of 0.07 m. Stratigraphic reconnaissance was carried out using a 1 m long half-cylinder Duits gouge sampler with extension rods. Larger samples for laboratory analysis were retrieved using either a modified Livingstone-type sampler (Merkt and Streif 1970) or 0.5 m and 1 m long Russian-type

Table 3.1   Pollen and diatom statistics

Pollen (Σ Total land pollen, TLP)

Site	Levels	Maximum	Minimum	Median	Mean	Standard deviation
M4D	22	208	164	204	202	8.8
M29B	49	596	100	217	240.6	98.6

Diatoms (Σ Total valves)

M4B	12	301	197	210.5	220	27.8
M29B	21	276	197	222	222.5	19.1

samplers. Preparation of samples for pollen and diatom analysis followed standard procedures (Battarbee 1979, Birks 1979). Prior to chemical treatment for pollen extraction, tablets of *Lycopodium* spores were added to a known volume of fresh sediment (Stockmarr 1971) in order that pollen concentration values could be calculated. Counting was undertaken on either a Zeiss or Vickers microscope at 400× and 625× magnification for pollen and diatoms respectively. Descriptive statistics for all levels counted are given in table 3.1.

Pollen analysis is used in this study to provide an independent age determination to supplement and verify radiocarbon dating, as an indicator of possible breaks in sedimentation and as a guide to changes in the local environment. Pollen identifications were made with reference to Faegri and Iversen (1974) and Moore and Webb (1978) and to extensive type-slide collections at Durham University and City of London Polytechnic. Diatom analysis is used to identify the broad changes in depositional environment through each main minerogenic unit. Diatom identifications were made with reference to Cleve-Euler (1951–55), Hendey (1964), Hustedt (1927–62) and van der Werff and Huls (1957–74) and the nomenclature follows Cleve-Euler. The count data were processed using the program NEWPLOT written by Dr I. Shennan and adapted for use on a microcomputer by the author. The program calculates 95 per cent confidence limits about the mean for each individual count. This provides an effective aid to pollen zonation since significant changes in taxa between levels can be readily identified where the confidence limits do not overlap. All pollen and diatom diagrams were zoned visually by assessing the number of significant changes present at each level. Samples for radiocarbon dating were taken using a 0.5 m long Russian-type sampler from four adjacent boreholes at Moniack 4B. In the laboratory, sub-samples of 5 cm thickness were cut from each core at the relevant lithostratigraphic boundaries and bulked to provide sufficient material for radiocarbon assay.

4.0 SITE DESCRIPTION AND STRATIGRAPHY

The Moniack site (NH 54 43) is located at the head of a sheltered embayment formed by the smaller section of the Beauly carse to the south-east of the Kirkhill ridge and 4 km from the contemporary shore of the Beauly Firth (figure 3.2). Three crag and tail features, the larger at Balchraggan reaching 60 m OD and a smaller, more complex, double form north-east of Cabrich together with linear ridges south of Moniack Castle and at Drumreach, suggest ice-movement from the south-west to north-east across the site. This direction conforms with the evidence of indicator erratics and striae from the area between the Beauly Firth and Loch Ness (Horne and Hinxman 1914).

A large alluvial fan deposited by the Moniack Burn has developed across the entire width of the embayment. The fan has an area of *c*.1.1 km² and its surface falls in altitude from *c*.41 m OD near the apex south-east of Moniack Castle to *c*.12 m OD near borehole 12. On morphological evidence alone Ogilvie (1923) suggested that this feature predated the main Flandrian rise in relative sea level since he stated that it 'is doubtful if the sea at the 25 to 30 ft [*c*.7.6 to 9.2 m] level passed the Moniack fan.' Initially, a stratigraphic investigation was undertaken to test this hypothesis and 58 boreholes were put down using a percussion drill and gouge sampler. All but three of the boreholes were located on the edge of the fan or to its landward in an area of surface peat covering *c*.0.8 km² which is divided by the eastern double crag and tail feature. The stratigraphic investigation showed that a complex sedimentary sequence of peat and intercalated minerogenic deposits, over 10 m thick in places, rests upon a minerogenic surface forming two depressions either side of the complex crag and tail feature (figures 3.3, 3.4 and 3.5).

The basal unit recorded by the stratigraphic survey is a light brown silty sand and gravel (boreholes 16–18, figure 3.4). However the small amount of sediment retained in the gouge sampler and its identification in only three boreholes makes an assessment of the provenance of this deposit difficult. In boreholes 25–28 the lowermost deposit is recorded as a grey or grey-pink sand and gravel. It is uncertain whether this deposit is the same as the basal unit or if it corresponds to a separate sand and gravel unit higher in the stratigraphy. It is therefore shown as undifferentiated sand and gravel on figure 3.4.

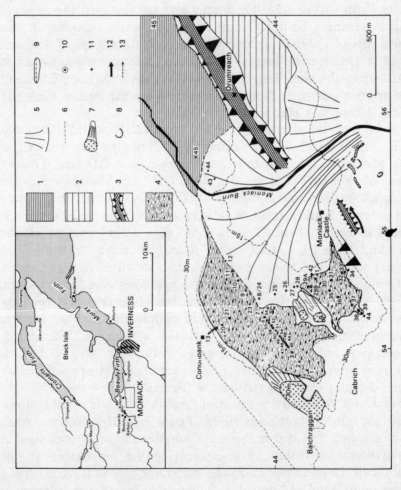

Figure 3.2 A map to show the location and landforms at Moniack and an inset map of the Cromarty, Beauly and Moray Firths, showing place names mentioned in the text. Key: 1, Kirkhill carse; 2, Undifferentiated Late Devensian marine deposits; 3, Ridge forms; 4, Surface peat; 5, Alluvial fan; 6, Boundary of fan uncertain; 7, Crag and tail forms; 8, Dead ice hollows; 9, Eskers; 10, Pollen, diatom and ¹⁴C sampling sites; 11, Boreholes; 12, Meltwater Channel; 13, Small channel form

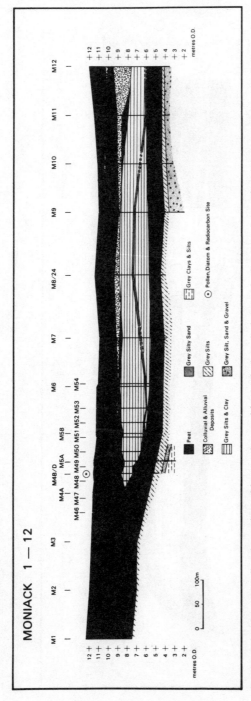

Figure 3.3 A generalised stratigraphic section at Moniack, boreholes 1-12, the locations of which are shown on figure 3.2

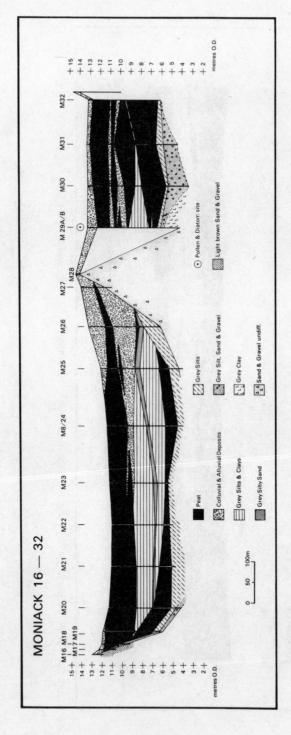

Figure 3.4 A generalised stratigraphic section through Late Devensian and Flandrian deposits at Moniack, boreholes 16-32, the locations of which are shown on figure 3.2

In several boreholes there is a minerogenic unit of grey clays, silts, sands and gravel lying between the basal sand and gravel and the lowermost of a series of peat layers. None of the boreholes contains an unambiguous, conformable contact with the basal sand and gravel and therefore the precise sequence of deposits postdating the basal unit is not known with certainty. However the sediments recorded can be divided into three or perhaps four sub-units (table 3.2). A distinctive layer of compact grey clays with some silt is overlain unconformably by a coarser layer of silt, sand and gravel which in turn is succeeded by a finer sub-unit composed predominantly of grey silts. A fourth sub-unit of grey silty sand may lie beneath the lower compact grey clay. This is suggested by the lowermost deposit recorded in borehole 37 which comprises 76 cm of blue-grey silty clay containing thin (*c.*1 cm) laminations of grey-white sand. Similarly in borehole 5A (figure 3.3) the lowermost deposit recorded, primarily of grey clay and silt, contains an increased proportion of silt and sand towards the base.

The available evidence for the sub-unit of compact grey clays with some silt (B(ii), table 3.2) is contained in boreholes 5A, 29A, 36 and 37. Shell fragments, presumed to be marine, were noted within this layer in boreholes 29A and 36 (figure 3.5). In general the layer is composed of an homogeneous compact grey clay that is difficult to penetrate even with a percussion drill. The maximum recorded thickness of the sub-unit is *c.*200 cm in borehole 36. In 5A, there is a higher silt content together with dark grey to black mottles of presumed sulphide-rich areas. The maximum altitude reached by the sub-unit is 6.7 m OD in borehole 37 above which it is truncated by a coarser layer of silt, sand and gravel. This latter sub-unit (B(iii), table 3.2) is variable in thickness and rises across the site from *c.*3.5–4 m OD between boreholes 12 and 9 to reach 4.7 m OD in borehole 20. To landward of 20 however, the surface of the layer rises more steeply to attain over 11 m OD in borehole 17 (figure 3.4). Above the coarser silt, sand and gravel is a sub-unit predominantly composed of grey silts which thins to landward, reaching a maximum altitude of 7.3 m OD in borehole 37 and *c.*7.5 m OD in both 1 and 19.

A widespread biogenic layer, usually comprising a compact, dry, herbaceous peat lies above the lower minerogenic sequence. The lower contact has an overall seaward slope in the north-western depression, falling from *c.*7.5 m to 4.4 m OD between boreholes 1 and 12, a distance of *c.*1.2 km (figure 3.3). The peat unit shows variation in composition across the site. For instance, in borehole 20 there is a basal layer of yellow-brown, well-humified bryophyte peat, perhaps reflecting enhanced

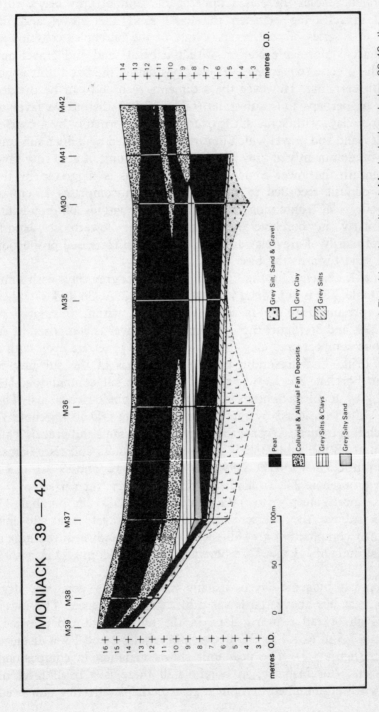

Figure 3.5 A stratigraphic section through the Late Deversian and Flandrian deposits at Moniack, boreholes 39-42, the locations of which are shown on figure 3.2

Table 3.2 Generalised lithostratigraphy at Moniack

E		Peat-colluvial/alluvial fan deposits.
D	(iii)	Grey silty clay/alluvial fan deposits.
D	(ii)	Grey micaceous silty sand.
D	(i)	Grey silty clay.
C		Peat.
B	(iv)	Grey silt.
B	(iii)	Grey silt, sand and gravel.
B	(ii)	Grey compact clay.
B	(i)	Grey silty sand?
A		Light brown (pink) silt, sand and gravel.

groundwater levels at the foot of the slope. In borehole 9 the sub-peat surface is at a slightly lower altitude compared to surrounding boreholes and within the peat at this location and at 8/24 and 23 there are 2 thin layers of light brown organic silt, too thin to be shown on figures 3.3 and 3.4, that suggest the presence of a small water body. Finally, a larger component of woody detritus in the peat at 2, 3, 4, 9 and 33 suggests that areas of the site may have been dry enough to support tree growth during formation of the lower peat. The upper contact of this peat falls from a maximum altitude of $c.8.6$ m OD landward of borehole 19 to 6.1 m OD at 12.

Lying above the peat is a further minerogenic unit comprised of 3 sub-units (table 3.2). Stratigraphically above the peat is a sub-unit of grey silty clay (D(i), table 3.2) which in turn is overlain by a coarser, thinner, layer of grey micaceous silty sand (D(ii), table 3.2). The surface of the latter ranges in altitude from $c.6.1$ m OD In borehole 11 to $c.10$ m OD in borehole 1. To landward of 51 there is evidence of erosion across the lower peat and the layer forms a separate tapering wedge of sediment (figure 3.3). Above the layer is a thin *Phragmites* peat which extends seaward as far as borehole 51. Further seaward another layer of grey silty clay is present above the grey micaceous silty sand reaching an altitude of $c.8.5$ m OD between 48 and 4A in the north-western depression and $c.9.3$ m OD in borehole 29B in the south-eastern depression (figures 3.3 and 3.4).

A further widespread peat layer occurs above the grey silty clay and forms the surface deposit over much of the site. Nearer to the alluvial fan, however, a number of layers composed of varying proportions of clay, silt, sand and gravel and including herbaceous and woody detritus are intercalated within the peat. There are three such layers at borehole 29B.

In general these layers thicken towards the Moniack alluvial fan and are interpreted as material of fluvial origin laid down by the Moniack Burn.

4.1 Site Biostratigraphy

Two locations were chosen for further detailed microfossil study. Borehole 29B in the south-eastern depression contains a complex stratigraphy of six biogenic and six minerogenic layers (figure 3.4). It was considered typical of boreholes nearer to the Moniack alluvial fan and was investigated to provide information on the influence of this feature on sedimentation at the site. Boreholes 4B and 4D are situated in the north-western depression and contain a simpler stratigraphy. These boreholes are *c*.5 m apart and were sampled at different times, 4B for diatoms and material for radiocarbon dating and 4D for pollen. This location was chosen because it is close to the landward limit of grey silty clay deposition where the thin grey micaceous silty sand layer lies directly on the lower peat and is separated from the grey silty clay above by a thin *Phragmites* peat (figures 3.2 and 3.3).

Moniack 29B (NH 5454 4368)

A core was taken from 29B using a modified Livingstone-type sampler. A summary of the stratigraphy is presented in table 3.3 and a more detailed description is given in Haggart (1982). The basal layers were not sampled because sediment below 718 cm was not retained in the sampling chamber. A nearby borehole taken with a smaller diameter gouge sampler penetrated to 895 cm (4.7 m OD) and proved a layer of compact grey silty clay containing shell fragments beneath the light grey sand and gravel. Fifty samples were analysed for pollen between 700 and 140 cm. The percentage frequency pollen diagram is presented in figure 3.6 and shows levels between 700 and 220 cm. It is divided into seven local pollen assemblage zones:

	cm from surface		
M29B1	700	– 670	Cyperaceae-Gramineae
M29B2	670	– 611.5	*Betula-Corylus/Myrica*
M29B3	611.5	– 444	*Pinus*
M29B4	444	– 394	*Alnus-Pinus*
M29B5	394	– 293	Gramineae-*Alnus*
M29B6	293	– 269.5	*Salix*-Gramineae
M29B7	269.5	– 200	*Alnus-Corylus/Myrica*-Gramineae

Table 3.3 The stratigraphy at Moniack-29B

Litho-unit	Depth (cm)	Altitude (m OD)	Description
	0–99	12.33–13.32	Not sampled
27–31	99–211	11.21–12.33	Dark brown herbaceous peat.
21–26	211–270	10.62–11.21	Brown and grey silts and sands.
20	270–285	10.47–10.62	Dark brown detrital peat. *Betula* sp. fruit and leaf fragments at 284 cm.
19	285–296	10.36–10.47	Grey silty clay with organic bands.
17–18	296–333	9.99–10.36	Dark brown herbaceous and detrital peat. *Hippuris vulgaris* seed at 296 cm, *Potamogeton natans* seed at 311 cm, *P. cf. alpinus*, *Juncus* sp. seeds at 330 cm.
16	333–393	9.39–9.99	Grey brown clayey silt. *Betula* sp. fruit and *Juncus effusus*-type seed at 333 cm, *Carex rostrata* seed at 334 cm.
15	393–398	9.34–9.39	Grey-brown clayey peat.
10–14	398–603	7.29–9.34	Grey silty clay.
8–9	603–626	7.06–7.29	Dark brown, dry, crumbly peat.
4–7	626–650	6.82–7.06	Grey silts, *Menyanthes* and *Carex* sp. seeds at 649 cm.
3	650–688	6.44–6.82	Dark brown herbaceous peat. *Juncus articulatus* type seed at 685 cm.
2	688–705	6.27–6.44	Light grey organic clay.
1	705–718	6.14–6.27	Light grey sand and gravel.

Thirty-two levels were routinely scanned for diatoms. In all levels below 600 cm diatoms were absent or too scarce to count. At 649 cm and 645 cm only a few fragments attributable to *Pinnularia* sp. and *Cymbella* sp. remained. At 294, 240, 230 and 216 cm diatoms were present though sparse in number and as all species encountered had fresh and fresh-brackish affinities, these counts were discontinued. The remaining 21 levels between 600 and 269 cm are presented in figure 3.7. The diagram is divided into three diatom assemblage zones:

cm from surface

M29BD1	600	– 450	*Paralia sulcata-Grammatophora oceanica*
M29BD2	450	– 396.5	*Diploneis interrupta*
M29BD3	396.5	– 269	*Tabellaria fenestrata*

MONIACK 29B

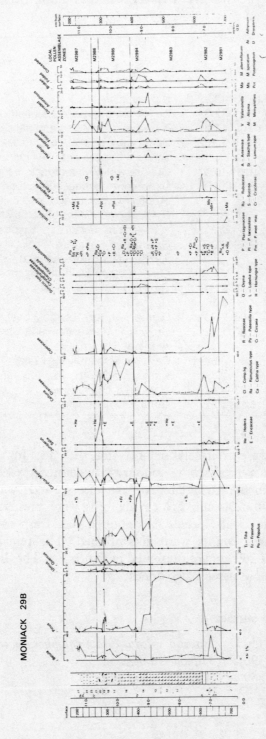

Figure 3.6 A relative percentage frequency pollen diagram from Moniack 29B. The stratigraphy is drawn up using symbols after Troels-Smith (1955); each denotes 25% presence. The numbers to the left of the stratigraphic column refer to the litho stratigraphic unit numbers used in a detailed description of the core by Haggart (1982). The sum used for the pollen frequency curves is (Total Land Pollen + Group)

MONIACK 29B

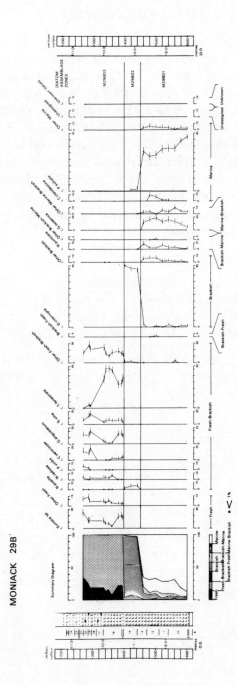

Figure 3.7 A diatom diagram from Moniack 29B. The sum used is the number of total valves counted. Salinity classes follow van der Werff and Huls (1957–1974). Full diatom counts are given in Haggart (1982)

Moniack 4B (NH 5411 4393) and 4D (NH 5410 4392)

Material for diatom analysis was taken using a 0.5 m long Russian-type sampler at 4B and on a separate occasion for pollen analysis using a 1 m long Russian-type sampler from 4D, *c*.5 m to the south-west. The ground surface altitude is the same for both boreholes yet the depths of stratigraphic horizons differ. A summary of the main stratigraphic units recorded at both these boreholes is presented in table 3.4. A more detailed description is given in Haggart (1982). An adjacent borehole taken with a smaller diameter gouge sampler penetrated to 595 cm and proved the lower peat overlies a unit of grey silt at 5.6 m OD. Twenty-two levels were analysed and counted for pollen between 453 and 270 cm. The percentage frequency diagram is presented in figure 3.8 and is divided into four local pollen assemblage zones:

cm from surface

M4D1	452 – 447.5	*Pinus*-Gramineae
M4D2	447.5 – 421	*Pinus*
M4D3	421 – 403	*Pinus*-Gramineae
M4D4	276 – 270	*Alnus-Pinus-Corylus/Myrica*

Twelve levels were counted for diatoms between 471 and 400 cm. The diatom diagram is presented in figure 3.9 and it is divided into five assemblage zones:

Table 3.4   M4B and M4D generalised stratigraphy

M4B Litho-Unit	Depth (cm)	Altitude (m OD)	M4D Litho-unit	Depth (cm)	Altitude (m OD)	Description
10	0 –289	8.70–11.59	12	0–260	8.99–11.59	Dark brown herbaceous peat.
8–9	289 –419	7.40–8.70	6–11	260–403	7.56– 8.99	Grey organic clay.
6–7	419 –435	7.24–7.40	5	403–419	7.40– 7.56	Dark brown herbaceous peat with *Phragmites* sp.
3–5	435 –468.5	6.905–7.24	3–4	419–443	7.16– 7.40	Grey clay-silt.
2	468.5–472	6.87 –6.905	2	443–447	7.12– 7.16	Grey micaceous silty fine sand.
1	472 –490	6.69 –6.87	1	447–540	6.19– 7.12	Dark brown herbaceous peat.

MONIACK 4D

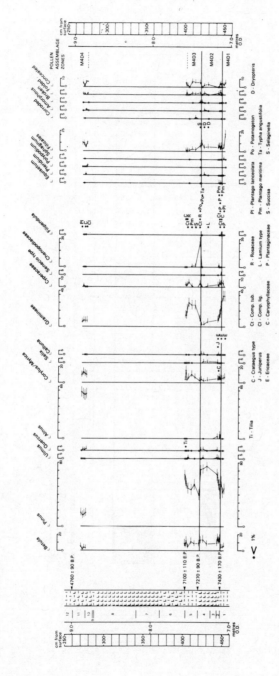

Figure 3.8 A relative percentage frequency pollen diagram from Moniack 4D. The conventions are the same as for figure 3.6

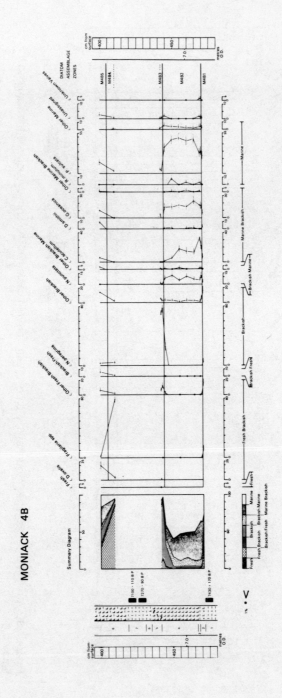

Figure 3.9 A diatom diagram from Moniack 4B

cm from surface

M4BD1	471	– 470.5	*Paralia sulcata-Fragilaria* sp.
M4BD2	470.5	– 444	*P.sulcata-Grammatophora oceanica*
M4BD3	444	– 442	*Navicula peregrina*
M4BD4	410	– 405	*Fragilaria* sp.
M4BD5	405	– 400	*Diploneis ovalis-P.sulcata*

4.2 Radiocarbon Dating

Four peat horizons were selected from borehole 4B for radiocarbon assay. This borehole was chosen because it is located close to the landward limit of grey silty clay deposition and where the thin *Phragmites* peat separates the grey micaceous silty sand layer from the grey silty clay (figures 3.3 and 3.8). Further details are given in table 3.5.

Table 3.5 Radiocarbon dates from Moniack

Site	National grid reference	Altitude (m OD)	Depth (cm)	Laboratory code	Age (^{14}C yrs BP)
M4B	NH 5411 4393	8.71–8.76	283–288	Birm 1124	4760± 90
M4B	NH 5411 4393	7.35–7.40	419–424	Birm 1125	7100±110
M4B	NH 5411 4393	7.28–7.33	426–431	Birm 1126	7270± 90
M4B	NH 5411 4393	6.82–6.87	472–477	Birm 1127	7430±170

4.3 Evidence for Sea-level Change at the Site Scale

One of the earliest marine deposits recorded at Moniack is represented by the sub-unit of grey compact clay containing shell fragments which is present in boreholes 5A, 29A, 36 and 37. In 5A the sub-unit is sulphide-rich while in 37 the lower 75 cm contains thin laminations of grey-white sand which grade upward into grey clay. Similar stratigraphic situations are common elsewhere in Scotland (Peacock 1981) and suggest quiet water deposition in proximity to an ice front. If this were the case at Moniack, meltwater probably entered the catchment via a low col at *c*.30 m OD, 800 m west of Balchraggan (figure 3.2).

Lying stratigraphically above the silty clay is the coarser layer of silt, sand and gravel. Only four out of 16 boreholes penetrate the entire layer and these give an average thickness of 48 cm. The layer is present across the width of the site and rises in a landward direction both to the north-west between boreholes 20 and 17 (figure 3.4) and also to the south-east between 37 and 39 (figure 3.2). This suggests the layer has a marine origin and represents a much higher energy environment than that in which the underlying grey clays were deposited.

The grey silt sub-unit which overlies the silt, sand and gravel layer is similarly interpreted as being of marine origin. The surface altitude of this sub-unit rises landward to wedge out at *c*.7.5 m OD in both the north-western and south-eastern depressions. The average thickness of this layer is 53 cm (n=14) though this masks a distinct difference between the two depressions. In the south-eastern depression the layer tends to be thinner and contains a higher organic content.

At 29B the upper part of this sub-unit contains bands of organic material including the bryophyte *Fontinalis* at 600 cm. The lowermost pollen spectrum at 700 cm (figure 3.6) is dominated by Cyperaceae (76%) and Gramineae (13%) with total arboreal pollen only reaching 3 per cent total pollen + spores. The presence of *Typha latifolia* and *Equisetum* with the grasses, sedges and *Fontinalis* suggests an open reedswamp environ-ment with shallow pools of still or slowly flowing fresh water. The pools were probably colonised by *Typha latifolia* with the grasses, sedges and *Salix* inhabiting slightly drier locations. Seeds of *Jucus articulatus*-type within the lower peat at 685 cm suggest that rushes could also have been an important component of the vegetation. No unequivocal evidence for a marine influence is present in the lowermost count though the presence of Chenopodiaceae pollen may point to saltmarsh environments in the vicinity. The transition to peat is marked by an increase of total pollen concentration, though nearly all is still contributed by Cyperaceae. A decline in the representation of *Equisetum* and the disappearance of *Typha latifolia* may suggest a slight lowering of the local water table as peat growth commenced. There is no indication of a break in deposition and therefore the transition to peat may be termed a regressive contact within this borehole. At the site scale, it seems likely that the lithological change from grey silt to peat records the conformable replacement of marine by terrestrial conditions and can be regarded as a regressive overlap (Tooley 1982).

No radiocarbon dates are available for peat initiation at 29B though the age of this lower regressive overlap can be estimated using the pollen stratigraphy. The frequency of *Corylus/Myrica* pollen rises to 28 per cent at 655 cm at the beginning of pollen zone M29B2 (figure 3.6). At Barnyards, 4 km to the north-west, a radiocarbon date spanning the *Corylus/Myrica* rise and peak gave an age of 9200±100 BP (Hv 10010,

Haggart 1986) which is well within the age range for the *Corylus/Myrica* maximum at other sites in Scotland. This correlation implies that peat growth began in a reedswamp environment on the former marine surface prior to *c.*9200 BP.

Between 650 and 620 cm (figure 3.6) there is a return to minerogenic sedimentation. This is preceded by an increase in Cyperaceae, *Filipendula* and *Selaginella* percentages which suggests a slightly higher local watertable. *Menyanthes* and *Myriophyllum alterniflorum* pollen at 650 cm and a *Menyanthes* seed at 649 cm indicate shallow, oligotrophic, still or slowly moving fresh water. Routine scanning for diatoms encountered only a few fragments of *Pinnularia* sp. and *Cymbella* sp. which is in accord with this interpretation. In adjacent boreholes there is no correlative of this horizon which appears to be limited in extent and may relate to a small channel deposit. Pollen spectra above the minerogenic layer reflect a return to open reedswamp environments with low total tree pollen percentages (6–11 per cent TP+S) accompanied by a rise in the frequency of *Equisetum* spores and Gramineae pollen.

The grey silty clay sub-unit which lies above the lower peat contains abundant marine and marine-brackish diatoms including *Paralia sulcata* which reaches 85 per cent in borehole 29B at 600 cm (figure 3.7). At this location the contact is erosional though in most other boreholes there is a transition between the peat and overlying grey silty clay. Therefore at the site scale this lithostratigraphic change demonstrating an increase in the marine influence may be termed a transgressive overlap (Tooley 1982). There are no radiocarbon dates for the 29B borehole though the age can be estimated using the pollen stratigraphy. *Pinus* pollen rises from 11 to 71 per cent TLP between 620 and 603 cm, the latter depth being within the bottom 1 cm of the overlying grey silty clay. The *Pinus* rise therefore corresponds with a major lithostratigraphic change and this makes it extremely difficult to assess whether the count for *Pinus* at 620 cm is the first indicator of the regional rise of this pollen type or whether the subsequent dominance of *Pinus* in the grey silty clay is the result of local over-representation. *Pinus* pollen is well known to be differentially concentrated in marine and estuarine sediments (Godwin 1975).

In a recent study of the distribution of *Pinus sylvestris* in Britain, Bennett (1984) suggests that pollen diagrams with *Pinus* pollen in excess of 20 per cent TP imply the local presence of the tree. The count of 11 per cent TLP at 620 cm may therefore relate to the expansion phase of *Pinus* into the local area prior to its establishment at the site. Elsewhere in Scotland the expansion of *Pinus* has been dated to between *c.*8250 and *c.*7880 BP in Wester Ross and Sutherland (Birks 1972, Pennington *et al.*

1972), at c.7970 BP in the Cairngorms (O'Sullivan 1975) and at c.7870 BP in Morar (Harkness 1981). Bennett (1984) suggests that *Pinus sylvestris* had become established in a belt stretching from the Grampians to Wester Ross and including the inner Moray Firth estuaries by c.7500 BP. It seems likely therefore that the contact in 29B at 7.3 m OD was eroded after c.7800 BP.

A radiocarbon date of 7100±110 BP (Birm 1125, table 3.5) from borehole 4B at an altitude of 7.4 m OD marks the return of marine sedimentation near to the landward limit of grey silty clay deposition. The overlap does show an altitudinal gradient, falling seaward from 7.8–c.6 m OD between boreholes 48 and 12 (figure 3.3), which suggests the possibility of time-transgressive development. However the available evidence is insufficient to prove this conclusively since the 29B data are based on pollen evidence from an erosional contact.

To the north and north-west of the Moniack alluvial fan the thin sub-unit of grey micaceous silty sand occurs within the grey silty clay and landward of 51 it forms a separate tapering wedge of sediment within peat that lies stratigraphically below the landward limit of grey silty clay (figure 3.3). At 4B the layer is only 3.5 cm thick and lies unconformably on the lower peat. The upper 5 cm of this peat has been radiocarbon dated to 7430±170 BP (Birm 1127, table 3.5). It is overlain by a fining upwards sequence c.34 cm thick and then by the thin *Phragmites* peat (figure 3.8).

A diatom count immediately above the erosion contact at 471 cm contains a mixture of species from fresh-brackish, brackish, marine-brackish and marine environments (figure 3.9). For example there is a proportion of fresh-brackish forms such as *Achnanthes lanceolata*, *Fragilaria bidens*, *F.brevistriata* and *Rhopalodia gibba*, all of which are alkaliphilous and epiphytic species. The brackish component is provided by *Diploneis interrupta*, *Navicula digitoradiata*, *N.peregrina* and *Nitzschia navicularis*. Of these brackish forms *N.peregrina* favours higher vegetated saltmarshes while *N.digitoradiata* and *N.navicularis* have a wider environmental tolerance. *Scoliopleura tumida*, present 1 cm above this level at 470 cm, is another brackish form and is commonly found on bare estuarine sand (Round 1960). The marine-brackish component at 471 cm is represented by the epiphyte *Grammatophora oceanica v. macilenta* and *Cocconeis scutellum* both of which reflect deeper yet still nearshore waters (Edsbagge 1965). Finally, there is a proportion of fully marine diatoms including *Paralia sulcata*, *Rhabdonema minutum* and *Hyalodiscus stelliger*.

Such a mixed diatom spectrum within the lowest 1 cm might support the stratigraphic interpretation that the layer was produced following an erosive incursion of sediment-laden water from a seaward direction that passed through sublittoral, and over the intertidal saltmarsh and fresh-brackish reedswamp environments. There is no evidence for any species of exclusively freshwater affinity within the grey micaceous silty sand layer which reinforces the conclusion that deposition occurred from seaward to landward. However, the diatom content is not homogeneous through the layer and certain consistent changes do occur. The two succeeding counts at 470 and 469 cm show a rise in marine and marine-brackish forms to 77 and *c.*80 per cent of total valves respectively. The pollen spectra at nearby 4D likewise show changes through the layer with Gramineae falling consistently from 26 to 9 per cent and *Pinus* rising from 41 to 65 per cent TLP between 447 and 443 cm (figure 3.8). The distinctive lithology of the layer within the finer silty clays to seaward, the diatom content and the evidence of erosion *c.*350 m to landward of the contemporaneous saltmarsh and reedswamp environments indicate at the very least a considerable lateral landward extension of the marine influence.

In borehole 4B *Paralia sulcata*, reaching 49 per cent of total valves at 455 cm, dominates the diatom assemblage within the *c.*34 cm thick clay silt that lies above the grey micaceous silty sand layer and proves continued marine conditions. A return to more brackish environments is indicated, however, by a rise in the frequency of *Navicula peregrina* to 77.6 per cent of total valves at 433 cm (figure 3.9). The inference of a decrease in the marine influence is reinforced by the decrease in the particle size and in increase in organic content. Changes in the proportion of Gramineae and *Pinus* pollen are a mirror image of those at the lower contact of the minerogenic layer and confirm a return to reedswamp environments. High Chenopodiaceae values of 31 per cent TLP at 420 cm (figure 3.8) suggest this may have been preceded by an episode of saltmarsh development. This consistent, conformable change in environ-ment showing a reduction in the marine influence indicates the contact is a regressive overlap (Tooley 1982). A radiocarbon date on the lower 5 cm of *Phragmites* peat directly overlying the transition zone from the clay silt gave an age of 7270±90 BP (Birm 1126, table 3.5). This date implies that the deposition of the grey micaceous silty sand and overlying clay silt was of short duration. The upper 5 cm of the thin *Phragmites* peat gave a radiocarbon age of 7100±110 BP (Birm 1125, table 3.5) which indicates that this peat also formed over a short period lasting no more than 600 ^{14}C years taking the standard errors into account, and probably much less.

Deposition of the marine silty clay probably continued without major interruption in borehole 29B because there is no equivalent of the grey

micaceous silty sand layer and overlying *Phragmites* peat as found at 4B.
There is in fact little change in either the pollen or diatom content in
borehole 29B until higher in the stratigraphy, between 450–440 cm
(figure 3.7). At 450 cm there is a marked change to a brackish diatom
assemblage with species such as *Diploneis interrupta* and *D.ovalis*
indicating an upper saltmarsh environment and *Navicula pusilla* suggesting
periodic sub-aerial conditions (Round 1960). Between 488 and 440 cm
Pinus pollen frequencies decline from 77 to 26 per cent and there is a
complementary rise in the frequency of *Alnus* pollen (figure 3.6). The
pollen and diatom evidence implies that environments conducive to the
growth of alder fen landward of a saltmarsh were being created near to
this sampling site as marine conditions receded. A similar environmental
change, also at the time of the Boreal-Atlantic transition, has been
reported from Newferry in N.Ireland (Smith 1984).

Again there is difficulty in assessing the age of this change in
environment from the pollen stratigraphy alone since the biostratigraphic
change coincides with a lithostratigraphic change from marine silty clay to
a brackish silty clay with increased organic content. This suggests that the
Alnus rise at the site is greatly influenced by local conditions. However,
two radiocarbon dates from nearby sites with similar stratigraphies,
Barnyards and Arcan Mains, place the local rational *Alnus* limit at prior to
5500 BP and *c*.5800 BP respectively (Haggart 1986). At both these sites
the *Alnus* rise occurs during the transition to more brackish environments
and beneath the dated peat layer which marks the return to terrestrial
conditions. This similarity in pollen stratigraphy and depositional
environment recorded at all three sites suggests that an age estimate of
c.5600 BP can be placed on the thin peat layer between 393–398 cm
which marks the highest altitude reached by marine and brackish
sediments in borehole 29B (figure 3.6).

A radiocarbon date on the lowermost 5 cm of surface peat overlying the
grey silty clay at 4B gave an age of 4760±90 BP (Birm 1124, table 3.5) for
the regressive overlap at this location. This date is *c*.800 ^{14}C years younger
than the age estimate for the same overlap at 29B. However the altitude of
the overlap is *c*.60 cm lower at 4B and the date may only reflect a younger
age for peat initiation at this lower altitude.

In the south-east depression the stratigraphy above the grey silty clay is
extremely complex. In borehole 29B there is a series of three minerogenic
and three biogenic layers. All the minerogenic layers contain fresh or
fresh-brackish diatoms to the exclusion of any forms that are tolerant of
higher salinities (figure 3.7). This confirms that the regressive contact at
9.3 m OD marks the end of marine and brackish conditions at 29B. The

overlying minerogenic layers are interpreted as being entirely of freshwater origin, most probably fluvial or alluvial deposits formed by the renewed development of the Moniack alluvial fan.

Only a small number of borings were put down through the surface of the fan and all of these are located towards its edge (figure 3.2). Nevertheless, certain conclusions can be drawn concerning the relative timing of alluvial fan activity. Firstly, the lower peat is continuous in all boreholes except those in which it has been eroded by subsequent marine action. Secondly, in all boreholes save those nearer to the alluvial fan, the marine grey silty clay is similarly undisturbed. Finally, in certain boreholes minerogenic material of non-marine origin is commonly present at altitudes above that of the marine grey silty clay. The evidence demonstrates a period of alluvial fan extension contemporary with and postdating the culmination of marine conditions at the site. Prior to this time, the Moniack alluvial fan had not completely restricted the access of more saline water from the north-east, though what effect any variation in the width of the constriction had on palaeotidal ranges is unknown. Boreholes 43, 44 and 45 to the east of the fan show little consistency in stratigraphy and do not help resolve the problem.

5.0 RELATIVE SEA-LEVEL CHANGE IN THE BEAULY FIRTH AREA

The Beauly Firth area has undergone perhaps as much as 42 m of glacio-isostatic uplift since *c*.9600 BP (Haggart 1982). The interplay of isostatic uplift together with the restoration of interglacial sea levels does provide a strong *a priori* argument for relative sea-level change as the single most important influence in determining the nature and timing of changes in coastal environments within the area. Despite this, other factors such as changes in coastal geography, hydrological regime and local sediment supply may be equally as important in certain circumstances. Because the Moniack site lies landward of a potential barrier to marine incursion, doubt has to be expressed concerning the regional applicability of the stratigraphic sequences recorded because these changes in sedimentary regime may ultimately relate to variations in the coastal geography at the entrance to the site and only indirectly, if at all, to relative sea-level change within the Beauly Firth area. The only effective way to isolate local site factors and assess the relevance of the site within the local area is to compare the record with that established from other sites that do not have the same potential difficulties in interpretation. Two other sites in the area have been studied in detail, Barnyards (NH 52 47) and Arcan

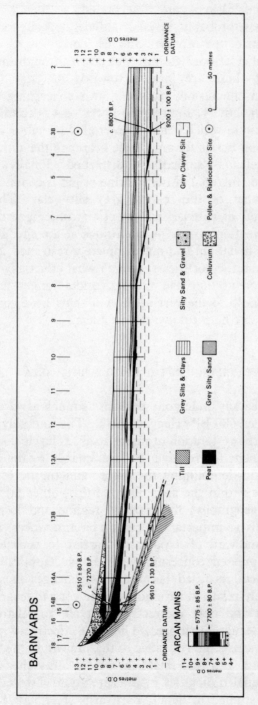

Figure 3.10 Stratigraphic sections through Late Devensian and Flandrian deposits at Barnyards and Arcan Mains. Radiocarbon dated locations are indicated by an arrow and a standard error following the date; ages estimated using pollen analysis are indicated by c. pre-fixing the date

Mains (NH 43 53). A generalised stratigraphy for both these sites is presented in figure 3.10 and the relevant radiocarbon data are given in table 3.6.

Table 3.6   Radiocarbon dates from Barnyards (BY) and Arcan Mains (AM)

Site	National grid reference	Altitude (m OD)	Depth (cm)	Laboratory code	Age (^{14}C yrs BP)
BY3B	NH 5283 4673	1.94–1.99	388–393	Hv 10010	9200±100
BY14B	NH 5226 4708	8.76–8.81	141–146	Birm 1122	5510± 80
BY14B	NH 5226 4708	6.59–6.64	358–363	Birm 1123	9610±130
AM	NH 4963 5358	9.00–9.05	126–131	Hv 10012	5775± 85
AM	NH 4963 5358	7.23–7.28	303–308	Hv 10013	7700± 80

Barnyards is located at the head of the Beauly Firth on a relatively open coast (figure 3.1). The stratigraphy (figure 3.10) is similar to that at Moniack but lacks the extensive surface peat and colluvial or alluvial deposits. The Late Devensian stratigraphy contains, as at Moniack, three sub-units. A lower minerogenic sub-unit of grey silts and clays is overlain by a coarser silt, sand and gravel which in turn is overlain by a clayey silt. The regressive overlap of a widespread peat layer above these silts formed between 9610±130 BP (Birm 1123, table 3.6) and 9200±100 BP (Hv 10010, table 3.6) and demonstrates a fall in relative sea level (Haggart 1986). The transgressive overlap began to form at c.8800 BP and reflects a rise in relative sea level. Prior to the end of this rise a thin micaceous silty sand layer was deposited and landward of BY14A (figure 3.10) it lies unconformably on the lower peat surface. A thin and patchy upper peat lies above the marine deposits at Barnyards. A radiocarbon date of 5510±80 BP (Birm 1122, table 3.6) on the regressive overlap near to the landward limit of marine sedimentation suggests that the reduction in marine conditions, caused by a fall in relative sea level, occurred prior to this date.

Arcan Mains is located in lower Strathconon (figure 3.1). The stratigraphy shows considerable variation probably attributable to a number of riverine cut and fill episodes. In the borehole sampled for pollen, diatoms and radiocarbon dating, peat began to form on a minerogenic surface at 5.4 m OD prior to the rise in *Corylus/Myrica* pollen which is dated to before c.9200 BP in the area (Haggart 1986). Renewed clastic deposition, initially with a freshwater, then with a more marine diatom flora, began after 7700±80 BP (Hv 10013, table 3.6) at *c.*7.3 m OD. A further layer of peat at 9 m OD succeeded the clastic layer after 5775±85 BP (Hv 10012, table 3.6; Haggart 1982).

These two sites provide data for comparison with the Moniack evidence. The earliest marine deposit at Moniack, the grey compact clay, is probably the correlative of the grey silts and clays which lie above till at Barnyards. As at Moniack, these silts and clays occupy a position below the coarser layer of silt, sand and gravel which was deposited during the Loch Lomond Stadial. These fine-grained deposits were therefore laid down between ice-sheet deglaciation and before the Loch Lomond Stadial, probably between *c.*13 500 and *c.*11 000 BP.

The coarser layer of silt, sand and gravel which overlies and truncates the compact clays is considered to be the equivalent of the buried gravel layer described from seaward of the Moniack alluvial fan by Sissons (1981). The layer occurs at altitudes above *c.*3.5 m OD at Moniack and therefore must correlate with the surface of marine erosion to landward of the Main Lateglacial Shoreline, the altitude of which Sissons places at between 1.1 and 2.6 m OD. Therefore the layer at Moniack was probably laid down during the period after the formation of the Main Lateglacial Shoreline yet before the climatic amelioration at the beginning of the Flandrian, most probably between 10 500–10 000 BP, and it reflects a rising relative sea level.

The marine silts which lie above the equivalent of the buried gravel layer at Moniack can be correlated with the extensive sequence of grey silts which were laid down before the development of the lower peat at Barnyards (figure 3.10, Haggart 1986). Deposition of these silts covers a time period from the end of the Loch Lomond Stadial through to the early Flandrian. If a high relative sea level at the end of the Loch Lomond Stadial (represented by the buried gravel layer at *c.*10–11 m OD) is accepted then the silt were deposited initially during a period of falling relative sea level which was followed by a stillstand or minor rise. The maximum altitude reached by these silts is 6.6 m OD at Barnyards and 7.5 m OD at Moniack.

The Late Devensian stratigraphy at Moniack is therefore directly comparable to that at Barnyards and beneath the Kirkhill carse. This suggests that factors operating at least on a regional scale within the Beauly Firth area are responsible and that the changes recorded closely reflect relative sea-level change. The buried gravel layer deposited during the Loch Lomond Stadial has been identified on both sides of the Moniack alluvial fan and confirms that the extent of the latter was limited at this time.

The regressive overlap of the lower peat at Moniack began to form earlier than *c*.9200 BP in borehole 29B at 6.4 m OD. Though no dating evidence exists to confirm an age gradient, the fall in altitude from 7.5 to 4.3 m OD between boreholes 1 and 9 (figure 3.3) suggests time-transgressive development. At Barnyards, a similar overlap declines to seaward from 6.6 to 1.9 m OD. The two radiocarbon dates of *c*.9600 BP and *c*.9200 BP at the landward and seaward extremes of the overlap, together with pollen evidence, suggest its formation took *c*.400 ^{14}C years. Therefore the lower regressive overlap at Moniack began to form during a period of falling relative sea level in the area and is not merely caused by a site-specific period of peat growth. Furthermore, if the landward limit of marine sedimentation immediately prior to overlap formation is assumed to be contemporaneous at both sites it implies that in comparison with Barnyards, the overlap at Moniack is restricted in time to the earlier two-thirds of this period of falling relative sea level.

The transgressive overlap of the lower peat at Moniack began to form later than *c*.7800 BP in borehole 29B at 7.3 m OD and at *c*.7100 BP in 4B. Though no age gradient can be proved for the overlap, since the 29B data are from an erosional contact, the rise in altitude from *c*.6 to 7.8 m OD between boreholes 12 and 8 (figure 3.3) again suggests time-transgressive development. At Barnyards, a similar overlap rises to landward from 2.1 to 7.9 m OD. Therefore the transgressive overlap above the lower peat at Moniack formed during a period of rising relative sea level in the area and is not solely the result of local site factors. If the landward limit of marine sedimentation immediately postdating the formation of the overlap is assumed to be contemporaneous at both sites, the evidence from Moniack represents only the later one-third of this rise in relative sea level. The preservation of evidence from the earlier two-thirds of the period of falling sea level and the later one-third of the following rise at Moniack is probably due to the location of the site at the head of a sheltered embayment. Evidence from the intervening time period probably lies to seaward of the Moniack alluvial fan. However, three boreholes put down to seaward of the fan (figure 3.2) showed little internal consistency and confirm Sissons' (1981) suggestion that the Flandrian stratigraphy in the area between the fan and the present coast has been complicated by a number of fluvial erosional and depositional episodes.

The thin, grey micaceous silty sand layer, dated to between *c*.7400 and *c*.7250 BP at Moniack also occurs at Barnyards. This concurrence at both sites proves that the layer has more than local site significance at Moniack and must relate to a period of erosion and higher energy deposition within the Beauly Firth area. However there is no equivalent of the thin

Phragmites peat above the silty sand layer at Barnyards. This means that though there is strong lithostratigraphic and biostratigraphic evidence for a reduction in the marine influence at Moniack at this time, it may only represent the return to equilibrium conditions at the site following an extreme event. It remains doubtful therefore that the regressive overlap above the grey micaceous silty sand at Moniack, though representing a negative tendency at the site scale, was formed following a fall in relative sea level within the local area.

The upper regressive overlap began to form after *c*.5600 BP at Moniack. At Barnyards and Arcan Mains, similar overlaps date from *c*.5500 BP and *c*.5800 BP. This coincidence of tendencies again suggests that factors operating at least on the local area scale, most probably a fall in relative sea level, were responsible.

After *c*.5600 BP the Moniack alluvial fan appears to have undergone considerable lateral extension, eventually reaching across the full width of the Moniack Burn lowland. There are three possible mechanisms to explain this resurgence in alluvial fan activity. Firstly, the presence of marine conditions prior to *c*.5600 BP may have provided an effective mechanism to transport alluvial material away from the site. Once marine conditions had receded, debris could have built out across the newly-exposed surface. However there is no evidence for a similar period of deposition during the time of low relative sea level represented by the lower peat at Moniack. A second explanation could be that the removal of marine conditions coincided approximately with the Boreal/Atlantic transition, a time traditionally considered to mark the change to a wetter climate (Godwin 1975). The runoff from the Moniack Burn catchment may have increased sufficiently at this time to entrain and transport a greater volume of larger grade sediment. Thirdly, the destruction of the natural forest by man (which has increased in scale from the late mesolithic toward the present) may have provided conditions conducive to alluvial fan deposition through soil erosion and increased runoff within the catchment. It is also possible that all three mechanisms may have operated together to effect a resurgence in alluvial fan activity.

The evidence from Moniack, Barnyards and Arcan Mains has been summarised in a diagram showing the chronology of positive and negative tendencies of relative sea level (figure 3.11). The thin *Phragmites* peat overlying the micaceous silty sand layer at Moniack represents a local negative tendency yet it is considered doubtful whether this corresponds to a fall in relative sea level. The data are amalgamated to form a composite chronology for the inner Moray Firth area. Sections of the chronology not covered by radiocarbon data have been interpolated with

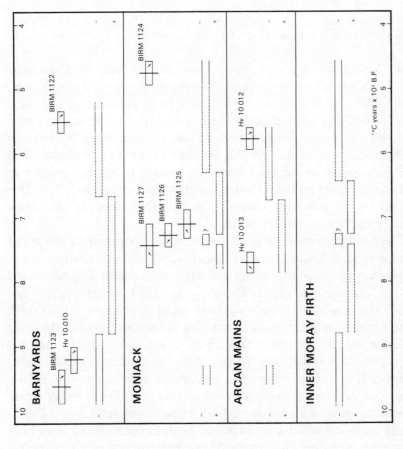

Figure 3.11 Summary chronology of positive (+) and negative (−) tendencies of relative sea-level at Moniack, Barnyards and Arcan Mains during the Flandrian Age. Radiocarbon data are shown with error boxes of 2σ about the mean. Dotted lines denote uncertainty. The data are amalgamated to form a summary chronology for the inner Moray Firth estuaries

reference to stratigraphic indicators of sea-level movement. The boundaries have been placed half-way between securely dated points. This device should not be mistaken as an attempt to force unwarranted accuracy on the scheme, rather as an unbiased attempt to produce a complete chronology. As further data are collected, the boundaries will become better defined.

6.0   COMPARISONS WITH OTHER AREAS OF SCOTLAND

The Late Devensian marine clays deposited at both Moniack and Barnyards lie below a coarser layer predominantly composed of silt, sand and gravel. This coarser layer is considered to be of Loch Lomond Stadial age. If the underlying clays predate the Loch Lomond Stadial, they may correlate with the lower Findon beds of the Cromarty Firth (Peacock *et al*. 1980) and by extension the Clyde beds of western Scotland. The coarser layer appears to correlate with the surface of marine erosion to landward of the shoreline beneath the Kirkhill carse (Sissons 1981). This suggests the layer was laid down after the formation of the Main Lateglacial Shoreline in eastern Scotland.

Several authors have recently questioned the interpretation of the age of the Main Lateglacial Shoreline in south-east Scotland and the direction of sea-level movement prior to, during and after its formation (Browne and Jarvis 1983, Paterson *et al*. 1981, Browne *et al*. 1984). They suggest that the Main Lateglacial Shoreline may have formed prior to *c*.11 000 BP during the Lateglacial Interstadial when isostatic recovery and eustatic sea level were in equilibrium and that relative sea level fell during the following Loch Lomond Stadial, cutting deep channels into the estuarine fill of the Forth and Tay valleys to a maximum depth of *c*.−30 m OD. This seems contrary to the evidence from the western Forth valley where there is stratigraphic evidence for a high relative sea level of *c*.12 m at *c*.10 300 BP while ice stood at its maximal Loch Lomond Readvance limit at the Menteith moraine (Sissons 1966). In the absence of any available conclusive stratigraphic evidence for the inner Moray Firth, it is intended to follow Sutherland (1984) in accepting Sissons' model as the simplest explanation of the available evidence.

The lower peat at both Moniack and Barnyards began to form under a falling relative sea level which began immediately prior to *c*.9600 BP. In the western Forth valley, pollen investigations have been carried out on peat overlying the Main Buried Beach at four sites. The evidence from East Flanders Moss (Durno 1956), West Flanders Moss (Newey 1966),

Bield and The Homesteads (Brooks 1972) confirms that the underlying beach deposits ceased to accumulate prior to c.9600 BP. This is supported by two radiocarbon dates of 9524±67 BP (SRR 72) and 9640±140 BP (I 2796) from the correlative of the Main Buried Beach near its shoreline at Carey in lower Strathearn (Cullingford *et al.* 1980). The age, stratigraphic relationships and pollen stratigraphies of the lower peat and underlying estuarine deposits at Moniack and Barnyards are therefore directly comparable with the peat and underlying beach deposits in the western Forth valley and lower Strathearn. The landward limit of marine-estuarine sedimentation preceding peat growth at Moniack and Barnyards is similarly correlated with the Main Buried Shoreline of south-east Scotland (Sissons 1976).

It is not known if a correlative of the Low Buried Beach of the western Forth valley exists in the Beauly Firth area. The present evidence is best explained by one period of falling relative sea level between c.9600 and later than c.9200 BP followed by the main Flandrian rise in relative sea level (figure 3.12). The relative sea-level curve for the western Forth valley shows three early Flandrian minima. The first is at c.9800 BP, the second at c.8900 BP between the formation of the Main and Low Buried Shorelines. The third is at c.8500 BP between the formation of the Low Buried Shoreline and the beginning of the rise to the Flandrian marine limit (Sissons and Brooks 1971). The relative sea-level curve for lower Strathearn (figure 3.12) shows two minima at c.8900 BP and c.7900 BP. More stratigraphic control and dating are needed before firm correlations can be made. However there are three possible interpretations. Firstly, the sites studied in the Beauly Firth area are at too high an altitude for a lower beach to be detected. Secondly, the inferred age of c.8800 BP for the initiation of the transgressive overlap at Barnyards may be in error (Haggart 1986). Thirdly, the rate of isostatic recovery in the inner Moray Firth during the early Flandrian may have been sufficiently different from that of the western Forth valley and lower Strathearn to militate against the formation of an equivalent to the Low Buried Shoreline.

The thin micaceous silty sand horizon at both Moniack and Barnyards has correlatives at other sites on the east coast of Scotland. These include Easter Ofference in the western Forth valley (Smith *et al.* 1985), St. Michael's in East Fife (Morrison *et al.* 1981), five sites in the Montrose Basin (Smith *et al.* 1980, Smith and Cullingford 1985) and Waterside in the Ythan valley (Smith *et al.* 1983). Ten radiocarbon dates from peat above and below the layer suggest it was probably deposited between c.7200 and c.6850 BP. The stratigraphic setting of the layer at these sites, within finer marine silts and clays and the evidence of

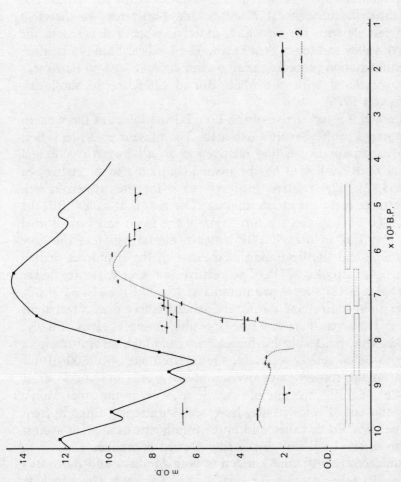

Figure 3.12 Time/altitude graph comparing relative sea-level curves from the western Forth valley and the Lower Strathearn with the index points from the inner Moray Firth area: 1, the western Forth valley (Sissons and Brooks 1971); 2, Lower Strathearn (Cullingford et al. 1980). Index point altitudes from the inner Moray Firth area are shown with arrows and one standard deviation for each ^{14}C date. The inner Moray Firth points refer only to the measured index point altitudes: there is no attempt to reconstruct former sea-level altitudes. The arrows denote tendencies of relative sea-level movement for each index point. The summary chronology for the inner Moray Firth estuaries (from figure 3.11) is shown at the bottom of the figure

penetration of saline water across contemporaneous saltmarsh and reedswamp environments suggests it was deposited during a brief period of high energy sedimentation, most probably a North Sea storm surge of great magnitude (Smith *et al.* 1985).

There may be some evidence for diachroneity in the formation of the highest Flandrian shoreline, the Main Postglacial Shoreline, with distance from the proposed centre of isostatic uplift. In the western Forth valley, the Main Postglacial Shoreline was abandoned prior to *c.*6500 BP at *c.*14 m OD, in lower Strathearn prior to *c.*6100 BP at *c*10–11 m OD and in East Fife prior to *c.*5800 BP at *c.*8–9 m OD (Morrison *et al.* 1981). The evidence from the inner Moray Firth area suggests that the Flandrian marine limit was reached prior to *c.*5800 BP. Each of these age estimates is derived from radiocarbon dates on peat immediately overlying Flandrian marine silts and clays close to the landward limit of deposition. However, differences in the thickness of material sampled and the fact that the Main Postglacial Shoreline has not been traced as a continuous feature between these areas means the resolution offered by the present evidence is too coarse either to prove or disprove diachroneity.

7.0 CONCLUSIONS

Detailed lithostratigraphic and biostratigraphic evidence and radiocarbon dating from Moniack provide information about the changing marine and terrestrial environments. Comparisons with other available evidence from the Beauly Firth area suggests that within the resolution of the techniques used, the major influence on sedimentation at Moniack has been relative sea-level change within the local area rather than local site characteristics. A major lateral expansion of the Moniack alluvial fan began after *c.*5600 BP and although at present it is a major element in the landscape, prior to 5600 BP it did not restrict the incursion of saline waters from the north-east. Ogilvie's (1923) assertion that the sea at the 25 to 30 ft level (7.6 to 9.2 m OD), did not pass the fan is therefore incorrect.

The most detailed evidence for changes in relative sea level in the Beauly Firth area is for the Flandrian Age. The nature and timing of these changes show many similarities with the Forth-Tay model and correlatives of the Main Buried and Main Postglacial Shorelines have been described. One exception to these correlations may be the absence of an equivalent to the Low Buried Beach of the western Forth valley. The question remains whether this discrepancy results from insufficient data in the present study.

The good agreement between the Beauly Firth and the Forth and Tay areas indicates that in the present study it has been possible to reconcile a shoreline-based approach with an approach based on the study of individual sites in an uplifted area. In reality the two approaches differ only in emphasis, with shoreline studies providing proportionately more information on relative dating, altitude and isostatic recovery while sites such as those investigated in the present study provide proportionately more information on 'absolute' age, environmental change and rates of sea-level change. More of both types of study are needed for the Beauly Firth area so that the current scheme of relative sea-level change can be refined. Once the boundaries between positive and negative movements in sea level have been defined more precisely it will be possible to measure the extent and diachroneity of sea-level movement and crustal movement between areas having different uplift histories.

ACKNOWLEDGEMENTS

I would like to thank Drs M. J. Tooley, I. Shennan, J. D. Peacock, J. J. Lowe, D. E. Smith and R. M. Tipping for their advice on many aspects of this work. Plant macrofossil identifications were kindly undertaken by Dr P. A. GreatRex. I am grateful to M. Teed, D. Lecore, A. Ellis and E. Oliver who drew the maps and diagrams. Stratigraphy was recorded and samples taken with the permission of Mr Munro of Cononbank, Mrs Gunn of Cabrich, Mr Forbes of Wellhouse, Mr Peterkin of Barnyards and Mr Stirling of Arcan Mains. The field assistance of R. Jowett, J. Jowett, A. M. Wilson, G. Coston, R. M. Tipping and R. G. Ward is gratefully acknowledged. Much of the work was undertaken whilst in receipt of an NERC/CASE research studentship at Durham University. I should like to thank Dr M. A. Geyh, *Niedersächsisches Landesamt für Bodenforschung*, Hannover, West Germany for undertaking some of the radiocarbon assays. A grant from Durham University Staff Research Fund enabled the balance of the assays to be undertaken in the Department of Geology, University of Birmingham. Finally I would like to thank Liz Haggart for helpful comment and improvements to the text.

Revised typescript received 1986, January.

REFERENCES

Battarbee, R. W. 1979: Diatoms in lake sediments. In B. Berglund (ed.), *Palaeohydrological changes in the temperate zone in the last 15 000 years.*

Subproject B, Lake and mire environments, Lund: University of Lund, Department of Quaternary Geology, vol. II, pp. 177–225.

Bennett, K. D. 1984: The post-glacial history of *Pinus sylvestris* in the British Isles. *Quat. Sci. Rev.*, 3, 133–55.

Birks, H. H. 1972: Studies in the vegetational history of Scotland III. A radiocarbon dated pollen diagram from Loch Maree, Ross and Cromarty, *New Phytol.*, 71, 731–54.

Birks, H. J. B. 1979: Pollen analysis. In B. Berglund (ed.), *Palaeohydrological changes in the temperate zone in the last 15 000 years. Subproject B, Lake and mire environments*, Lund: University of Lund Department of Quaternary Geology: vol. II, pp. 133–67.

Brooks, C. L. 1972: Pollen analysis and the Main Buried Beach in the western part of the Forth valley. *Trans. Inst. Br. Geogr.* 55, 161–71.

Browne, M. A. E., Graham, D. K. and Gregory, D. M. 1984: Quaternary estuarine deposits in the Grangemouth area, Scotland. *Rep. Br. Geol. Surv.*, 16 (3), 1–14.

Browne, M. A. E. and Jarvis, J. 1983: Late Devensian marine erosion in St. Andrews Bay, east-central Scotland. *Quaternary Newsletter*, 41, 11–17.

Cleve-Euler, A. 1951–55: Die Diatomëen von Schweden und Finland. *Kungl. Svenska Vetensk. Akad. Handl.* Ser. 4: 2(1), 1–163; 3(3), 1–153; 4(1), 1–158; 4(5), 1–255; 5(4), 1–232.

Cullingford, R. A., Caseldine, C. J. and Gotts, P. E. 1980: Early Flandrian land and sea-level changes in lower Strathearn. *Nature*, 284, 159–61.

Durno, S. E. 1956: Pollen analysis of peat deposits in Scotland. *Scott. Geogr. Mag.*, 72, 177–87.

Edsbagge, H. 1965: Vertical distribution of diatoms. *Svensk.bot.Tidskr.*, 59, 463–68.

Faegri, K. and Iversen, J. 1974: *Textbook of Pollen Analysis*. 3rd edn. Oxford: Basil Blackwell.

Firth, C. R. 1984: Raised shorelines and ice limits in the inner Moray Firth and Loch Ness areas, Scotland. Unpublished PhD Thesis, CNAA, Coventry (Lanchester) Polytechnic.

Godwin, H. 1975: *The History of the British Flora*. 2nd edn. Cambridge: Cambridge University Press.

Haggart, B. A. 1982: Flandrian sea-level changes in the Moray Firth area. Unpublished PhD Thesis, University of Durham.

Haggart, B. A. 1986: Relative sea-level change in the Beauly Firth, Scotland. *Boreas*, 15, 191–207.

Harkness, D. D. 1981: Scottish Universities Research and Reactor Centre radiocarbon measurements IV. *Radiocarbon*, 23, 252–304.

Hendey, N. I. 1964: *An introductory account of the smaller algae of British coastal waters. Part V, Bacillariophyceae (Diatoms)*. London: HMSO.

Horne, J. and Hinxman, L. W. 1914: The geology of the country around Beauly and Inverness. *Mem. Geol. Surv. Gt. Br.*

Hustedt, F. 1927–62: *Die Kieselalgen, Deutschlands, Österreichs und der Schweiz unter Berücksichtigung der übrigen Länder Europas sowie der angrenzenden Meeresgebiete.* Leipzig: Akad. Verlag.

Merkt, V. J. and Streif, H. 1970: Stechrohr-Borgeräte für Limnische und Marine Locker sedimente. *Geol. Jb.*, 88, 137–48.

Moore, P. D. and Webb, J. A. 1978: *An Illustrated Guide to Pollen Analysis.* London: Hodder and Stoughton.

Morrison, J., Smith, D. E., Cullingford, R. A. and Jones, R. L. 1981: The culmination of the Main Postglacial Transgression in the Firth of Tay area, Scotland. *Proc. Geol. Ass.*, 92, 197–209.

Newey, W. W. 1966: Pollen-analysis of sub-carse peats of the Forth valley. *Trans. Inst. Br. Geogr.*, 39, 53–9.

O'Sullivan, P. E. 1975: Early and middle Flandrian pollen zonation in the eastern Highlands of Scotland. *Boreas*, 4, 197–207.

Ogilvie, A. G. 1914: The physical geography of the entrance to Inverness Firth. *Scott. Geogr. Mag.*, 30, 21–35.

Ogilvie, A. G. 1923: The physiography of the Moray Firth coast. *Trans. R. Soc. Edin.*, 53, 377–404.

Paterson, I. B., Armstrong, M. and Browne, M. A. E. 1981: Quaternary estuarine deposits in the Tay-Earn area, Scotland. *Rep. Inst. Geol. Sci.*, 81/7.

Peach, B. N. 1912: The geology of Ben Wyvis, Carn Chuinneag and the surrounding country. *Mem. Geol. Surv. Gt. Br.*.

Peacock, J. D. 1975: Scottish late and post-glacial marine deposits. In A. M. D. Gemmell (ed.), *Quaternary studies in north-east Scotland*, Aberdeen: Quaternary Research Association, 45–9.

Peacock, J. D. 1977: Subsurface deposits of Inverness and the inner Cromarty Firth. In G. Gill (ed.), *The Moray Firth area Geological Studies*, Inverness Field Club, 103–4.

Peacock, J. D. 1981: Scottish Late-Glacial marine deposits and their environmental significance. In J. Neale and J. Flenley (eds), *The Quaternary in Britain*, Oxford: Pergamon, 222–36.

Peacock, J. D., Graham, D. K. and Gregory, D. M. 1980: Late and post-glacial marine environments in part of the Inner Cromarty Firth, Scotland. *Rep. Inst. Geol. Sci.*, 80/7.

Pennington, W., Haworth, E. Y., Bonny, A. P. and Lishman, J. P. 1972: Lake sediments in northern Scotland. *Phil. Trans. R. Soc. B.*, 264, 191–294.

Read, H. H., Phemister, J. and Ross, G. 1926: The geology of Strath Oykell and lower Loch Shin. *Mem. Geol. Surv. Gt. Br.*

Read, H. H., Ross, G. and Phemister, J. 1925: The geology of the country around Golspie, Sutherlandshire. *Mem. Geol. Surv. Gt. Br.*

Round, F. E. 1960: The diatom flora of a salt marsh on the river Dee. *New Phytol.*, 59, 332–48.

Shennan, I. 1983a: Flandrian and Late Devensian sea-level changes and crustal movements in England and Wales. In D. E. Smith and A. G. Dawson (eds), *Shorelines and Isostasy*, London: Academic Press, 255–83.

Shennan, I. 1983b: A problem of definition in sea-level research methods. *Quaternary Newsletter*, 39, 17–19.

Shennan, I., Tooley, M. J., Davis, M. J. and Haggart, B. A. 1983: Analysis and interpretation of Holocene sea-level data. *Nature*, 302, 404–6.

Sissons, J. B. 1966: Relative sea-level changes between 10 300 and 8300 BP in part of the carse of Stirling. *Trans. Inst. Br. Geogr.*, 39, 19–29.

Sissons, J. B. 1976: *The Geomorphology of the British Isles: Scotland*. London: Methuen.

Sissons, J. B. 1981: Late-glacial marine erosion and a jökulhlaup deposit in the Beauly Firth. *Scott. J. Geol.*, 17, 7–19.

Sissons, J. B. 1983: Shorelines and isotasy in Scotland. In D. E. Smith and A. G. Dawson (eds), *Shorelines and Isostasy*. London: Academic Press, 209–25.

Sissons, J. B. and Brooks, C. L. 1971: Dating of early postglacial land and sea-level changes in the western Forth valley. *Nature*, 234, 124–7.

Smith, A. G. 1984: Newferry and the Boreal-Atlantic Transition. *New Phytol.*, 98, 35–55.

Smith, D. E. and Cullingford, R. A. 1985: Flandrian relative sea-level changes in the Montrose basin area. *Scott. Geogr. Mag.*, 101, 91–105.

Smith, D. E., Cullingford, R. A. and Brooks, C. L. 1983: Flandrian relative sea-level changes in the Ythan valley, north-east Scotland. *Earth Surface Processes and Landforms*, 8, 423–38.

Smith, D. E., Cullingford, R. A. and Haggart, B. A. 1985: A major coastal flood during the Holocene in eastern Scotland. *Eiszeitalter Gegenw.*, 35, 109–18.

Smith, D. E., Morrison, J., Jones, R. L. and Cullingford, R. A. 1980: Dating the Main Postglacial Shoreline in the Montrose area, Scotland. In R. A. Cullingford, D. A. Davidson and J. Lewin (eds), *Timescales in Geomorphology*, Chichester: John Wiley, 225–45.

Smith, J. S. 1963: Notes on post-glacial gullying. *Scott. Geogr. Mag.*, 79, 176–7.

Smith, J. S. 1966: Morainic limits and their relationship to raised shorelines in the east Scottish Highlands. *Trans. Inst. Br. Geogr.*, 39, 61–4.

Steers, J. A. 1937: The Culbin Sands and Burghead Bay. *Geogr. J.*, 90, 498–528.

Stockmarr, J. 1971: Tablets with spores used in absolute pollen analysis. *Pollen et Spores*, 13, 615–21.

Sutherland, D. G. 1984: The Quaternary deposits and landforms of Scotland and the neighbouring shelves: a review. *Quat. Sci. Rev.*, 3, 157–254.

Synge, F. M. 1977: Land and sea-level changes during the waning of the last regional ice-sheet in the vicinity of Inverness. In G. Gill (ed.), *The Moray Firth Area Geological Studies*. Inverness Field Club, 88–102.

Synge, F. M. and Smith, J. S. 1980: *A field guide to the Inverness area*. Quaternary Research Association.

Tooley, M. J. 1982: Sea-level changes in northern England. *Proc. Geol. Ass.*, 93, 43–51.

Troels-Smith, J. 1955: Karakterisering af løse jordarter. *Danm. geol. Unders.*, IV, 3, 10, 73pp.

Van der Werff, A. and Huls, H. 1957–74: *Diatomeënflora van Nederland.* (8 parts). Published privately by A. van der Werff, Westzijde 13a, De Hoef, (U), The Netherlands.

4

Holocene sea-level changes in the North Sea Region

Ian Shennan

1.0 INTRODUCTION

The extensive low-lying coastal zones that border the southern North Sea and the sequences of uplifted shorelines and lake basins in Scandinavia and Scotland have been systematically studied for over 100 years to elucidate the factors of local and regional significance which have controlled erosional and depositional processes in the palaeocoastal zone during the Holocene epoch. As a result of the research work carried out by individuals and groups from numerous universities, state and federal survey and research institutions in all the countries bordering the North Sea the database potentially available for analysing the causes and effects of changes in sea level is larger than for any other area of similar size in the world. Perhaps it is the volume and variety of data that have so far precluded any detailed synthesis at the regional scale.

Mörner (1980a) has indicated that the region can be utilized as an immense sea-level laboratory and later in this paper some of the 'experiments' that can be performed will be illustrated. Apart from Mörner, most recent authors have been content to deal with relatively detailed descriptions of local-scale evidence. The important volume on *'The Quaternary History of the North Sea'* (Oele *et al.* 1979) contained many details of sea-level changes in each national coastal sector of the area but summarizing the great amount of data was only dealt with at a broad and descriptive level (Oele and Schüttenhelm 1979). The sea-level data from the Netherlands were used as a model to illustrate the general changes in the area during the Holocene (Jelgersma 1979) but little attempt was made to analyse and quantify the different relationships discussed by the rest of the authors in the book. Much of the evidence in the book will be used later, together with a selection from many of the publications which have appeared since.

It is not the aim here to provide a summary of research papers that have recently appeared dealing with sea-level changes in the North Sea but rather to investigate some of the methods that can be applied in trying to synthesize the available data. It is realized that such an approach has many pitfalls. Sea-level researchers are very protective about their own field area and the interpretation of the local events recorded there. Attempts to summarize published data lead to judgements that must be made using a poorer database, since full details about stratigraphy, sampling problems, laboratory analysis, *i.a.* are rarely available. Even if such details were published, attempts to synthesize the evidence on a regional scale would result in problems of assimilation, leaving no time to perform the regional analyses. The explosion of detailed data from interdisciplinary research makes the task of synthesis increasingly difficult. The problem to be addressed is how best to utilize the information that has been collected to answer questions relevant at one temporal and spatial scale to phenomena expressed at a different resolution.

2.0   SEA-LEVEL DATA AND PALAEOGEOGRAPHIC ENVIRONMENTS

All studies of past sea levels depend on being able to identify a feature of erosion or a deposit, the formation of which has been controlled by sea level. The accuracy of the reconstructed level will depend on quantifying the altitudinal and temporal relationships. The identification of the 'indicative meaning' and age of 'sea-level index points' has been discussed by many authors (e.g. van de Plassche and Preuss 1978, Shennan 1982a, Kidson 1982) and there has been some move towards standardization of approach and terminology due in no small part to the international co-operation encouraged by the INQUA Shorelines Commission and the two IGCP Projects; Project 61 which ran from 1974 to 1982 and its successor, Project 200, which runs until 1987. These organizations have encouraged an awareness of the need for scientific accuracy in all aspects of sea-level research – the importance of consistency between different workers in their use of terminology and methods of measurement, description and presentation of results. Rigorous adherence to operational definitions and repeatable methods of analysis have been shown to allow meaningful correlations to be made between the sea-level records from different areas using data collected by different authors (Shennan *et al.* 1983). Moves have been made to compile the various sea-level data in the form of atlases of sea-level curves (Bloom 1977, 1982, Grant 1985, Ota *et al*. 1981) and as a computer based databank of radiocarbon dated sea-level index points (Preuss 1979a, Tooley 1982a). Little use has been made, up to the present at least, of the datasets in any regional- or global-scale analyses. Newman *et al*. (1980) have illustrated the potential benefits of a computer based analysis but a shortfall in the necessary detail and accuracy required of such databases has precluded wide acceptance of the conclusions (Shennan 1987).

The North Sea region (figure 4.1) offers an excellent opportunity to isolate variables which combine to produce the coastline response to variations in sea level. It has been argued that the area is small enough to have acted uniformly to any past changes in geoid configuration (Mörner

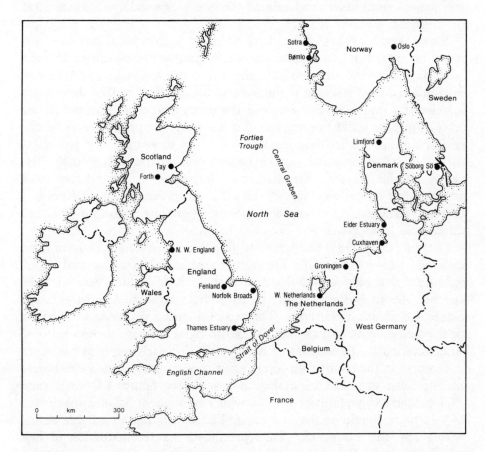

Figure 4.1 A map of the North Sea and adjacent countries, showing the locations of sites mentioned in the text

1976a, 1980a) and also exhibits a wide range of environments so that many other important variables such as isostatic history, coastal morphology, sediment supply, freshwater discharge, tidal range, exposure to storms, long term crustal movements and human activity can be evaluated. Each of these variables can be shown to control the registration of sea level at a relevant scale and a careful search of the published literature would soon reveal that each one has at some time been used to explain the difference between the sea-level records from two or more areas. Yet it is the wide range of palaeogeographic coastal environments from the area that allows the importance of different processes to be assessed. Mörner (1969, 1971) has argued that the variety of sea-level index points available in south-west Sweden, the ability to trace the evidence over many hundreds of kilometres and then to test the conclusions from other areas around the North Sea make the region ideal for studying sea-level changes.

National political boundaries have no effect on geological processes but it can be argued that interpretation of geological evidence can be affected (e.g. Hughes 1980). National differences arise due to variations in the way in which sea-level research is funded and organised as well as differences in scientific approach. For example the interpretation of changes in sea level is likely to differ to some extent if it is made the prime reason for the research project rather than just one result of a more extensive geological survey or of an essentially archaeological research project. Equally, the nature of the present coast has some influence on the relative rôles attributed to various local factors since it is much easier to argue a point if current analogues are available. Some examples showing national differences in approach are discussed below.

Hafsten (1979, 1983) has presented fifteen relative sea-level curves from different parts of Norway. They are based mainly on the analysis of sediments that have accumulated in basins which became isolated from the sea due to isostatic uplift. Other indicators studied include beach ridges and abrasion platforms. The sea-level curves discussed by Hafsten were based on both radiocarbon and biostratigraphical age determinations. The variation in the amount of isostatic uplift largely explains the gross differences in the relative sea-level curves, e.g. ranging from a Pre-Boreal marine limit of +220 m in the Oslo area (see figure 4.1) to a Late Weichselian marine limit of +32 m, with a subsequent Atlantic maximum of +11 m, at Bømlo on the west coast. The distribution of suitable basins within any single area may have precluded the reconstruction of low amplitude oscillations that may have occurred during the period between the earliest marine limit and the present. Hafsten (1983) quotes recent investigations which suggest that the Holocene shoreline oscillations reported from southern Sweden (Mörner 1976b) are not recorded in the Norwegian sea-level curves and previous recognition of oscillations, particularly in south-west Norway, is due to 'stratigraphical misinterpretation'. The debate will no doubt continue and will only be resolved with the continuation of scientific analysis of the field evidence using detailed methods of palaeoenvironmental reconstruction. Two examples of such research are given by Krzywinski and Stabell (1984) and Kaland (1984, Kaland *et al.* 1984) and their published curves are used in the analyses described later in this paper since they are based on stratigraphic, microfossil and radiocarbon analyses, rather than some of the other curves described by Hafsten.

Since Mörner first published the results of his work (1969) his sea-level curve has been up-dated in light of new information (Mörner 1976b) and remains a most valuable summary of the local and regional evidence. Some of the original differences in the interpretation of the Swedish data appear resolved although there remain some points of debate (e.g. Eriksson 1979). Nevertheless, Mörner's curve has been proposed as a regional eustatic curve (Mörner 1980a). The validity of the concept of regional eustasy, at the scale of the North Sea region, and the magnitude of other local and regional factors calculated using Mörner's curve as a eustatic baseline are investigated in section 4.

Denmark occupies an interesting location in terms of sea-level analysis since it lies on the boundary between the areas to the north which exhibit net crustal uplift since the last glaciation and those to the south which reveal apparent crustal subsidence. The detail of sea-level research in the area has been discussed by Petersen (1981, 1984a,b), Krog (1979, 1984) and Mörner (1976b). Apart from the relative curve from Söborg Sö (Morner 1976b) it appears difficult to construct any local or regional sea-level analyses due to the paucity of the data (Krog 1979). The recent summaries given by Petersen (1984a) and Krog (1984) both depend to a large extent on data collected over 40 years ago. An incomplete sea-level curve from the Limfjord area has been presented by Petersen (1984a).

Sea-level changes on the North Sea coast of Germany have been investigated by many research workers from numerous state survey organizations and universities. The detail from their combined studies probably cannot be surpassed elsewhere. Interdisciplinary studies utilizing geological, palaeoecological, archaeological and pedological methods of analysis have provided a wealth of information and advanced many original points of debate. A summary of the major regional features of sea-level change is provided by Behre *et al.* (1979) who also discuss some of the more contentious issues, such as how a curve drawn through the sea-level index points, from a subsiding area, plotted on a time-altitude graph will appear smooth yet the palaeoecological evidence indicate fluctuations in the water-table. The various published relative sea-level curves show similar characteristics, i.e. a generally smooth curve, perhaps with some changes in the rate of sea-level rise; but there are differences in the interpretation of controlling factors which operate at a more local scale. Just one example of this is the greater weight attributed to atmospheric and hydrographic variations through time by Linke (e.g. 1984) compared to other workers who have stressed the role of off-shore sandy barrier systems (e.g. Streif 1979). Linke has concentrated his field investigations in the area south of Cuxhaven, an area presently without extensive offshore barrier systems and open to the effects of North Sea storms, whereas others have worked with the palaeoenvironments of barrier island coasts (e.g. Streif 1972) or major river estuaries (e.g. Preuss 1979b) where the final registration of a change in sea level will be affected by different local factors.

The number of radiocarbon datapoints available from the German coast is large enough to allow chronostratigraphic and numerical methods of analysis to be explored for separating local and regional phenomena. Barckhausen *et al.* (1977), Streif (1978) and others have developed a method of integrating lithostratigraphy and chronostratigraphy as a basis for the mapping, classification and ultimate interpretation of Holocene coastal stratigraphy. The scheme has been successfully applied elsewhere (e.g. Baeteman 1981) and appears a more reliable method for correlating between areas than the earlier scheme of Brand *et al.* (1965). Geyh (1971, 1980) has pioneered the analysis of the temporal distribution of radiocarbon dated samples from the palaeocoastal zone using the cumulative frequency histogram methods, subsequently adopted by others (e.g. Roeleveld 1974, Morrison 1976, Shennan 1979, Berendsen 1984) and likely to be a very important method as more data become available in computer compatible form (e.g. Tooley 1982a, Shennan *et al.* 1983). Preuss (1979a) developed a package of computer programs for the analysis and display of sea-level data from the IGCP Project No. 61 data bank and even though there has been a loss of momentum since the end of Project 61 in 1982, the role of computer based analyses is certain to increase in the future once the technology becomes more widely adopted.

The Dutch sector of the North Sea coastal zone has been studied as intensively as the German part. Indeed the work of Jelgersma (e.g. 1961, 1966, 1979, 1980) is probably the most quoted from the North Sea area. Her original work has stood for over 25 years with little modification. Her arguments for relying on compaction free basal peat samples to construct past sea levels are well known and have been widely commented on elsewhere (e.g. Tooley 1978, Shennan 1987) and further comments here would be superfluous. As with the German situation, the general sequence of events is well known for most parts of The Netherlands and much of the recent work has been concentrated on very detailed analysis of local factors. Mapping and classification of sequences to reveal the degree of synchroneity of coastal changes remains important (e.g. Roeleveld 1976, van de Plassche 1985) so that the spatial variability of coastline response to sea-level change can be evaluated. Van de Plassche (1980, 1981, 1984 and pers. comm. 1985) has explored the relationships between ground-water levels, peat growth, peat compaction and river flood-basin effects in a series of detailed local-scale analyses where the necessary altitudinal resolution is in the order of a few decimetres. Compaction prevents the clear effect of any other factors being evaluated. Other local-scale phenomena have been discussed, for example, man's response to sea-level changes (Louwe Kooijmans 1976); the relationship between sedimentation in the perimarine zone and that at the coast (Berendsen 1984); and the problem of relating dune formation to the consequences of sea-level change, man or climate (Roep 1984, Jelgersma *et al.* 1970).

Recent work in Belgium has concentrated on mapping the sediments of the coastal plain. In an aim to recognize the importance of both local and regional sedimentary changes Baeteman (1981) has proposed the adoption of the classification scheme of Barckhausen *et al.* (1977) and has shown that it can be integrated with an explanation of the evolution of the sea-level controlled sediments (Baeteman 1985). However no detailed summary of the vertical changes in sea level associated with the vertical and spatial changes in sediment types has been published.

The evidence for sea-level changes on the North Sea coast of the United Kingdom is concentrated in sheltered estuaries. There is a narrower range of paleoenvironments compared to the continental coasts but there are major differences resulting from the variation of crustal movements (e.g. Jardine 1979, Shennan 1983, Sissons 1983). These are mainly glacio-isostatic responses although a longer term subsidence factor may be significant.

Particularly detailed studies in the Thames estuary (Devoy 1979, 1982) have revealed the importance of both crustal movements and local sedimentary and tidal conditions in controlling relative sea-level move-ments. Devoy (1982) has clearly demonstrated that the trend of sea-level change does not conform to a simple exponential curve although the amplitude and wavelength of periods of oscillation cannot be precisely specified. Different approaches by Alderton (1983) and Shennan (1986), using evidence from the Norfolk Broads and the Fenland respectively, show that while the trend of sea-level change can only be represented by an error band, variations in the rate of sea-level rise are evident. Actual falls of sea level are within the range of the error bands using the data so far available.

Important conclusions have emerged from detailed analysis of the estuaries in Scotland (see for example Haggart, chapter 3). Shoreline studies have revealed both a generalized picture of isostatic uplift, reaching a maximum of *c*.40–50 m for the western Forth since *c*.11 000–10 250 BP, and marked deformation of individual shorelines over short distances (Sissons 1983). Smith (Smith *et al*. 1980, 1983, 1985a) has successfully integrated the stratigraphic and morphologic approaches to the study of sea-level changes. Outstanding questions remain. First, the diachroneity of the shoreline or sedimentary sequence representing the maximum Holocene relative sea level for areas affected by different rates of isostatic uplift, and secondly, the significance of a persistent silty-sandy layer found in the sedimentary sequence of many of the estuaries. This layer has a marine origin and a series of similar radiocarbon dates may suggest it is the result of a major storm event (Haggart, chapter 3, Smith *et al*. 1985b).

The sediments from beneath the North Sea provide much information about the early Holocene development of the region. Eden *et al*. (1978) argue that variable rates of crustal subsidence for the Tertiary, Quaternary and since the Late Weichselian glacial maximum are the combination of long term tectonic subsidence and glacio-isostatic movement and may lend support to the theory of a peripheral bulge around the glaciated areas. Recent analysis of geophysical and geological data has resulted in revision of the stratigraphy (Stoker *et al*. 1985); some of the subsidence rates may require recalculation and the conclusions may require revision.

Jansen *et al*. (1979) have summarized the Late Quaternary and Holocene development of the North Sea, revealing a maximum fall of sea level to about −110 m. Sedimentation in the deeper parts ended around 8500 BP but the rise of sea level across the shallower areas is recorded by peat, freshwater and brackishwater clays, tidal flat deposits and sand waves. Radiocarbon and pollen data provide a general record of the rise of sea level (e.g. Behre *et al*. 1979, Jansen *et al*. 1979, Jelgersma *et al*. 1979, Ludwig *et al*. 1981). The connection between the North Sea and Strait of Dover was effected about 8300 BP (Jansen *et al*. 1979), temporarily the Dogger Bank remained an island but by 7800–7500 BP the present circulation pattern was established (Jelgersma *et al*. 1979, Stabell and Thiede 1985). The unconsolidated deposits became important sediment sources for the tidal flat, beach and sand dune environments which now contain a record of sea-level changes inland of the present coastline.

Mörner (1976b, 1979, 1980a,b) has attempted to use some of the data from the region to evaluate processes of more than local significance. Indeed he states 'the regional eustatic curve for north-west Europe is calculated such that it should not be affected by any local palaeoenvironmental changes – on the contrary, it is the tool for deciphering local effects' (Mörner 1980c, pp. 397–8).

It must be an aim of sea-level researchers to be able to specify the temporal and spatial resolution of the variables considered to control processes operating at the coastline. The difficulties and possible approaches in using the North Sea sea-level laboratory can be illustrated employing recent sea-level records from localities around the area.

3.0 THE SEA-LEVEL LABORATORY: DATA SOURCES

Analysis of sea-level information at the scale of the North Sea region involves the use of many different types of data collected by different workers. Such data have been filtered, some have been rejected, others have gained extra significance as key locations. Each data point has gone through some stage of interpretation and therefore the database and subsequent analysis is dependent, to varying degrees, on decisions made by the original research worker.

IGCP Project 61 included two themes aimed at developing a consistency in the collection and availability of raw sea-level data. These were the 'Manual for sample collection and evaluation of sea-level data' (van de Plassche, unpublished draft), which has yet to appear in print, and the computer databank of radiocarbon dated sea-level index points (Preuss 1979a). The latter has not become a basis for either global or regional synthesis, no doubt due to the great demands on manpower in data collection, verification and programming which were limited by funding in IGCP Project 61 and have no funding under IGCP Project 200. Thus one route for undertaking regional scale research is rather restricted, even though promising results have been forthcoming from a number of studies based on small data sets (e.g. Preuss 1979a, Flemming 1982, Shennan *et al.* 1983).

If the relatively raw data are not available, either not published or not adequately collated in a centralised databank, then regional synthesis can be based on either sea-level change chronologies, i.e. changes through time with no quantification of altitudinal changes, or the comparison of sea-level altitudes through time. Both approaches depend on the methods of description, analysis, classification and presentation of the data by the original authors and the problems for subsequent analysis can be illustrated by the following example.

3.1   Classification of changes in sea level

Figure 4.2 shows a sequence of intercalated freshwater peats and brackish-marine clastic deposits. Samples are taken at 'A' to 'T', each is radiocarbon dated and the microfossils analysed. For the sake of argument 'A' to 'F' and 'L' to 'Q' all reveal an increasing marine influence, i.e. positive tendency of sea-level movement, which due to significant altitudinal changes can be related to a rise in local relative sea level. Equally, samples 'G' to 'K' and 'R' to 'T' reveal negative tendencies of sea-level movement, related to a fall in local relative sea level. This model illustrates the argument about fluctuations of sea-level being interpreted from regressive overlaps. Given ample supplementary evidence (e.g. Sissons and Brooks 1971) such an interpretation may be unequivocal but this will not always be the case. In this example the true chronology is a rise of sea level 5000–4500 BP and 4000–3500 BP and a fall 4500–4000 BP and 3500–3000 BP. These would be approximately the time limits defined as periods of positive tendency and periods of negative tendency of sea-level movement using the methods discussed by Shennan (1982a,b, 1983). A difference of a few decades would arise depending on the method used to define the boundaries, e.g. for the mean age of 3400±120 and 3600±50 the unweighted average is 3500 whereas the average, weighted by the standard errors (Olsson 1979) is 3570±46 BP. A similar result is obtained if the boundary age is represented by the age at which the histograms (Geyh 1971) for dates on the regressive overlap attain a value greater than those on the transgressive overlap (Shennan 1982a).

Tooley (1982b) and Shennan (1982a) have already discussed the ambiguous use of the terms transgression and regression. Unless the method of definition is clearly stated then correlations between different areas are meaningless. Unfortunately changes in sea level do not always form a good basis for mapping Holocene sediments. Where much of the sea-level research follows on from work carried out for mapping (e.g. many of the research workers in Germany, the Netherlands and Belgium are associated with mapping institutes) lithostratigraphic and chronostratigraphic correlations are based on the peat layers (e.g. Roeleveld 1976, Jelgersma *et al.* 1979, Streif 1978, Baeteman 1981). The problems of

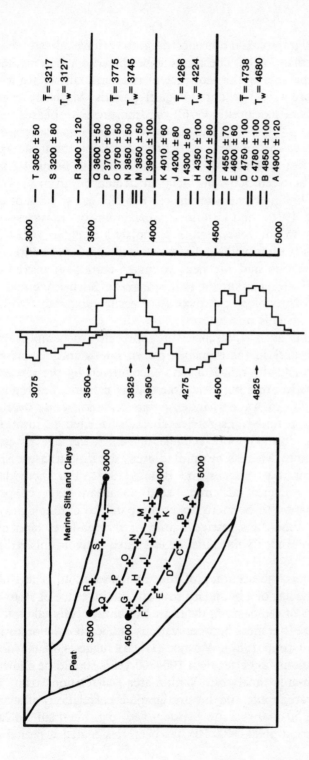

Figure 4.2 A diagram showing an hypothesized chronology of transgressive/regressive overlaps. Dated samples are obtained from locations 'A' to 'T' and various methods of defining chronostratigraphic intervals are illustrated and discussed in detail in the text. The stratigraphic section is shown on the left, cumulative frequency histograms are in the centre and the temporal distribution of dated samples, 'A' to 'T' is shown on the right

combining lithostratigraphy and chronostratigraphy have already been discussed (e.g. Baeteman 1981). The chronologies based on such methods are not directly comparable to the sequence of rises and falls of sea level hypothesized in figure 4.2. The chronological periods, variously called transgressive intervals (Roeleveld 1976) or transgressive phases and subphases (Jelgersma *et al.* 1979) and equated to the lithostratigraphic units; regressive intervals or phases, are defined by taking the mean ages for the start and end of peat growth. For the sequence in figure 4.2 the end of peat growth between 5000 and 4500 BP would be given as 4738 (unweighted mean), 4680 (weighted mean) or 4825 BP (as the peak of the histogram, Roeleveld 1976), and is termed a maximum of transgression. Similarly the maximum of regression is calculated as 4266, 4224 or 4275 BP. A transgressive interval is defined as the time interval between a maximum of transgression and the next youngest regression maximum (Roeleveld 1976) and a regression interval *vice versa*. Such a method of definition produces a chronology not directly or easily comparable with a chronology of rises and falls of sea level.

The reasons behind such differences of approach are complex but perhaps reveal differences in the demands placed on an analysis of sea-level related deposits and the range of data encountered by the research worker or institution. In areas bordering the southern North Sea the age and altitudinal variation of sea-level index points on a particular overlap may not reveal a clear time-transgressive character related to location, thus classification is deemed more reliable on the mean age of peat initiation or termination, whereas in uplifted areas the time-transgressive nature may be clearer (e.g. Sissons and Brooks 1971). For those data summarized by chronological schemes based on mean dates of peat initiation and termination to be more easily compared to chronologies of sea-level change the time-transgressive nature of the sea-level tendency dated by each sea-level index point must be evaluated to avoid misleading comparisons.

A further problem is the accuracy of the time resolution. The exact method of defining the age of a boundary may give a difference of 50 to 70 years; standard errors of radiocarbon dates are not always fully taken into account and there are differences between various radiocarbon laboratories (International Study Group 1982). Mörner (1980a) suggests that a time resolution for correlations no better than 100–200 years should be allowed for during between-area analyses. Within-area correlations can be enhanced by lithostratigraphic and biostratigraphic correlation, allowing significant periods of 50–200 years to be identified (e.g. Shennan 1982a). For example, the period 5600–5400 BP has been designated a period of negative tendency of sea-level movement in the Fenland on the basis of stratigraphy, pollen, diatom and radiocarbon data. Using a similar method Tooley (1982b) has identified a period of regressive overlap 5435–5250 BP. Given the limitations discussed it could be argued that the evidence from two areas indicates a synchronous *c*.200 year period of negative tendency within the range 5600–5200 BP. Where such decisions about time-shifting individual chronologies are made to enhance correlation between different areas (e.g. Mörner 1976b) they should be explicitly stated since they can make a great difference to the final results and to future synthesis. However, synchronous changes in dominant tendencies of sea-level movement have been demonstrated without involving such arguments (e.g. Shennan *et al.* 1983).

Without accepted standard methods of data analysis and presentation of results it is not easy to collate the data from different areas to provide a regional synthesis. But with due consideration of the limits of the data and a suitable choice of temporal and spatial scale the relevant factors can be investigated.

4.0 THE NORTH SEA AND EUSTASY

It has been shown (Shennan *et al.* 1983) that, by using a consistent method of analysis, data from published sources can be utilized to identify periods when the tendencies of sea-level movements in three geographically distinct areas seem to be controlled by regional factors. Many controls over coastal changes are possible and sea-level change is just one. Where other factors, such as fluctuations in sediment supply or storminess, are considered more important, how such changes can have the same effect in the different areas requires an explanation. Another conclusion could be that the synchroneity between the records is due to chance. Established correlations require continued exploration to enhance further their explanation.

The factors that can be considered as controlling relative sea-level changes and coastal development show a great variation in spatial and temporal scales which are relevant to their study and identification. Within-estuary, i.e. local, studies are required to investigate the effects of sediment supply, consolidation, river basin flood storage, local tide variation and coastal geomorphic changes (e.g. Devoy 1979, van de Plassche 1980, 1981, 1984, Robinson 1982). These require a relative time resolution of the order of 50–100 years, obtained by a combination of radiocarbon methods, archaeology and lithostratigraphic correlation.

Regional effects such as glacio-isostasy, tectonic movements and eustasy require different methods of analysis, with a different time resolution, at best 100–200 years, since chronostratigraphic correlation is now dependent on radiocarbon dating and other methods of absolute or relative dating such as palaeomagnetism. Lithostratigraphic correlation is less helpful in such investigations.

To identify absolute, rather than relative, changes certain factors must be held constant. Other factors can then be varied relative to the constant factors to establish whether or not the data fit the proposed model (e.g. Flemming 1982). Mörner (1980a) has argued that the North Sea area will act uniformly to global-scale geoid changes during the Holocene, and therefore his curve represents the 'regional eustatic curve'. This curve is subject to the same types of error as all sea-level curves. Some of these errors have been reduced, but certainly not eliminated. Nevertheless it can be used to compute the possible effects of other variables, of both local and regional significance. On a regional scale the concept of regional eustasy will be tested. If it is a valid concept then a single curve can be used to isolate various factors that affect different areas within the region. Whether Mörner's curve is correct on this basis can then be evaluated. Factors operating as controlling variables at the sub-regional level may be illustrated by assessing the differences between local sea-level curves and the proposed regional eustatic curve. Possible factors to be considered include glacio-isostasy, hydro-isostasy, long term crustal movements, palaeo-tidal changes and sediment compaction. Indeed the crustal movements involved in the glacio-isostatic processes consequent upon the melting of the last icesheet may well have resulted in a change in the configuration of the geoid within the North Sea.

The approach taken here is to use the regional eustatic curve proposed by Mörner, to investigate these various hypotheses using the evidence available from mainly published sources, and including the inherent weaknesses of some of these data. Major consistencies and residuals can then be evaluated. This approach is considered at two scales.

4.1   Local sea-level tendencies and eustasy

Where detailed evidence is available for changes in sea-level tendencies for a small homogenous area the local responses to the proposed eustatic changes can be evaluated. Mörner (e.g. 1969, 1976b) made such comparisons to validate his regional eustatic curve. In order to identify the limits of resolution that may be obtained in fitting the local to the regional eustatic records the evidence from the Fenland can be used (Shennan 1986).

Table 4.1 Ages and altitudes of the regional eustatic curve used for comparison with other curves. Data obtained from the text of Mörner (1971, 1976b) and checked against diagrams from Mörner (1980, 1984)

Data Point	Carbon–14 Age (BP)	Sidereal Age	Altitude (m)
PTM – 1	8800	8500	– 18.6
PR – 1	8500	8000	– 20.4
PTM – 2	7000	7700	– 10.0
PR – 2	6750	7500	– 10.3
PTM – 3A	6450	7350	– 7.0
PR – 3A	6380	7250	– 7.2
PTM – 3B	6250	7100	– 6.0
PR – 3B	6100	6950	– 6.3
PTM – 4	5850	6700	– 4.1
PR – 4	5500	6350	– 4.7
PTM – 5A	4980	5825	– 1.7
PR – 5A	4650	5475	– 2.7
PTM – 5B	4600	5400	– 1.5
PR – 5B	4450	5000	– 2.1
PTM – 6	4050	4100	– 0.3
PR – 6	3400	3500	– 1.4
PTM – 6/7	3000	3150	– 0.3
PR – 6/7	2900	3000	– 1.3
PTM – 7	2500	2600	+ 0.6
PR – 7	2375	2425	– 0.8
PTM – 8	2300	2300	0.0
PR – 8	2100	2100	– 0.9
PTM – 9	1550	1550	+ 0.1
PR – 9	1300	1300	– 0.8
PTM – 10	1000	1000	0.0

Mörner (1976b) suggests that the maxima of the eustatic sea-level oscillations are known to the nearest 0.1 m. The altitudes of the minima were more difficult to establish, but in subsequent papers they are claimed to be equally well established (e.g. 1979). Such an accuracy is significantly different from those suggested by other authors (e.g. Kidson 1982, Shennan 1982a). To facilitate comparative analysis the curve was stored on computer file as a sequence of altitudes for each ten years between 8800 and 1000 BP using the fixed points for the maxima and minima shown in table 4.1. The remaining points were interpolated using a half wavelength sine curve passing through each pair of alternating maxima and minima. The solution was considered easier than digitising the published curve. The error induced by this approximation is only of the order of a few centimetres, and insignificant in comparison to the other factors considered. Only major factors of the modelled relationships are considered within the analysis. At a later stage (section 4.2) a coarser approximation of the regional curve is used to investigate how stable the observed relationships are, dependent upon changes in the original assumptions. The modelled curve is shown in figure 4.3. Using the regional eustatic curve as a baseline, the average linear rate of subsidence in the Fenland for the last 6500 radiocarbon years, i.e. the period for which evidence is available, is estimated as c0.91 m /1000 years, although there is some evidence to suggest that the subsidence was not linear (Shennan 1986). This is an average figure, taking into account the errors within the Fenland data. However, by taking the linear solution as a first approximation and the regional eustatic curve, predicted and observed responses recorded in the Fenland can be compared.

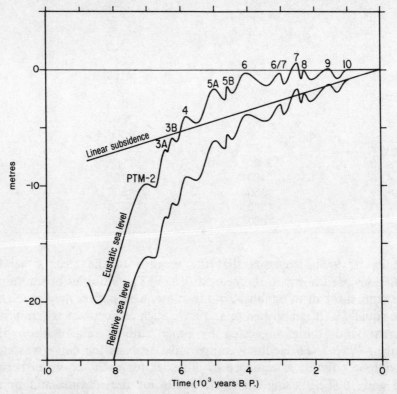

Figure 4.3 Computed regional eustatic sea-level curve calculated using a half wavelength sine curve passing through each pair of alternating maxima and minima defined by Mörner (1971, 1976b, 1980, 1984) and listed in table 4.1. The average linear rate of subsidence in the Fenland for the past 6500 radiocarbon years is estimated at c. 0.91 m /1000 years (Shennan 1986). The resulting predicted relative sea-level curve is calculated from the eustatic and subsidence factors

The relative sea-level curve calculated from the regional eustatic curve and the linear subsidence curve (figure 4.3) contains more oscillations than the sea-level band derived from the field data (figure 4.4). The field data curve was not compensated for the the effects of sediment consolidation therefore some of the discrepancies in altitude, less than *c*.1 m, may not be significant. The two diagrams show that the Fenland coastal sedimentary system consisting of alternations between marine tidal-flat deposits and peat beds does not react equally to all eustatic oscillations in that the number of periods of reduced rates of sea-level rise, which may include falls of sea-level, shown by the sea-level band (figure 4.4) is less than the number of eustatic oscillations (figure 4.3). Further analysis of the Fenland and eustatic data illustrates how such areas react to changes in sea level.

The rate of change in sea level calculated from the computed relative sea-level curve can be compared to the sea-level tendency chronology (figure 4.5). The periods of negative tendency identified from empirical analysis of the field data and the computed periods showing negative rates of sea-level change all fall within the 100–200 year time resolution expected for regional correlation. There is also a suggestion that there is a consistent lag-time between sea-level change and the registration of a negative tendency in such sedimentary environments. Other sedimentary environments need not show a similar lag-time. The effect within the Fenland is shown on figure 4.6. Each period of negative tendency of sea-level movement in the Fenland prior to 2500 BP can be explained by a single sedimentary model. The periods of negative tendency after 2500 BP are not well recorded by sediment sequences, but more by archaeological and historical evidence, and are not considered further here. Prior to each period of negative tendency there is a major period of sea-level rise. Short periods of rapid change seem important in delaying the registration of a negative tendency, shown by the rises of sea level culminating the PTM–3B and PTM–5B (figures 4.5 and 4.6). Following the major period of sea-level rise there is a period of falling sea level. Rather than reacting instantly to changes in sea-level movement the sedimentation and vegetation systems require some time to adapt to the new parameters. Negative tendencies become established, represented by extensive growth of peat over marine–brackish deposits, vegetation successional change and decomposition layers within peat beds (Shennan 1986). Whilst negative tendencies are occurring the formerly wet fens dry out and the detrital peats and turfas become oxidised. Only later because of positive tendencies of sea-level movement and recrudescence of peat growth does the decomposition layer become sandwiched. Once established, a period

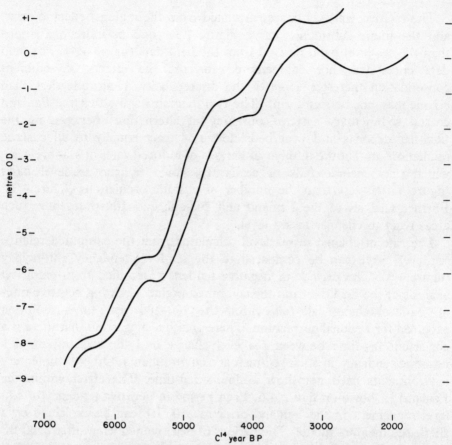

Figure 4.4 A relative sea-level band (mean highwater of spring tides) for the Fenland derived from an analysis of field and laboratory data (after Shennan 1986). This relative sea-level band should be compared with the predicted relative sea-level curve in fig. 4.3, allowing for a correction to a common tide level. At present, MHWST is 3.32 ± 0.13 m above mean tide level, and 3.80 ± 0.07 m above Ordnance Datum

of negative tendency of sea-level movement is only terminated by the next period of significant sea-level rise. Only the major changes of the relative sea-level curve have so far been recorded in the sedimentary sequence and the smaller oscillations appear to go unrecorded, but this may also be a reflection of the limited spatial distribution of data points from within the Fenland.

Mörner (1976b) suggests that the amplitude of the falls in sea level is maximal at 1 m and a somewhat smaller figure should be expected in theory. The combined effect of smaller amplitude oscillations and a slight change in their time limits (PTM–6/7 to 3300 BP, PR–3B to 6200 BP, PR–4 to 5400 BP and PR–5B to 4340 BP) produces a perfect match of

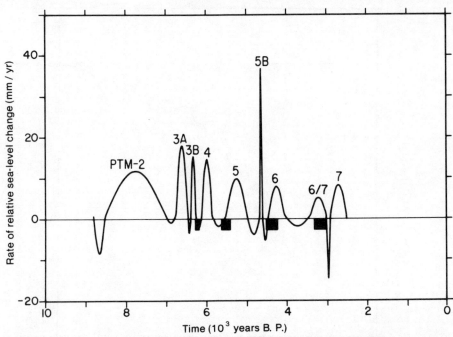

Figure 4.5 Rate of change in sea level for the Fenland calculated from the computed relative sea-level curve (fig. 4.3) with the periods of negative tendencies of sea-level movement (Shennan 1982a) shown as black rectangles. The associated PTM periods for the regional eustatic sea-level curve are indicated (after Mörner 1976b)

negative tendencies with rates of sea-level change but the lag-effect model showing the response to the major sea-level rises and periods of alternating sea-level movement still holds and is the simplest explanation (figure 4.7). Even though a detailed match can be shown by considering small variations of the modelled or empirical data, these variations are well within the specified accuracy of the dataset. No manipulation is required. The sea-level chronology and sediment sequence in the Fenland clearly has a regional eustatic origin, and a wider coverage of data points from the Fenland may be expected to reveal further fluctuations in the tendency chronology and relative sea-level band.

4.2 Regional effects and eustasy

The interaction between eustasy, glacio-isostasy and tectonic movements can be analysed by comparing published sea-level curves, noting the methods of analysis and interpretation of the original authors, with the regional eustatic curve.

Relative sea-level curves have been chosen to give a reasonable spatial

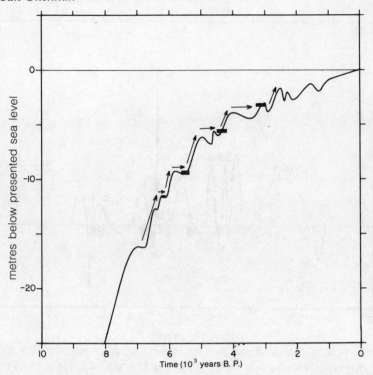

Figure 4.6 The computed relative sea-level curve for the Fenland (fig. 4.3) and the periods of negative tendency of sea-level movement (black rectangles) derived from empirical data. The arrows are added to emphasise the correlation between each period of negative tendency of sea-level movement with major changes in trend of the predicted sea-level. The altitudes of the rectangles are not significant; they do not show the altitudes obtained from the field data

cover of the North Sea region and the altitudes of each curve at 500-radiocarbon-year intervals were estimated using a 1 mm square grid on a transparent sheet. The accuracy with which each curve could be estimated is shown, along with the data used, in table 4.2. The original curves were related to different baselines, e.g. mean sea level, mean high tide level. The values in table 4.2 all relate to altitudes above or below this datum line given for the present on the original sea-level curve (figure 4.8).

The relevant eustatic value was subtracted from the relative sea-level altitude for each time point to give a basic uplift or subsidence value that could be further analysed. With a eustatic curve showing fluctuations and a relative sea-level curve also containing fluctuations the combination of the two curves may be affected by the extent to which the fixed 500-year datapoints coincide with the maxima or minima on either curve. There are a number of ways to treat the situation. Firstly the data can be pretreated,

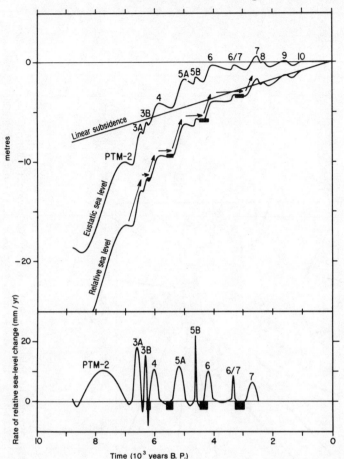

Figure 4.7 Recalculated eustatic and relative sea-level curves and rate of relative sea-level movement compared with the periods of negative sea-level tendency in the Fenland. The recalculated curves were based on theoretical considerations and the age errors to be expected during correlation at the regional scale. These adjustments result in a "best-fit" solution between the computed and empirical data, but do not alter the interpretations obtained from the unadjusted results (figs 4.5; 4.6)

for example by correlating the maxima and minima of the two curves and then just using the coincident maxima values. This was the method used by Mörner (1976b) for comparing the PTM maxima with those for the relative curve from north-west England (Tooley 1974). This involved an allowance of up to 300 years difference in the age of maxima considered equivalent. An alternative method is adopted here where the time interval is kept constant and the values of each curve taken at that point. This

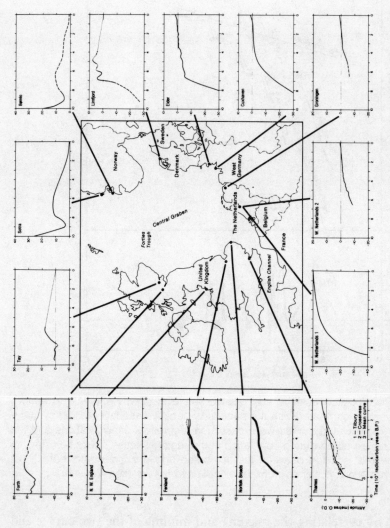

Figure 4.8 Fourteen relative sea-level curves from around the North Sea and one from North-west England drawn on a uniform scale. The original source for each area is indicated within the text. Dashed lines indicate a decrease in the reliability of the curve noted by the original author. The dotted section for the Forth curve indicates even lower reliability noted by the author; the dotted section for the Tay and Limfjord curves are extrapolations made for this chapter. The curve from North-west England is included to allow comparisons to be made with earlier analyses using similar methods

Table 4.2 Relative sea-level data obtained from available relative sea-level curves for 500 year intervals

Altitudes (m) of relative sea level at the time indicated on the conventional C–14 timescale. These data were measured relative to the altitude at which the curve intercepted the axis at 0BP, or relative to the tidal datum mentioned by the original author. All data are therefore standardized as deviations from the present datum, i.e. the reference water level is taken into consideration.

	Reference water level	Accuracy[a] of data (m)	Altitudes (m) at conventional C–14 age																	
			500	1000	1500	2000	2500	3000	3500	4000	4500	5000	5500	6000	6500	7000	7500	8000	8500
Tay Estuary	MHW	0.06	0.63	1.25	1.88	2.50	3.13	3.75	4.38	5.00	5.63	6.25	6.88	7.50	7.90	6.10	3.00	−1.30	1.80
Forth Estuary	MHW	0.15	0.27	0.95	2.04	3.53	4.21	3.66	5.02	8.10	9.10	10.10	10.00	11.00	12.30	12.30	11.40	7.60	4.10
North-west England	MHWST	0.15	1.40	1.12	0.56	0.56	0.84	0.0	−1.40	−0.84	−0.70	−2.80	−3.08	−4.20	−4.20	−5.59	−14.27	−13.99	
Fenland: maximum	MHWST	0.05				−1.55	−2.40	−2.75	−2.80	−4.75	−5.10	−7.40	−9.50	−10.80	−11.95				
Fenland: minimum	MHWST	0.05				−4.00	−4.10	−3.40	−3.90	−5.30	−6.25	−8.95	−10.20	−11.70	−12.50				
Fenland: mean	MHWST	0.05				−2.78	−3.25	−3.08	−3.35	−5.03	−5.68	−8.15	−9.85	−11.25	−12.23				
Norfolk Broads: maximum	MHWST	0.15				−1.31	−1.94	−4.44	−5.07	−5.69	−6.31	−6.53	−6.84	−7.46	−8.19	−10.28	−13.19	−16.94	
Norfolk Broads: minimum	MHWST	0.15				−2.15	−3.82	−5.28	−5.90	−6.53	−6.94	−7.15	−7.46	−7.98	−8.61	−11.32	−14.23	−18.87	
Norfolk Broads: mean	MHWST	0.15				−1.43	−2.88	−4.86	−5.49	−6.11	−6.63	−6.84	−7.15	−7.72	−8.40	−10.80	−13.71	−17.91	
Thames Estuary: mean	MHWST	0.15		−0.88	−1.76	−2.65	−3.23	−3.82	−4.70	−5.59	−6.47	−7.35	−8.24	−9.56	−10.59	−12.65	−14.41	−17.94	−31.24
Crossness	MHWST	0.15		−0.88	−2.20	−3.23	−3.82	−3.82	−3.52	−4.41	−8.53	−8.24	−8.24	−9.71	−12.06	−13.24	−14.71	−17.94	−31.24
Tilbury	MHWST	0.15		−0.88	−2.20	−3.23	−3.82	−5.00	−6.32	−8.82	−10.29	−11.03	−10.88	−10.00	−12.06	−13.53	−14.71	−17.94	−31.24
West Netherlands 1	MSL	0.12	0.00	−0.25	−0.50	−1.00	−1.50	−2.25	−3.00	−4.00	−5.00	−6.25	−7.75	−10.25	−13.25	−17.50	−23.75	−34.54	
West Netherlands 2	MHW	0.05	−0.28	−0.70	−0.95	−1.27	−1.58	−1.96	−2.66	−3.89	−5.00	−6.27	−7.53	−9.00	−8.89				
Gröningen	MHW	0.05	−0.42	−0.83	−1.22	−1.44	−1.77	−2.06	−2.50	−3.33	−4.44	−5.77	−6.89	−8.89					
Cuxhaven	MSL	0.10	−0.19	−1.80	−2.10	−2.20	−2.30	−2.70	−3.30	−4.30	−5.77	−6.00	−8.00	−14.20	−18.30	−23.00	−28.50	−35.50	
Eider Estuary	MHW	0.40	−1.00	−1.15	−1.54	−1.73	−2.31	−2.31	−4.62	−3.85	−5.77	−6.54	−6.92	−11.92	−20.77	−31.92	−42.69		
Limfjord	MSL	0.15	0.60	1.19	1.67	2.26	2.86	3.33	3.81	4.52	5.95	7.38	3.33	3.57	3.57	3.10	−11.76	−19.00	−23.53
Bømlo	MHW?	0.25	0.50	1.00	1.60	2.25	3.00	3.75	4.25	4.60	5.25	6.00	7.50	8.80	9.50	9.50	9.00	7.00	4.00
Sotra	MHW?	0.25	0.10	0.50	1.00	2.00	2.80	3.75	5.30	6.75	8.00	9.25	10.25	11.00	11.25	11.00	10.25	7.00	2.75
Eustatic sea level (m) with regressions			0.0	0.0	0.0	−0.82	0.60	−0.30	−1.34	−0.31	−1.95	−1.71	−4.70	−5.54	−7.30	−10.00	−12.60	−17.80	−20.40
Eustatic sea level (m) – no regressions			0.0	0.0	0.0	0.04	0.60	−0.30	−0.30	−0.30	−1.23	−1.75	−3.13	−4.89	−7.29	−10.00	−12.36	−14.78	−17.17
Sidereal timescale (Mörner 1976, 1984)			500	1000	1500	2000	2600	3150	3650	4050		5200	5950	6350	6850	7400	7700	7800	8000
Sidereal timescale (Klein et al. 1982) mean age			560	918	1430	1933	2558	3200	3790	4538	5195	5733	6228	6928	7400	7800	7500	8000	
Conventional C–14 age			500	1000	1500	2000	2500	3200	3500	4000	4500	5000	5500	6000	6500	7000	7500	8000	8500

[a] This figure relates to the accuracy of the measurement of the altitude from the diagram showing the original sea-level curve, not the inferred accuracy of the sea level reconstructed from empirical data.

method was used by Sissons (1967, Sissons and Brooks 1971) and Cullingford *et al.* (1980). The greatest potential errors will arise where the curve reveals a rapid rate of change around the data points, where a small shift in time would give a different, perhaps significantly different, altitude. To lessen this effect the analyses have been duplicated using a eustatic curve which has been interpolated by a straight line between each successive pair of maxima (from table 4.1), i.e. the short term fluctuations have been removed (table 4.2).

For each relative sea-level curve the eustatic values, using the two eustatic variables, were subtracted and a scatterplot for each showing resultant uplift or subsidence was produced. Each scatterplot was inspected and the time period identified where a linear trend was apparent. The linear trend was calculated in eight separate ways. These eight methods are the possible combinations of two possible choices for three conditions, i.e. the linear regression calculated with a constant term or forced through the origin; the eustatic curve with modelled regressions or interpolated as a straight line between the maxima only; and a radiocarbon or sidereal timescale. These combinations are illustrated by eight columns of three ticks in table 4.3. The radiocarbon to sidereal timescale conversion was obtained from Mörner (1976b, 1984), and checked against the values given by Klein *et al.* (1982).

The various linear trends are summarized in table 4.4. Each curve will be discussed subsequently but a few general comments can first be made. The constant term shows how close the trend passes to the origin. A large deviation from zero could indicate a number of factors, such as the statistical effect of calculating a linear function to a non-linear relationship,

Table 4.3 Methods used for calculating linear trends of uplift/subsidence. Each method utilizes one of the alternatives for each of the three conditions which affect the calculation of linear trends.

Method No.	1	2	3	4	5	6	7	8
Best-fit linear regression with constant term	✓		✓		✓		✓	
Best-fit linear regression, through origin		✓		✓		✓		✓
Eustatic curve, with regressions	✓	✓			✓	✓		
Eustatic curve, with no regressions			✓	✓			✓	✓
Radiocarbon years	✓	✓	✓	✓				
Sidereal years					✓	✓	✓	✓

or a misinterpretation regarding the relationship of the sea-level index points or the sea-level curve to the correct tide level. Given the accuracy of the data a constant term less than 1.0 m is probably not important. The eustatic curve without regressions produces generally smoother uplift/ subsidence plots, with reduced uplift or enhanced subsidence. The sidereal time scale flattens out both rates of uplift and subsidence. For the discussions of each area the scatterplots calculated from the eustatic curve without regressions are used since a number of authors do not show low amplitude oscillations in sea level and the scatterplots would then tend to reflect the eustatic oscillations superimposed on a longer term trend. Where the two eustatic curves reveal significantly different scatterplots such differences are discussed. The results from each area are now outlined, with the curve used for data collection specified.

The Fenland, United Kindom (Shennan 1986, figure 14). Relative sea-level changes in the Fenland are summarised by a sea-level band and three analyses have been carried out, using the maximum, minimum and mean values at each time point. The values for the 'minimum' analyses show the lowest correlation coefficients and largest constant terms (table 4.4), indicating that the minimum line of the sea-level band is unlikely to relate to a constant reference water level, and is certainly not equivalent to mean high water of spring tides. In addition the Fenland data were not adjusted for the effects of sediment consolidation and it should be expected that the best estimate of past tide levels would be represented by the mean or maximum curves.

The average linear rate of subsidence over the past 6500 radiocarbon years, combining the mean and maximum data sets, is 0.93 ± 0.07 m/1000 yr, and 0.81 ± 0.08 m/1000 yr over the past 7400 sidereal years (figures 4.9 and 4.10). There are no consistent deviations from the linear trends except for some indication of enhanced subsidence since 5500 BP (also noted in Shennan 1986) with the reduced trend from 6500–5500 BP being noted in other curves, see below. The significance of this trend cannot be assessed adequately with the current database.

The Norfolk Broads, United Kingdom (adapted from Alderton 1983, figure 101). These data, like the Fenland, have been summarized as a band and similarly the 'minimum' analysis could be rejected. No linear solution can explain all the data points on either the maximum or mean scatterplots (figures 4.9 and 4.10). Two factors additional to linear subsidence seem to be important. Firstly the data from the Norfolk Broads are from sites up to 30 km from the present coast, along relatively

Table 4.4 Summary of linear trends of uplift/subsidence in the North Sea Region

	Cases used (yr BP)[a]	Radiocarbon timescale			Sidereal timescale		
		Constant (m)	Rate (m/1000 yr)	Regression coefficient	Constant (m)	Rate (m/1000 yr)	Regression coefficient
Tay Estuary	0–5000	−0.35	1.60	0.98	−0.10	1.40	0.98
			1.46			1.36	
		−0.41	1.53	0.98	−0.18	1.34	0.99
			1.37			1.27	
Forth Estuary	0–5000	−1.23	2.42	0.97	−0.88	2.11	0.97
			1.92			1.79	
		−1.29	2.34	0.96	−0.97	2.06	0.98
			1.83			1.70	
North-west England	0–5500	0.78	−0.00	−0.06	0.57	0.08	0.19
			0.29			0.27	
		0.69	−0.09	0.25	0.62	−0.06	−0.19
			0.16			0.15	
Fenland: maximum	0,2000–5500	0.14	−0.87	−0.88	−0.07	−0.74	−0.88
			−0.84			−0.75	
		−0.05	−0.94	−0.91	−0.28	−0.79	−0.92
			−0.95			−0.86	
Fenland: mean	0,2000–5500	−0.41	−0.86	−0.87	−0.62	−0.73	−0.87
			−0.97			−0.87	
		−0.61	−0.93	−0.89	−0.84	−0.78	−0.90
			−1.08			−0.98	
Fenland: minimum	0,2000–5500	−0.96	−0.85	−0.83	−1.17	−0.72	−0.83
			−1.10			−0.99	
		−1.16	−0.92	−0.85	−1.39	−0.77	−0.85
			−1.22			−1.10	
Norfolk Broads: maximum	0,1500, 2000, 6000–7500	−0.19	−0.47	−0.97	−0.27	−0.41	−0.95
			−0.51			−0.47	
		−0.47	−0.46	−0.93	−0.55	−0.41	−0.92
			−0.57			−0.52	
Norfolk Broads: mean	0,1500, 2000, 6000–7000	−0.40	−0.52	−0.94	−0.51	−0.46	−0.91
			−0.62			−0.57	
		−0.68	−0.52	−0.90	−0.79	−0.45	−0.87
			−0.68			−0.62	
Norfolk Broads: minimum	0,1500, 2000, 6000–7000	−0.83	−0.55	−0.88	−0.97	−0.48	−0.84
			−0.74			−0.68	
		−1.11	−0.55	−0.84	−1.25	−0.47	−0.81
			−0.80			−0.74	
Thames Estuary: mean	0,1000– 5000	−0.01	−1.12	−0.96	−0.29	−0.95	−0.95
			−1.13			−1.05	
		−0.11	−1.19	−0.98	−0.42	−1.00	−0.96
			−1.23			−1.14	

	Cases used (yr BP)[a]	Radiocarbon timescale			Sidereal timescale		
		Constant (m)	Rate (m/1000 yr)	Regression coefficient	Constant (m)	Rate (m/1000 yr)	Regression coefficient
Thames Estuary: Tilbury	0,1000– 5000	0.83	−2.00	−0.97	0.39	−1.71	−0.97
			−1.69			−1.57	
		0.73	−2.06	−0.98	0.27	−1.75	−0.98
			−1.79			−1.66	
Thames Estuary: Crossness	0,1000– 5000	−0.05	−1.16	−0.90	−0.23	−1.02	−0.92
			−1.18			−1.10	
		−0.15	−1.22	−0.93	−0.36	−1.06	−0.95
			−1.28			−1.19	
Western Netherlands 1	0–7000	0.27	−0.49	−0.88	0.19	−0.42	−0.87
			−0.42			−0.38	
		0.15	−0.55	−0.95	0.06	−0.48	−0.95
			−0.51			−0.46	
Western Netherlands 2	0–5000	0.13	−0.53	−0.87	−0.07	−0.46	−0.88
			−0.47			−0.44	
		0.75	−0.60	−0.96	−0.02	−0.52	−0.96
			−0.57			−0.53	
Groningen	0–5500	−0.16	−0.55	−0.83	−0.27	−0.47	−0.83
			−0.61			−0.60	
		−0.08	−0.71	−0.98	−0.22	−0.60	−0.98
			−0.74			−0.68	
Cuxhaven	0–6000	−0.32	−0.65	−0.86	−0.45	−0.56	−0.86
			−0.76			−0.69	
		−0.27	−0.79	−0.94	−0.42	−0.68	−0.94
			−0.86			−0.80	
Eider Estuary	0–5000	−0.43	−0.61	−0.76	−0.57	−0.51	−0.74
			−0.78			−0.73	
		−0.49	−0.68	−0.89	−0.66	−0.57	−0.86
			−0.88			−0.51	
Limfjord	0–5000	−0.64	1.69	0.96	−0.44	1.50	0.98
			1.43			1.33	
		−0.71	1.62	0.45	−0.53	1.44	0.98
			1.34			1.24	
Bømlo	0–5000	−0.45	1.56	0.98	−0.21	1.36	0.98
			1.38			1.29	
		−0.51	1.49	0.98	−0.29	1.31	0.99
			1.29			1.20	
Sotra	0–5000	−1.57	2.29	0.96	−1.25	2.01	0.98
			1.66			1.54	
		−1.63	2.21	0.96	−1.35	1.95	0.98
			1.57			1.45	

[a] Cases used refer to those data points identified as indicating a linear trend on the scatterplots (figures 4.9 and 4.10). The calculations were made using original data from table 4.2; the scatterplots (figures 4.9 and 4.10) are diagrammatic summaries of the results and do not indicate the resolution of the original data. The sidereal equivalents to the ages of the cases used can be obtained from table 4.2.

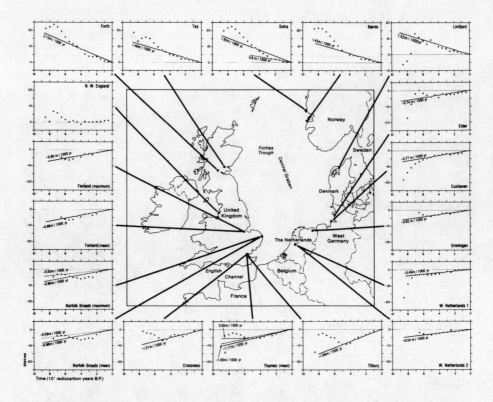

Figure 4.9 Computed uplift and subsidence from sites around the North Sea, using the radiocarbon timescale. Uplift/subsidence values relative to the regional eustatic sea-level curve (figure 4.3) were obtained for each area (table 4.2). Open circles indicate that the data were obtained by the author by extrapolation. The rate of uplift/subsidence is the mean value obtained by four methods of calculation (tables 4.3 and 4.4). Since the data points on the scatterplots are for the eustatic curve without regressions they will tend to appear slightly below the mean rate line shown, which is calculated from the data using the eustatic curve with regressions as well. These data were excluded from the scatterplots for clarity. The linear rates only relate to the time periods indicated in table 4.4; the lines on the scatterplots have been extended in some cases for ease of labelling. Non-linear relationships are evident for many areas before 6000 BP

narrow river valleys, with a spit diverting the river south as it reaches the coast. Changes in the tidal range, presently 1.9 m for spring tides at the open coast, are likely to have occurred in the past. An increase in range would have been shown as a positive residual from a linear trend. Secondly the data points for the period after 5000 BP are mostly from intercalated peats overlying 6–10 m or more of unconsolidated silts, clays and peats and are more susceptible to consolidation effects than the earlier index points which were generally from the transgressive overlap of a basal peat. The combination of a change in tidal range, resulting in positive residuals 7500–5500 BP, and consolidation, resulting in negative residuals 5000–1500 BP, would give a distribution as shown in figure 4.9 in addition to a linear rate of subsidence similar to that for the Fenland. This is shown as a dashed line and indicates the likely maximum rate. The minimum rate of -0.50 ± 0.07 m/1000 radiocarbon years (-0.45 ± 0.05 m/ 1000 sidereal years) is obtained if the tidal effect is ignored and greater importance attributed to the consolidation effect (dotted line on figures 4.9 and 4.10). The consolidation effect is not so important in the Fenland where index points obtained from near to the base of the unconsolidated sequence are used at intervals throughout the time period considered, unlike the Norfolk broads where such index points are only available in the oldest part of the chronology.

The Thames Estuary, United Kingdom (Devoy 1979, figure 29). Three curves of relative sea-level change have been presented by Devoy (1979); a mean curve, a fluctuating curve from Tilbury and a fluctuating curve from the Crossness area (figure 4.8). The latter is some 16 km upstream of Tilbury and the difference in altitudes of the two curves was attributed to differential subsidence within the estuary. Sediment consolidation and the effects of tidal amplitude and river discharge have been shown not to account fully for the within-estuary differences (Devoy 1979).

The subsidence curves for the three data sets (figures 4.9 and 4.10) reveal the differential crustal movements but also some consistent trends. A linear trend is only evidenced from 5000 BP onwards; the rates for the radiocarbon timescale are -1.89 ± 0.16 m/1000 yr at Tilbury, $-1.21\pm$ 0.05 m/1000 yr at Crossness and -1.17 ± 0.05 m/1000 yr for the mean curve and -1.67 ± 0.07 m/1000 yr, -1.09 ± 0.07 m/1000 yr and $-1.03\pm$ 0.08 m/1000 yr respectively for the sidereal timescale. For the period prior to 5000 BP there are significant deviations from these linear trends. A number of reasons can be suggested. The data point for 8500 BP was obtained by extrapolation from the original figure (Devoy 1979, figure 30). The curve at that point shows a very steep slope and the

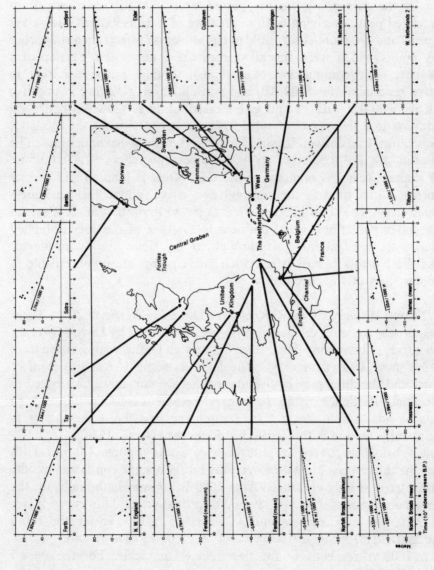

Figure 4.10 Computed uplift and subsidence from sites around the North Sea, using the sidereal timescale. Other details are given in the caption for figure 4.9, with further explanation in the text

extrapolation may be in error. However a maximum altitude is given by the Isle of Grain sea-level index point and this indicates that the points shown should be no more than 1 m higher at most. Thus, if the field data are correct, and there is no reason to doubt them, the residuals between the proposed eustatic curve and the Thames curves must be explained.

As with the Norfolk Broads a combination of tidal changes and consolidation must be considered. The stratigraphic and spatial distribution of the data points reveals that consolidation will not have had a significant effect. This conclusion is supported by Devoy's (1982) calculations of 0.3 to 0.9 m for the effect of consolidation in some of the index points. These will not remove the 5000 to 8000 BP effects shown on figure 4.9. The tidal parameters are unlikely to have remained stable throughout this period, especially during the connection of the English Channel to the North Sea and the establishment of the present circulation pattern in the North Sea region 8300–7500 BP. It is debatable whether such factors would explain the 7–11 m residual around 7500 BP, even with a reduction of 1 m in the residual by estimating the linear trend allowing for consolidation effects. Some tidal effect is probable, otherwise figure 4.9 reveals local uplift 8000–5500 BP which is difficult to account for. One possible explanation is the tidal effect combined with reduced or zero subsidence prior to 5500 BP followed by linear subsidence of between a minimum of 1.00 ± 0.05 m/1000 yr (allowing for consolidation effects) to 1.17 ± 0.05 m/1000 yr (data for the 'mean' curve and radiocarbon timescale).

North-west England, United Kingdom (Tooley 1978, figure 38). There is essentially a zero uplift rate for the past 5000 or 6000 radiocarbon years with an exponential decrease prior to then (figures 4.9 and 4.10). The index point 8000 BP (7900 sidereal years) appears as a 6 m negative residual, if an exponential curve, on the sidereal scale, for isostatic uplift of a formerly glaciated region was to be expected. The original relative sea-level curve shows a steep rise after 7800 BP, fixed by two index points. The 6 m residual can be partly explained by consolidation affecting the original sea-level index points and by using a sea-level band drawn through the error boxes of the data points (Tooley 1982b).

The results appear less precise than the correlations and rates of change noted by Mörner (1976b) but these reflect the decisions made about the accuracy of the original data, the method of analysis used and the repeatability of such a method.

The Forth Estuary, United Kingdom (Sissons 1967, figure 82 <4000 BP,

Sissons and Brooks 1971, figure 2, >4000 BP).   The rates of uplift shown in table 4.4 are given as a guide only since the original curve is poorly fixed post-4000 BP and a linear trend is an unsuitable summary of the points shown in figures 4.9 and 4.10. Similar to the North-west England plot the two oldest data points appear a few metres too low. In general the uplift curve shows a curvelinear decrease, continuing to the present.

The Tay Estuary, United Kingdom (Cullingford et al. 1980, figure 2).   The original relative sea-level curve is too incomplete to reveal anything more than broad trends in uplift (figures 4.9 and 4.10). The rates shown (table 4.4) are based on an interpolated linear fall of relative sea-level from 6000 BP to the present. The datum for 8000 BP was also interpolated from the original graph. There have been a number of detailed shoreline and stratigraphic studies from the area (e.g. Cullingford *et al.* 1980, Morrison, *et al.* 1981, Smith *et al.* 1985a) but no complete detailed relative sea-level curve has been produced.

The Western Netherlands 1 and 2 (1: Jelgersma 1980, figures 5 and 6, with corrections from van de Plassche 1980. 2: Louwe Kooijmans 1974, figure 14). These two curves should be considered as composites since both use index points from a wide geographical area, e.g. greater than the distance between the Thames Estuary and Norfolk Broads which were considered separately. For the period 0–6500 BP the two curves show very similar subsidence characteristics. Curve 1 shows, for the period 0–7000 BP, a subsidence rate of −0.49±0.05 m/1000 radiocarbon years, −0.44±0.04 m/1000 sidereal years. Curve 2 gives a best fit linear solution for 0–5000 BP only, the earlier period showing characteristics of reduced subsidence similar to other curves already discussed. In this case it may be the result of using one, rather imprecise, data point at the extreme of the data range. The average rates are very similar to curve 1 (table 4.4, figures 4.9 and 4.10). It should be noted that this method of analysis works at a quite different scale of resolution compared to the local comparisons made by Louwe Kooijmans (1974) and van de Plassche (1980) where differences of a few decimetres are analysed. The part of curve 1 pre-7000 BP is obtained from samples collected up to 160 km offshore. Such sites are likely to have undergone a subsidence history different to the onshore sites and the difference between the two parts of the subsidence curve need not be evaluated further given the current database.

Groningen District, The Netherlands (Roeleveld 1976, figure 56).   The relative sea-level curve is a summary of many stratigraphic and radiocarbon analyses but drawn through only ten fixed points. There is a clear linear trend 0–5500 BP of −0.65±0.08 m/1000 radiocarbon years (−0.59±0.08 m/1000 sidereal years, table 4.4, figures 4.9 and 4.10). There is a change in the nature of the scatterplot 6500–5500 BP. Whether this represents a change in the rate of subsidence, since a similar effect has been noted in a number of other analyses discussed, or a change in the tidal regime, requires more analysis. It could also be a result of the method employed for curve construction; the period relates to the oldest part of the curve where it is based on widely spaced data points. The linear trend calculated indicates slightly greater subsidence for the Groningen District of the Northern Netherlands than for the Western Netherlands (cf. Roeleveld 1976), although the differing spatial scales used in data collection must be taken into account.

Cuxhaven, West Germany (Linke 1982, figure 13). The relative sea-level curve represents an interpretation of the mean tide level, calculated from the altitudes of clastic deposits and intercalated peat deposits with the assumption that these represent fluctuations between very stormy phases and storm-free phases. During the former phases marine clastic sedimentation took place at higher elevations than during the latter. The subsidence scatterplots (figures 4.9 and 4.10) show a linear trend 0–6000 BP of −0.77±0.08 m/1000 radiocarbon years (−0.68±0.09 m/1000 sidereal years), with greater subsidence prior to that. The division is due to the same effect as noted for the West Netherlands 1 curve; the early part of the curve is based on data from the offshore zone, thus showing quite different subsidence effects.

The Eider Estuary, West Germany (Behre et al. 1979, figure IV – 24). This relative curve for mean high tide level movements is based on different interpretations than that of Linke (above) and shows fluctuations of a few decimetres amplitude, inferred from botanic and stratigraphic data. The accuracy with which the data could be obtained from the published curve is poor (table 4.2), therefore the variability of the points on the scatterplots (figures 4.9 and 4.10) is exaggerated. Nevertheless the linear trend 0–5000 BP of −0.74±0.11 m/1000 radiocarbon years (−0.66± 0.13 m/1000 sidereal years) is indistinguishable from the Cuxhaven curve. The nature of the earlier part of the curve is quite different. Prior to 7500 BP the curve is drawn from offshore samples, from areas of possible enhanced subsidence. As with other analyses discussed the 6500–5000 BP period reveals a reversed slope relationship. Whether this reflects a tidal, crustal or consolidation effect, or an effect due to the resolution of the data in this example, is unclear.

Limfjord, Denmark (Petersen 1984a, figure 2).   Data points for the period 500–3500 BP have been interpolated from the original sea-level curve. There were also few sea-level index points prior to 7500 BP and the altitudinal accuracy of the early part of the curve is poor. The linear trends given (table 4.4) act as a rough guide only but there are too few reliable fixed points to draw any firmer conclusions. The scatterplots (figures 4.9 and 4.10) suggest that the data points for 7500–8500 BP are anomalous.

Bømlo, Norway (Kaland 1984, figure 23).   The uplift scatterplots reveal a curvelinear relationship (figures 4.9 and 4.10) although a linear summary, 1.43±0.11 m/1000 radiocarbon years and 1.29±0.06 m/1000 sidereal years, appears adequate for the last 5000 years. This may be related to the 'double factor' uplift recognized for Scandinavia (Mörner 1980b) but it may be a limitation in the resolution of the data. The oldest index point appears a few metres too low.

Sotra, Norway (Kaland et al. 1984, figure 2).   The analysis of this curve produces similar results to Bømlo, except that the linear factor is poorly established, revealed by the larger constant terms for the best-fit linear solutions and the greater variability in the linear rates calculated by the different methods (table 4.4). A reduced linear uplift in the order of 0.8 m/1000 yr for the last 2500 years may be evident but this further confirms an overall curvelinear relationship (figure 4.9). The oldest data point is some metres too low; the next oldest appears too low on the diagrams (figures 4.9 and 4.10) but if the data points from the eustatic curve with regressions had been shown it would have appeared on the line of the curve.

4.3   General points

This regional analysis of relative sea-level curves has indicated how crustal movement, tidal variations and local sediment consolidation *may* interact and how such factors can be investigated given due consideration of the correct temporal and spatial scales. They are all dependent on the assumptions that a single sea-level curve can be adopted as a baseline and that the curve proposed by Mörner is the appropriate one. If the baseline is incorrect then the error will be recorded in the analysis of each curve.

The curves from the Fenland, Norfolk Broads, Thames Estuary (all three curves), Western Netherlands 1 and 2, Groningen and the Eider Estuary, i.e. most of the curves from the subsiding parts of the southern North Sea, revealed a decreased, or reversed, subsidence curve for the period *c.*6500–5000 BP (figure 4.9). The phenomenon does not totally disappear if the data calculated from the eustatic curve with regressions are plotted on figures 4.9 and 4.10 (such data were of course evaluated, see tables 4.3 and 4.4). If the baseline, i.e. eustatic, curve was in error any proposed correction would produce increased positive residuals in the uplift curves from Denmark, Norway, North-west England and Scotland. Alternative explanations would include the imprecision of the relative sea-level curves, which is possible for some of the cases only; changes in tidal range as the bathymetry of the coastal zone and estuaries of the North Sea changed, certainly a possible factor; sediment consolidation, most probable in at least one example; or a variation in the rate of subsidence, perhaps due to the increasing hydro-isostatic load.

The curves from the uplifted sites reveal that the data points for 8500 and 8000 BP (radiocarbon scale) show consistently low uplift values, a factor noted by Mörner (1976b) in his analysis of the north-west England data. This is a particularly difficult period for which to obtain precise time and altitude fixed points due to changes in the atmospheric carbon–14 content (Mörner 1971) and the rapid changes of sea-level between PTM–1 and PTM–2 (figures 4.3 and 4.8). Any slight alteration in the time factor, i.e the interpretation of the radiocarbon data *and* their error terms, in, *either* the eustatic curve *or* the relative curve would probably be sufficient to remove any significant residual from a smooth uplift curve, when converted to a sidereal timecale. Finally, the consistent deviations noted for these two time periods *may* be evidence to suggest that either the regional eustatic curve is in error, or that the geoid has changed configuration, on the scale of the North Sea during the Holocene, since no single baseline curve could adequately explain all the residuals from the present analyses. These observations require more detailed investigation when more data become available.

The mean linear rates of uplift and subsidence calculated for the last 5000 radiocarbon years (figure 4.9 and table 4.4) indicate a similar pattern to other analyses but the absolute rates vary. Flemming (1982) used a linear isostatic factor for the last 10 000 years as a first approximation. His suggestion that a cubic or quartic model would be better is clearly evidenced by the curves in figures 4.9 and 4.10. Analyses of tide gauge data (e.g. figure V–10 in Jelgersma 1979, Emery & Aubrey 1985, Rossiter 1972, Pugh and Faull 1982) also show comparable patterns of uplift and subsidence although particular detail must be paid to the length of record used and such data are poor indicators of trends applied to much longer periods (Pugh and Faull 1982). A more accurate three-dimensional expression of the distribution of uplift and subsidence through time, based on the data presented here, will allow a better modelling of the mass transfer and rates of flow associated with the mechanisms of glacial isostasy whereas current calculations are based on a series of uplift profiles (Mörner 1980b).

5.0 CONCLUSIONS

It has been shown that the North Sea region is indeed a sea-level laboratory from which various factors controlling relative sea level can be identified. These factors operate at different scales and can only be studied by the correct choice of temporal and spatial scales of resolution. The interaction between regional eustasy, crustal movements, tidal factors and local sedimentary environments has been illustrated and the results can form the basis for comparison with other studies which use quite different approaches, such as modelling the deformation of the Earth's crust or analysing the recent rates of sea-level change from tide gauge records.

While local scale factors will continue to be evaluated by research workers closely associated with the field data collection and subsequent sediment analysis, regional scale analyses can only progress with an increasing integrated computer based relational database. The flexibility and repeatability of approaches that can be explored using such a database were very evident during the research carried out for this paper. Numerical and graphical analysis of sea level data, the histogram methods discussed, sea-level curve modelling and statistical methods, offer very many possible lines for future research but the effort required to accumulate the required data into computer compatible form is almost beyond the capabilities of the co-operation fostered within the IGCP sea-level projects. Without an increase in such effort and co-operation, regional sea-level analyses will be held back by a lack of suitable and readily available data. Such data exist but are coded by local interpretations, methods of classification and presentation. Such methods are eminently suitable for local scale studies but differences between local based approaches hinder regional analyses. The sea-level data resources have been proven but they are not yet sea-level data reserves.

Revised typescript received 1986, January.

ACKNOWLEDGEMENTS

The author is grateful to Eileen Beattie and Kathryn Lund for typing the manuscript.

REFERENCES

Alderton, A. 1983: Flandrian vegetational history and sea-level change of the Waveney Valley. Unpublished Ph.D. Thesis, University of Cambridge.

Baeteman, C. 1981: An alternative classification and profile type map applied to the Holocene deposits of the Belgian coastal plain. *Bull. Soc. belge de Géologie*, 90, 257–80.

Baeteman, C. 1985: Development and evolution of sedimentary environments during the Holocene in the western coastal plain of Belgium. *Eiszeitalter Gegenw.*, 35, 23–32.

Barckhausen, J., Preuss, H. and Streif, H. 1977: Ein lithologisches Ordnung-sprinzip für das Küstenholozän und seine Darstellung in Form von Profiltypen. *Geol. Jb.*, A44, 45–77.

Behre, K.-E., Menke, B. and Streif, H. 1979: The Quaternary geological development of the German part of the North Sea. In E. Oele, R. T. E. Schüttenhelm and A. J. Wiggers (eds), The Quaternary History of the North Sea. *Acta Univ. Ups. Symp. Univ. Ups. Annum Quingentesimum Celebrantis*, Uppsala, 2, 85–113.

Berendsen, H. J. A. 1984: Quantitative analysis of radiocarbon dates of the perimarine areas in the Netherlands. *Geol. Mijnbouw*, 63, 343–50.

Bloom, A. L. 1977: *Atlas of Sea-level Curves*. IGCP Project 61. Ithaca, New York: Cornell University.

Bloom, A. L. 1982: Atlas of Sea-level Curves: Supplement. IGCP 61. Unpublished typescript.

Brand, G., Hageman, B. P., Jelgersma, S. and Sindowski, K. H. 1965: Die lithostratigraphische Unterteilung des marinen Holozäns an der Nordseeküste, *Geol. Jb.*, 82, 365–84.

Cullingford, R. A., Caseldine, C. J. and Gotts, P. E. 1980: Early Flandrian land and sea-level changes in Lower Strathearn. *Nature*, 284, 159–61.

Devoy, R. J. N. 1979: Flandrian sea-level changes and vegetational history of the lower Thames Estuary. *Phil. Trans. R. Soc. Lond.*, B285, 355–407.

Devoy, R. J. N. 1982: Analysis of the geological evidence for Holocene sea-level movements in south-east England. *Proc. Geol. Ass.*, 93, 65–90.

Eden, R. A., Holmes, R. and Fannin, N. G. T. 1978: Quaternary deposits of the Central North Sea, 6. Depositional environment of offshore Quaternary deposits of the Continental Shelf around Scotland. *Rep. Inst. Geol. Sci.*, 77/15.

Emery, K. O. and Aubrey, D. G. 1985: Glacial rebound and relative sea levels in

Europe from tide-gauge records. *Tectonophysics*, 120, 239–55.

Eriksson, K. G. 1979: Late Pleistocene and Holocene shorelines on the Swedish West Coast. In E. Oele, R. T. E. Schüttenhelm and A. J. Wiggers (eds), The Quaternary History of the North Sea. *Acta Univ. Ups. Symp. Univ. Ups. Annum Quingentesimum Celebrantis*, Uppsala, 2, 61–74.

Flemming, N. C. 1982: Multiple regression analysis of earth movements and eustatic sea-level changes in the United Kingdom in the past 9000 years. *Proc. Geol. Ass.*, 93, 113–25.

Geyh, M. A. 1971: Middle and young Holocene sea level changes as global contemporary events. *Geol. För. Stockh. Förh.*, 93, 679–92.

Geyh, M. A. 1980: Holocene sea-level history: Case study of the statistical evaluation of ^{14}C dates. *Radiocarbon*, 22, 695–704.

Grant, D. G. 1985: Atlas of sea-level curves – supplement. *Litoralia*, 11, 2–9. Newsletter of the INQUA Commission on Quaternary Shorelines.

Hafsten, U. 1979: Late and Post-Weichselian shore level changes in South Norway. In E. Oele, R. T. E. Schüttenhelm and A. J. Wiggers (eds), The Quaternary History of the North Sea. *Acta Univ. Ups. Symp. Univ. Ups. Annum Quingentesimum Celebrantis*, Uppsala, 2, 45–59.

Hafsten, U. 1983: Biostratigraphical evidence for Late Weichselian and Holocene sea-level changes in southern Norway. In D. E. Smith and A. G. Dawson (eds), *Shorelines and Isostasy*, London: Academic Press, 161–81.

Hughes, T. M. 1980: Genes and glacial history: a letter to the editor. *Boreas*, 9, 149.

International Study Group 1982: An inter-laboratory comparison of radiocarbon measurements in tree rings. *Nature*, 298, 619–23.

Jansen, J. H. F., van Weering, Tj. C. E. and Eisma, D. 1979: Late Quaternary sedimentation in the North Sea. In E. Oele, R. T. E. Schüttenhelm and A. J. Wiggers (eds), The Quaternary History of the North Sea. *Acta Univ. Ups. Symp. Univ. Ups. Annum Quingentesimum Celebrantis*, Uppsala, 2, 175–87.

Jardine, W. G. 1979: The western (United Kingdom) shore of the North Sea in Late Pleistocene and Holocene times. In E. Oele, R. T. E. Schüttenhelm and A. J. Wiggers (eds), The Quaternary History of the North Sea, *Acta Univ. Ups. Symp. Univ. Ups. Annum Quingentesimum Celebrantis*, Uppsala, 2, 159–74.

Jelgersma, S. 1961: Holocene sea-level changes in the Netherlands. *Meded. Geol. Sticht.*, C.VI, 7.

Jelgersma, S. 1966: Sea-level changes during the last 10 000 years. In J. S. Sawyer (ed.), Proceedings of the International Symposium at Imperial College, London, 18–19 April, 1966. *World Climate 8000 to 0 B.C.* London: Royal Meteorological Society, 54–69.

Jelgersma, S. 1979: Sea-level changes in the North Sea basin. In E. Oele, R. T. E. Schüttenhelm and A. J. Wiggers, (eds), The Quaternary History of the North Sea. *Acta Univ. Ups. Symp. Univ. Ups. Annum. Quingentesimum*

Celebrantis, Uppsala, 2, 233–48.

Jelgersma, S. 1980: Late Cenozoic sea-level changes in the Netherlands and the adjacent North Sea Basin. In N.-A. Mörner (ed.), *Earth Rheology, Isostasy and Eustasy,* Chichester: John Wiley, 435–47.

Jelgersma, S., Oele, E. and Wiggers, A. J., 1979: Depositional history and coastal development in the Netherlands and the adjacent North Sea since the Eemian. In E. Oele, R. T. E. Schüttenhelm and A. J. Wiggers (eds), The Quaternary History of the North Sea. *Acta Univ. Ups. Symp. Univ. Ups. Annum Quingentesimum Celebrantis,* Uppsala, 2, 115–42.

Jelgersma, S., de Jong, J., Zagwijn, W. H. and van Regteren Altena, J. F. 1970: The coastal dunes of the Western Netherlands; geology, vegetational history and archaeology. *Meded. Rijks. geol. Dienst.* N.S.21, 93–167.

Kaland, P. E. 1984: Holocene shore displacement and shorelines in Hordaland, western Norway. *Boreas,* 13, 203–42.

Kaland, P. E., Krzywinski, K. and Stabell, B. 1984: Radiocarbon - dating of transitions between marine and lacustrine sediments and their relation to the development of lakes. *Boreas,* 13, 243–58.

Kidson, C. 1982: Sea-level changes in the Holocene. *Quat. Sci. Rev.,* 1, 121–51.

Klein, J., Lerman, J. C., Damon, P. E. and Ralph, E. K. 1982: Calibration of radiocarbon dates: tables based on the consensus data of the Workshop on Calibrating the Radiocarbon Time Scale. *Radiocarbon,* 24, 103–50.

Krog, H. 1979: Late Pleistocene and Holocene shorelines in Western Denmark. In E. Oele, R. T. E. Schüttenhelm and A. J. Wiggers (eds), The Quaternary History of the North Sea. *Acta. Univ. Ups. Symp. Univ. Ups. Annum Quingentesimum Celebrantis,* Uppsala, 2, 75–83.

Krog, H. 1984: The Quaternary of Vendsyssel. *INQUA Subcommission on Shorelines of Northwestern Europe. Field Conference 1984 September 15–21. Excursion Guide. North Sea Coastal Zone between Jade Bay and Jammer Bight.* Hannover: NLFB, 81–90.

Krzywinski, K. and Stabell, B. 1984: Late Weichselian sea-level changes at Sotra, Hordaland, Western Norway. *Boreas,* 13, 159–202.

Linke, G. 1982: Der Ablauf der holozänen Transgression der Nordsee aufgrund von Ergebnissen aus dem Gebiet Neuwerk/Scharhorn. *Probleme d. Küstenforsch i. südl. Nordseegebiet,* 14, 123–57.

Linke, G. 1984: Arensch (south of Cuxhaven). *INQUA Subcommission on Shorelines of Northwestern Europe. Field Conference 1984, September 15–21. Excursion Guide. North Sea Coastal Zone between Jade Bay and Jammer Bight,* Hannover: NLFB, 22–7.

Louwe Kooijmans, L. P. 1974: *The Rhine/Meuse delta: Four studies on its prehistoric occupation and Holocene geology.* Leiden: E. J. Brill.

Ludwig, G., Müller, H. & Streif, H. 1981: New dates on Holocene sea-level changes in the German Bight. *Spec. Publs. Int. Ass. Sediment.,* 5, 211–19.

Mörner, N.-A. 1969: The Late Quaternary history of the Kattegatt Sea and the Swedish West Coast. *Sver. geol. Unders.* Serie C, 640, 1–487.

Mörner, N.-A. 1971: Eustatic changes during the last 20 000 years and a method for separating the isostatic and eustatic factors in an uplifted area. *Palaeogeogr., Palaeoclimatol., Palaeoecol.*, 9, 153–81.

Mörner, N.-A. 1976a: Eustasy and Geoid Changes. *J. Geol.*, 84, 123–51.

Mörner, N.-A. 1976b: Eustatic changes during the last 8000 years in view of radiocarbon calibration and new information from the Kattegatt region and other north-western European coastal areas. *Palaeogeogr., Palaeoclimatol., Palaeoecol.*, 19, 63–85.

Mörner, N.-A. 1979: South Scandinavian sea-level records: a test of regional eustasy, regional palaeoenvironmental changes and global paleogeoid changes. *Proceedings of the 1978 International Symposium on coastal evolution in the Quaternary São Paulo, Brasil (1979)*, 77–103.

Mörner, N.-A. 1980a: The northwest European 'sea-level laboratory' and regional Holocene eustasy. *Palaeogeogr., Palaeoclimatol., Palaeoecol.*, 29, 281–300.

Mörner, N.-A. 1980b: Eustasy and geoid changes as a function of core/mantle changes. In N.-A. Mörner (ed.), *Earth Rehology, Isostasy and Eustasy*, Chichester: Wiley, 535–53.

Mörner, N.-A. 1980c: Late Quaternary sea-level changes in north-western Europe: a synthesis. *Geol. För. Stockh. Förh.*, 100 (for 1978), 381–400.

Mörner, N.-A. 1984: Planetary, solar, atmospheric, hydrospheric and endogene processes as origin of climatic changes on the earth. In N.-A. Mörner and W. Karlén (eds), *Climatic Changes on a Yearly to Millennial Basis*, Dordrecht: Reidel, 483–507.

Morrison, I. A. 1976: Comparative stratigraphy and radiocarbon chronology of Holocene marine changes on the western seaboard of Europe. In D. A. Davidson and M. L. Shackley (eds), *Geoarchaeology*, London: Duckworth, 159–75.

Morrison, J., Smith, D. E., Cullingford, R. A. and Jones, R. L. 1981: The culmination of the Main Postglacial Transgression in the Firth of Tay area, Scotland. *Proc. Geol. Ass.*, 92, 197–209.

Newman, W. S., Marcus, L. F., Pardi, R. R., Paccione, J. A. and Tomecek, S. M. 1980: Eustasy and deformation of the geoid: 1000–6000 radiocarbon years BP. In N.-A. Mörner (ed.) *Earth Rheology, Isostasy and Eustasy*, Chichester: Wiley, 555–67.

Oele, E. and Schüttenhelm, R. T. E. 1979: Development of the North Sea after the Saalian glaciation. In E. Oele, R. T. E. Schüttenhelm, and A. J. Wiggers (eds), The Quaternary History of the North Sea. *Acta Univ. Ups. Symp. Univ. Ups. Annum Quingentesimum Celebrantis*, Uppsala, 2, 191–216.

Oele, E., Schüttenhelm, R. T. E. and Wiggers, A. J. (eds) 1979: The Quaternary History of the North Sea. *Acta Univ. Ups. Symp. Univ. Ups. Annum Quingentesimum Celebrantis*, Uppsala, 2, 1–248.

Olsson, I. U. 1979: Radiometric dating. In B. E. Berglund (ed.), *Palaeohydrological changes in the last 15,000 years*. IGCP 158B. Lake and mire environments. Project guide, II. Specific methods, 1–38. Lund: Department of Quaternary Geology.

Ota, Y., Matsushima, Y. and Moriwaki, H. 1981: *Atlas of Holocene Sea-level records in Japan.* Japanese Working Group IGCP Project 61. Yokohama: Yokohama National University.

Petersen, K. S. 1981: The Holocene marine transgression and its molluscan fauna in the Skagerrak-Limfjord region, Denmark. *Spec. Publs. Int. Ass. Sediment.*, 5, 497–503.

Petersen, K. S. 1984a: The Holocene marine history of the Limfjord Area. *INQUA Subcommission on Shorelines of Northwestern Europe. Field Conference 1984, September 15–21. Excursion Guide. North Sea Coastal Zone between Jade Bay and Jammer Bight.* Hannover: NLFB, 74–80.

Petersen, K. S. 1984b: Late Weichselian sea levels and fauna communities in northern Vendsyssel, Jutland, Denmark. In N.-A. Mörner and W. Karlén (eds), *Climatic Changes on a Yearly to Millennial Basis*, Dordrecht: Reidel, 63–8.

Plassche, O. van de 1980: Holocene water-level changes in the Rhine-Meuse delta as a function of changes in relative sea level, local tidal range, and river gradient. *Geol. Mijnbouw*, 59, 343–51.

Plassche, O. van de 1981: Sea level, groundwater and basal peat growth – a reassessment from The Netherlands. *Geol. Mijnbouw*, 60, 401–8.

Plassche, O. van de 1984: Causes of a Late-Atlantic swamp-forest submergence in the central Rhine/Meuse delta. In N.-A. Mörner and W. Karlén (eds), *Climatic Changes on a Yearly to Millennial Basis*, Dordrecht: Reidel, 205–14.

Plassche, O. van de 1985: Time-limit assessment of some Holocene transgressive and regressive periods in the Northern Netherlands. *Eiszeitalter Gegenw.*, 35, 43–8.

Plassche, O. van de and Preuss, H. 1978: IGCP Project 61. Sea-level movements during the last deglacial hemicycle (ca 15 000y). Explanatory guidelines for completion of the computer form for sample documentation. Unpublished typescript. Amsterdam/Hannover: IGCP.

Preuss, H. 1979a: Progress in computer evaluation of sea-level data within the IGCP Project No. 61. *Proceedings of the 1978 International Symposium on coastal evolution in the Quaternary. São Paulo, Brasil, (1979)*, 104–34.

Preuss, H. 1979b: Die holozäne Entwicklung der Nordseekuste im Gebiet der östlichen Wesermasch. *Geol. Jb.*, A53, 3–84.

Pugh, D. T. and Faull, H. E. 1982: Tides, surges and mean sea-level trends. In *Shoreline Protection*, Institution of Civil Engineers, University of Southampton, 14–15 September 1982. London: Thomas Telford Ltd, 45–55.

Robinson, M. 1982: Diatom analysis of Early Flandrian lagoon sediments from East Lothian, Scotland. *J. Biogeogr.*, 9, 207–21.

Roeleveld, W. 1976: The Holocene evolution of the Groningen marine-clay district. *Berichten van de Rijksdienst voor het Oudheidkundig Bodemonderzock*, vol. 24. Supplement.

Roep, Th. B. 1984: Progradation, erosion and changing coastal gradient in the coastal barrier deposits of the Western Netherlands. *Geol. Mijnbouw*, 63, 249–58.

Rossiter, J. R. 1972: Sea-level observations and their secular variation. *Phil. Trans. R. Soc. Lond.*, A272, 131–9.

Shennan, I. 1979: Statistical evaluation of sea-level data. *Sea Level: Information Bull. of IGCP Project No. 61*, 1, 6–11.

Shennan, I. 1982a: Interpretation of Flandrian sea-level data from the Fenland, England. *Proc. Geol. Ass.*, 93, 53–63.

Shennan, I. 1982b: Problems of correlating Flandrian sea-level changes and climate. In A. F. Harding (ed.), *Climatic Change in Later Prehistory*, Edinburgh: University Press, 52–67.

Shennan, I. 1983: Flandrian and Late Devensian sea-level changes and crustal movements in England and Wales. In D. E. Smith and A. G. Dawson (eds), *Shorelines and Isostasy*, London: Academic Press, 255–83.

Shennan, I. 1986: Flandrian sea-level changes in the Fenland. II: tendencies of sea-level movement, altitudinal changes, and local and regional factors. *Journal of Quaternary Science*, 1, 155–79.

Shennan, I. 1987: Global analysis and correlation of sea-level data. In R. J. Devoy (ed.), *Sea Surface Studies: a global view*, Beckenham: Croom Helm, 198–230.

Shennan, I., Tooley, M. J., Davis, M. J. and Haggart, B. A. 1983: Analysis and interpretation of Holocene sea-level data *Nature*, 302, 404–6.

Sissons, J. B. 1967: *The Evolution of Scotland's Scenery*, Edinburgh: Oliver & Boyd.

Sissons, J. B. 1983: Shorelines and Isostasy in Scotland. In D. E. Smith and A. G. Dawson (eds), *Shorelines and Isostasy*, London: Academic Press, 209–25.

Sissons, J. B. and Brooks, C. L. 1971: Dating of Early Postglacial Land and Sea Level Changes in the Western Forth Valley. *Nature*, 234, 124–127.

Smith, D. E., Cullingford, R. A. and Brooks, C. L. 1983: Flandrian relative sea-level changes in the Ythan Valley, Northeast Scotland. *Earth Surface Processes and Landforms*, 8, 423–38.

Smith, D. E., Dawson, A. G., Cullingford, R. A. and Harkness, D. D. 1985a: The Stratigraphy of Flandrian relative sea-level changes at a site in Tayside, Scotland. *Earth Surface Processes and Landforms*, 10, 17–25.

Smith, D. E., Cullingford, R. A. and Haggart, B. A. 1985b: A major coastal flood during the Holocene in eastern Scotland. *Eiszeitalter Gegenw.* 35, 109–18.

Smith, D. E., Morrison, J., Jones, R. L. and Cullingford, R. A. 1980: Dating the Main Postglacial Shoreline in the Montrose area, Scotland. In R. A. Cullingford, D. A. Davidson and J. Lewin (eds), *Timescales in Geomorphology*, Chichester: Wiley, 225–45.

Stabell, B. and Thiede, J. 1985: The physiographic evolution of the Skagerrak during the last 15 000 years: Palaeobathymetry and palaeogeography. *Nor. geol. Tidsskr.*, 65, 19–22.

Stoker, M. S., Long, D. and Fyfe, J. A. 1985: The Quaternary succession in the central North Sea. *Newsl. Stratigr.*, 14, 119–28.

Streif, H. 1972: The results of stratigraphical and facial investigations in the coastal Holocene of Woltzeten/Ostfriesland, Germany. *Geol. För. Stockh. Förh.*, 94, 281–99.

Streif, H. 1978: A new method for the representation of sedimentary sequences in coastal regions. *Proceedings of the 16th Coastal Engineering Conference. ASCE/Hamburg. West Germany (August 28th–September 1, 1978)*, 1245–56.

Streif, H. 1979: Cyclic formation of coastal deposits and their indications of vertical sea-level changes. *Oceanis*, 5, 303–6.

Tooley, M. J. 1974: Sea-level changes during the last 9000 years in north-west England. *Geog. J.*, 140, 18–42.

Tooley, M. J. 1978: *Sea-level Changes in North-west England during the Flandrian Stage*. Oxford: Clarendon Press.

Tooley, M. J. 1982a: Introduction: IGCP Project No. 61 in the UK. *Proc. Geol. Ass.*, 93, 3–6.

Tooley, M. J. 1982b: Sea-level changes in northern England. *Proc. Geol. Ass.*, 93, 43–51.

5

Sea-level changes in the Mediterranean

Paolo A. Pirazzoli

1.0 INTRODUCTION

The Mediterranean is an excellent region for recording marks of former sea levels owing to the low tidal amplitude and the presence of numerous indicators of ancient shorelines.

The amplitude of the spring tide is very slight (usually less than 0.2 to 0.3 m), increasing a little only near the Strait of Gibraltar (0.9 m), the Gulf of Gabes (1.7 m) and in the North Adriatic (0.9 m).

The frequent occurrence of limestone along the coasts favours the development of forms of erosion (platforms, notches, sea caves) which remain for long periods. Even loose beach deposits often consolidate rapidly in the Mediterranean climate (beachrock, *panchina*) and are preserved for longer.

Encrusting of sessile organisms at a particular altimetric level (Vermetids, *Neogoniolithon*, barnacles) enables the position of an ancient sea level to be determined precisely, and sometimes an age to be obtained.

Innumerable vestiges of ancient civilisations have been left along the coasts, often clearly dated, so that sometimes they serve to determine the former sea level very precisely.

Finally, tectonic activity has resulted in the uplift or submergence of the marks of ancient shorelines, protecting them from the destructive impact of waves and so preserving them.

Although favourable for sea-level investigations, there are still too many areas in the Mediterranean which require further study. This makes it difficult to draw regional conclusions from the results at our disposal, particularly as there are numerous factors contributing to the relative variations in the sea level, and they refer to diverse scales.

In this paper, after having recalled the geodynamic forces tectonically deforming this area and described the shape of the present sea surface, changes in sea levels in the Mediterranean are reviewed and discussed, especially those since the last Interglacial.

2.0 THE GEODYNAMICAL CONTEXT

It would be unwise to interpret the distribution of the former shorelines without taking into account the geodynamical context of the Mediterranean region.

The Mediterranean Sea (figure 5.1) consists of a series of deep sedimentary basins stretching some 4000 kilometres between Gibraltar and the Black Sea. Together with the Alpine mountain chains with which they are closely associated, these basins occupy the junction between the African-Arabian and the Eurasian continents in a zone marked by earthquakes and volcanic eruptions.

The present situation was reached after a long geological history, the Alpine chains having formed progressively over the last 180 million years on the site of an ocean – Tethys – widening towards the East. Since the Atlantic Ocean opened up, Africa and Europe have formed two plates subject to certain movements in relation to each other: Africa rotated at 50° in a trigonometric direction in relation to Europe, reducing the eastern positions of Africa and Europe by 1500 km (Biju-Duval *et al.* 1976).

The present phase which began some 50 million years ago is that of a slow rotation of Africa around the focal point of Gibraltar, where the deformation is absorbed for the most part in a 500- to 600-km wide zone from north to south (*Groupe de recherche néotectonique de l'Arc de Gibraltar* 1977). The relative displacements between Africa and Europe remain slight (<1cm /yr), indicating a collision blocking the system. At the present time, this collision is pushing Turkey in a southwestern direction, where the only oceanic space remains. These geodynamic movements imply that great forces are at work in the lithosphere involving considerable tectonic movements.

The present narrowness of the Mediterranean, where the continental margins join (according to Biju-Duval *et al.* (1976), only 10 per cent of the surface of the Mediterranean basins is situated more than 100 km away from the continental shelves), has provoked a geologically rapid sedimentary aggradation of the basins at a sedimentation rate around 0.3 mm /yr for the last 5 million years. The result is that the crust is buried under *c*.10 km of sediment or more, and that the great deltas (Nile, Po, Rhône, Ebro) continue far undersea.

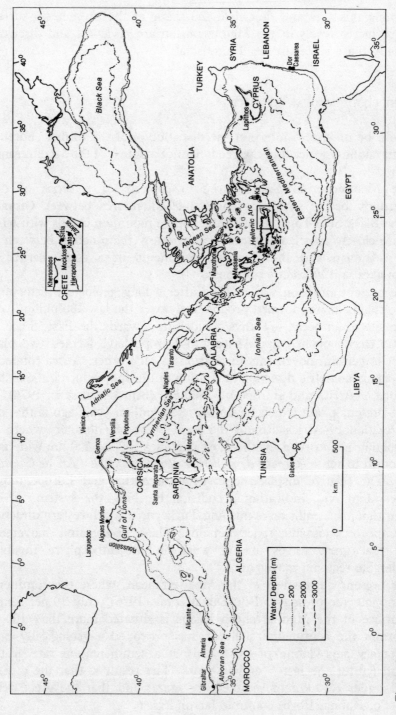

Figure 5.1 A map of the Mediterranean area. In the Hellenic Arc: A = Antikythira; M = Moni Khrisoskalitisas; Ka = Karpathos

Owing to the weight of the sediment, the basins in the Western Mediterranean have subsided at least 7 km, and in the Eastern Mediterranean, 6 to 15 km. This movement implies a progressive migration of the flexure of the continental margins towards the continent, with a general tendency towards a subsidence of the coast, overlaying in places the tectonic uplift movements caused by collision or subduction phenomena.

Subduction zones do indeed exist. The one associated with the Hellenic arc dates back to the Plio-Quaternary age and the distribution of seismic activity makes it possible to estimate that about 280 km of the plate have already disappeared beneath the arc. The situation in Calabria is more difficult to interpret; here the deep seismicity, which reaches a depth of 500 km towards the north-west, seems to stop between −200 km and the surface. This fact suggests an interruption of the subduction process, but this does not tally with the important vertical movements which occurred during the Quaternary.

The water balance is made necessarily fragile by these diverse tectonic forces; the Mediterranean is connected with the Atlantic Ocean and the Black Sea only by way of shallow, narrow straits which are affected by tectonic deformations. If, for instance, the Strait of Gibraltar closed up, as the present water budget shows a loss, the Mediterranean would dry up in the space of 3000 years with a probable drop in the sea level of some thousand metres. This phenomenon is certainly not new: it occurred during the Messinian (between 9 and 6 million years ago) when evaporite layers were deposited on the bottom of the basins. The sea-level rise which followed in the Pliocene, as soon as the strait reopened, was also some thousand metres high.

In the Quaternary the Strait of Gibraltar seems to have remained permanently open, although the gap has been gradually shoaling since the early Pliocene (Hsü 1974), and therefore the Mediterranean was affected by the glacio-eustatic variations of the Atlantic Ocean. The Black Sea, on the other hand, was linked to the Mediterranean only during the main Interglacial periods (Stanley and Blanpied 1980).

3.0 PRESENT MEAN SEA LEVEL

The mean sea level is an equipotential surface of the Earth's field of gravity and its position is influenced by the variations in density within the Earth and the Ocean.

3.1   Earth density effects

The mean sea surface topography of the Mediterranean Sea, deduced from data from the SEASAT satellite, shows the presence of differences in elevation as high as 50 m between a low situated in the Eastern Mediterranean and a high in the Gulf of Lions (Barlier *et al.* 1983 and figure 5.2). Geoid heights of figure 5.2, correspond to a reference ellipsoid of semimajor axis A = 6,378,140 m and flattening F = 1/298,257. The accuracy of this representation of the surface topography has been estimated to be better than 0.5 m on a global scale.

In the Western Mediterranean there is a generally increasing slope of 3 to 7 m of the sea surface (with respect to the reference ellipsoid) between North Africa and Europe. The difference in elevation reaches ~20 m between Libya and the Gulf of Genoa and more than 15 m between the Ionian Sea and the North Adriatic. Steep slopes appear near Southern Italy.

The most striking feature however is the marked depression in the Eastern Mediterranean, around the Hellenic arc, which marks the Ionian Trench, where subduction is active west of Crete, and stretches as it deepens around the transform faults of Pliny and Strabo (Le Pichon and Angelier 1979). The slope of the mean sea surface topography is particularly abrupt between this depression and the neighbouring Aegean Sea, which obviously constitutes a gravimetric sill between the Eastern Mediterranean and the Black Sea.

The relief of the sea surface topography reflects variations in density in the structure of the Earth, in relation to the geological history and the geodynamical context. Thus the relief accentuates progressively from west to east in proportion to the increasing relative displacements that have occurred (and are still occurring) between the African and Eurasian plates. The slopes become particularly steep near areas where subduction is active or fairly recent.

On the whole the slopes rise from Africa towards Eurasia and from the subducting zones towards the overthrusting zones; the region of the Calabrian arc however shows an opposite trend.

On account of the tectonic activities affecting the Mediterranean Basin, the relief of the sea surface topography is probably not static, but is gradually changing. In this respect the model proposed by Rizos (1983) foresees an accentuation of the present relief, with an increase in the slope of the geoid from west to east in the Mediterranean, of the order of 5–10 cm per century.

Figure 5.2 Mediterranean sea surface topography based on SEASAT altimeter data, according to Barlier et al (1983). Contour interval: 1 m

3.2 Oceanic effects

Of quite a different type, the dynamic calculations used in oceanography indicate variations in the sea surface height caused solely by oceanic effects. The reference levels are the isobaric surfaces, i.e. imaginary surfaces along which pressure remains constant. As the surface of the sea is also an isobaric surface, it is possible to calculate the eventual slope of the sea surface in relation to other deeper isobaric surfaces, provided the distribution of the sea-water density is known. Figure 5.3 shows the distribution of the mean dynamic level of the sea in the Mediterranean, according to Lisitzin (1965), who assumes a mean decrease of 5 dyn cm per 100 km between the Atlantic and the Mediterranean, and a subsequent lowering of about 15 dyn cm between latitudes 5°E and 20°E.

In the direction of the Black Sea, after the lowest point of the Aegean, the sea level rises about 10 dyn cm near the Dardanelles and 25 dyn cm near the Bosphorus. Altogether, when crossing these two passages, the sea level increases by 40 dyn cm. Finally, in the Black Sea, the mean sea level reaches minimal values in the central area of the sea and a maximum in the east, off the Caucasus coasts.

On the whole the dynamic variation in level is 80 cm between the Aegean Sea and the Alboran Sea, and 50 cm between the Aegean and the Eastern Mediterranean. These values can be considered the maximum variation in the mean sea level that may be caused by a climatic change when the quantity of sea water does not alter. Similarly, in the Eastern Mediterranean analysis of the foraminifera has shown that in comparison with the last glacial maximum (18 000 BP) the greatest changes in the winter sea-surface temperature ($-6°C$) and the sea-surface salinity ($-5‰$) occurred in the Aegean Sea, whereas the greatest changes in the maximum summer sea-surface temperature ($>4°C$) occurred in the southern and eastern parts of the Eastern Mediterranean (Thunell 1979). These variations, since the glacial maximum and during the Holocene, must have caused slight changes in the dynamic slopes of the sea surface. The differences in sea level which resulted remained however of the order of a few decimetres at the most.

4.0 FORMER SHORELINES

Marks of former sea levels are frequent along the Mediterranean coasts. Since the end of the last century elevated shorelines have been reported in several areas, at various elevations. Depéret (1918) published a review of

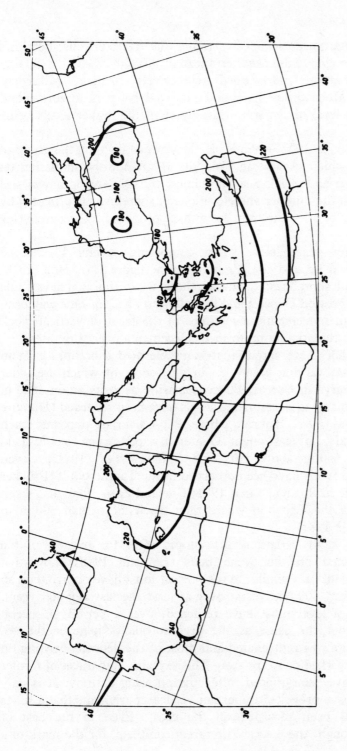

Figure 5.3 The distribution of mean sea level (dyn cm) in the Mediterranean and Black Sea, according to Lisitzin (1965, 1974). A dynamic metre has the dimensions of work and represents the work which must be done to move a unit mass the distance of one metre in the vertical direction. It is determined by the potential value gh. Choosing the dyn.m as a unit for the dynamic depth, we obtain D = gh/10. One dynamic metre corresponds therefore roughly to 1.02 geometrical metres

Pleistocene Mediterranean sea levels, stating that traces of four shorelines were present throughout the Mediterranean at 90–100, 55–60, 28–30 and 18–20 m in elevation and named respectively Sicilian, Milazzian, Tyrrhenian and Monastirian. Each shoreline was believed to correspond to the maximum level of a marine transgression, the higher levels being the older ones.

Forty years later, in 1957, when R. H. Hey began forming the group of correspondents, which became in 1961 the INQUA Subcommission on the Mediterranean and Black Sea Shorelines, the Depéret idea was still debated, although the number and elevations of shorelines investigated by various authors were often different from those proposed by Depéret (Hey 1984).

Another twenty years later, when comparing several Pleistocene shorelines observed around the Mediterranean (figure 5.4), Hey (1978) concluded that all shorelines, including those whose horizontal attitude had so greatly impressed Depéret and his followers, had in some way been displaced by earth movements, sometimes in the form of vertical block movements, with remarkably uniform displacements over wide areas.

Numerous authors have shown that many elevated shorelines exist in the Mediterranean, varying greatly in height, some of which are older than the Quaternary. In Greece, Pliocene marine deposits attain 1800 m in height and as many as eleven tiered levels have been recorded (Dufaure and Zamanis 1981). In Calabria, where Plio-Calabrian deposits reach 1400 m in altitude, at least eight Quaternary platforms rise in tiers between 0 and 650 m above sea level (Dumas *et al.* 1981); eleven Quaternary tiered levels have been observed in the Taranto Gulf (Brücker 1982), five to nine in Spain (Dumas 1981; Goy and Zazo 1986) and seven or eight levels in the Lebanon where they reach more than 300 m in altitude (Sanlaville 1981).

On the other hand variations in isotopic rates for oxygen in the carbonates collected on the ocean beds (Emiliani 1978) show that interglacial situations very similar to the present must have occurred on an average about every 100 000 years, over at least the last 700 000 years. Each time the sea level must have returned, over a period of several millennia, to about the same as the present one. Whenever the sea returned, the shore was rejuvenated and most of the deposits existing on the coast were reworked or swept away. This explains how traces of former ancient shores have been effaced, often disappearing entirely. It is only where tectonics have provoked important vertical movements that a series of shorelines has been recorded on the coast. Even in the best of circumstances though, these series are rarely complete, for the mark of a

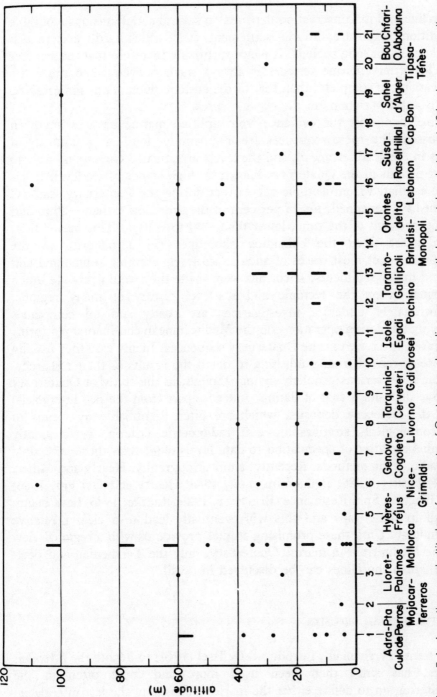

Figure 5.4 Locations and altitudes of segments of Quaternary shorelines apparently horizontal and at least 10 km long, according to Hey (1978). Points indicate altitudes which are precisely known, vertical lines the limits of uncertainty of those which are not

shoreline and its conservation depends on several simultaneous favourable conditions (exposure, erosion, settlement, etc.), which hardly ever remain unchanged for long periods. It is not surprising therefore that the number of Quaternary marine terraces is always smaller, even when the series appears more complete, than that of the eustatic fluctuations indicated by the isotopic variations in the oceanic cores.

Until now only the evidence from uplifted marine terraces has been discussed. But these sequences are fragmentary, found in a minority of areas in the Mediterranean, and the levels investigated correspond only to short periods of the Quaternary known for high stands of sea level. It has been estimated from isotopic curves that during the Quaternary sea level might have remained, for 75 per cent of the time, lower than −20 m and for 50 per cent of the time, lower than −40 to −50 m. This means that, even apart from the subsiding shorelines (in a majority in the Mediterranean) most traces of ancient sea levels are now submerged and buried under sediments. If corings were made they would provide much information on the tectonic and sea-level history of many regions. Unfortunately undersea investigations are costly and oil companies carrying out coring operations on the Mediterranean continental platforms are rarely interested in the Quaternary sequences. In any case they usually choose to refrain from publishing in detail the results of their research.

The most serious problem arising, though, in the study of Quaternary marine deposits is that of dating. Indeed, apart from the last interglacial and the Holocene deposits, which are often identifiable by means of palaeontological, stratigraphic and radiometric criteria, it frequently remains a matter of speculation to date levels older than those accessible by radiometric methods. Recently, aminostratigraphy (Hearty and Miller, 1984; Hearty, 1986; Belluomini *et al.*, 1986; Hearty and Dai Pra, 1986) and Electron Spin Resonance (Bruckner, 1986; Radtke, 1986) have begun to fill in some gaps and this will eventually lead to a clearer relative chronology. Until these promising studies provide us with a regional view of the Mediterranean marine Quaternary, only the Tyrrhenian and post-Tyrrhenian shorelines can be discussed in detail.

5.0 TYRRHENIAN DEPOSITS

The term 'Tyrrhenian', introduced by Issel (1914) to denote the *Strombus* layers, has since then been used more and more often in the Mediterranean to define either the marine deposits of the last interglacial or, by extension, the corresponding period of time.

Strombus bubonius Lmk from the Mediterranean, which is characteristic of the Tyrrhenian deposits, probably arrived with a host of fauna from the Senegambian shores, where it continues to live in the calm warm waters at depths varying between 1 and 4–5 m (Meco 1977). Between Senegambia and the Mediterranean, the coasts of Mauritania and Morocco are known today for the upwelling of cold oceanic waters creating an insuperable barrier for the *Strombus*.

According to Shackleton and Opdyke (1973), one feature of the last interglacial is the isotopic oxygen ratios in the oceanic sediments which are slightly higher than in the Holocene. This difference implies that temperatures were a little higher too, probably accompanied by climatic and oceanic modifications sufficiently important to impede, for a while at least, the persistent upwelling on the north-west coasts of Africa. It would then be possible for *S. bubonius* to cross the littoral upwelling zone which had hindered its expansion and penetrate into the Mediterranean. This favourable circumstance seems to have been exceptional during the Quaternary, so much so that *S. bubonius* is usually considered the most characteristic last interglacial deposit in the Mediterranean.

The fauna that usually accompanies *S. bubonius* in the Tyrrhenian deposits of the Mediterranean often includes, among the pelecypods: *Arca clathrata* Defrance (= *A. plicata* Chemnitz ?), *Glycymeris glycymeris* Linné, *Spondylus gaederopus* Linné, *Brachydontes puniceus* Gmelin (= *B. senegalensis* Lmk), *Tugonia anatina* Gmelin, etc., and among the gastropods: *Patella ferruginea* Gmelin, *Patella safiana* Lmk, *Polynices lacteus* Guilding (= *Natica lactea*), *Cymatium ficoïdes* Reeve, *Conus testudinarius* Bruguière, *Cypraea lurida* Linné, *Tritonidea viverrata* Kiener (= *Cantharus viverratus*), *Thais haemastoma* Linné, etc. Some of these species, however, have also been found in older deposits.

Three transgressive episodes are traditionally distinguished for the Tyrrhenian stage; they are called the ancient or lower Tyrrhenian, the Eutyrrhenian and the Neo-tyrrhenian.

Established by stratigraphical means in Tunisia, the Douira Formation (Paskoff and Sanlaville 1983), though devoid of any *Strombus* fauna, the ancient Tyrrhenian remains hypothetical in other regions. Attempts have been made to correlate it (Paskoff and Sanlaville 1982) with deposits in Spain, near Almeria and Alicante (Baena *et al.* 1981a,b, Zazo *et al.* 1981), with the 'pre-Enfean' in the Lebanon (Sanlaville 1977) and the 'Anfatian' in Morocco (Weisrock 1980). The age of this episode, if it is the same, has still to be determined and might be older than the last interglacial.

The Eu-tyrrhenian has been the easiest stratigraphic unit to establish, owing to the frequent presence of *S. bubonius*. According to Paskoff and

Sanlaville (1982) it would appear to be the major phase of the Tyrrhenian, with a large volume of littoral sediments often several metres thick. The fine deposits – sands which have now become more or less consolidated into sandstone – are often predominant. Numerous Mediterranean deposits are associated with the Eu-tyrrhenian, among which those of the Rejiche formations in Tunisia, Cala Mosca in Sardinia (Ulzega and Ozer 1982), II Fronte Formation in south Italy (Hearty 1986), and the Harounian deposits in Morocco.

The Neo-tyrrhenian phase, which has left discrete morphological traces, with the frequent appearance of *Strombus*, seems to have been brief. Neo-tyrrhenian sediments are often encased in the lower section of the Eu-tyrrhenian deposits which they partly rework. The Chebba formations in Tunisia, Santa Reparata in Sardinia, the Ouljian in Morocco, and many more deposits in Spain, France, Italy and Greece, all belong to the Neo-tyrrhenian.

Zazo *et al.* (1984) distinguish even a fourth Tyrrhenian episode with *Strombus* near Almeria, which has been dated 39 000±2000 yr by Th/U.

The main problem with the Tyrrhenian deposits is to date them with accuracy. Most of the material that has been used for Uranium-series measurements consists of mollusc shells, but the 'usefulness of ^{230}Th/^{234}U ratios in mollusca has *not* been demonstrated' (Stearns 1981, p. 16). Unlike coral, mollusc shells acquire their uranium after the death of the organisms and further uptake and/or exchange is common throughout the age of the sample. This means that ^{230}Th/^{234}U ages may measure the average time of addition and not the full age since the death of the organism. The fact that corals found in a *Strombus* layer near Taranto (Italy) have been dated at least 260 000 to 200 000 yr (Dai Pra and Stearns 1977) and pectuncles in Tyrrhenian deposits at Karpathos (Greece) have been dated 260 000 yr (Barrier 1979) makes it all the more uncertain, for these dates are prior to the latest interglacial. This makes many correlations speculative and also the fact that it was not until 1984, after some 25 years of its activity, that the INQUA Subcommission on Mediterranean Shorelines started to compile an inventory of the deposits that have been ascribed to the Tyrrhenian.

Elevation, the main criterion of the Depéret classification, cannot be accepted as a means of correlation, due to tectonic activity. Within Italy, the elevation of marine deposits ascribed to beaches of the last interglacial may vary from more than +120 m in Calabria to about −70 m under the lagoon of Venice. Dramatically tilted marine terraces have been reported in many localities. In some cases the pattern of the faults has given the marine terraces a stepped appearance, but this does not always mean there were multiple shorelines.

On a more regional scale, in southern Greece the elevation of Tyrrhenian deposits decreases systematically from the southernmost part of the Hellenic Arc, where the deposits reach elevations around 100 m in places, towards the north, where they disappear gradually underwater in the Aegean Sea (Keraudren 1970–72, Angelier 1979).

Joint stratigraphical and palaeontological criteria remain, for the time being, the most reliable approach, in order to distinguish different episodes in the Tyrrhenian stage, above all where contact surfaces exist between marine and continental sediments. Nevertheless, with the noteworthy exception of Almeria (Spain), where *S. bubonius* is present in four stepped marine sequences (Zazo *et al.* 1984), the occurrence of three Tyrrhenian episodes has not yet been demonstrated in the same profile, although the existence of at least two independent *Strombus* levels has been proved beyond doubt in many places.

Formations observed in the Mediterranean are often compared with those investigated in coral reef areas such as Barbados and New Guinea (Mesolella *et al.* 1969, Bloom *et al.* 1974), where the ages of morphologically distinct reef terraces are widely accepted as standards. Furthermore, when local datings seem unreliable or are not available, ages of the order of 125 000, 100 000 or 80 000 years are often attributed automatically to Tyrrhenian deposits. Nevertheless dates very close to these values have in fact been obtained in certain outcrops (see, for example, Angelier 1979, Barrier 1979, Bernat *et al.* 1978, Bruckner 1986, Dai Pra and Stearns 1977, Dumas 1977, Goy and Zazo 1986, Hearty 1986, Keraudren 1971, Radtke 1986, Stearns and Thurber 1965, although other dates differ considerably from these values.

6.0 HIGH SEA LEVELS DURING THE LAST GLACIATION

There are some data which suggest that there was a period following the Tyrrhenian, but before the Holocene, during which sea level was only slightly lower than the present level in the Mediterranean. Some radiocarbon assays attribute an age of about 30 000 BP to this level and even a Th/U age of some 39 000 yr has been obtained (Zazo *et al.* 1984).

It is true that the ages under review are towards the limit of radiocarbon dating and could therefore be considered as minimum ages. However, as pointed out by Giresse and Davies (1980), the existence of relatively warmer periods during the last glaciation has been shown from pedological, morphological, glaciological, phytogeographic and oceanic evidence. Reef complexes in New Guinea have given ages near 28 000, 45 000 and 65 000 BP for interstadial high sea levels that would have reached −45 m, −35 m and −20 m respectively in this area (Bloom *et al.* 1974).

In the Gulf of Gabes (Tunisia) the occurrence of a transgression, dated about 27 000 BP and reaching a level very close to the present one, has been deduced by Blanc-Vernet *et al.* (1979) from dinoflagellates and nanofossils, showing a normal degree of salinity, found above hypersaline deposits belonging to a former, older lagoon. Paskoff and Sanlaville (1983) ascribe the formation of a system of coastal dunes in Tunisia to a sea level, again about 27 000 BP at a height of approximately −5 m. Eolianites, formed within the period of the Würm glaciation, are reported too in Morocco, in Crete, in Spain and in Algeria. However ages of about 27 000 BP have also been obtained in South Tunisia for intertidal shells collected *in situ* between 35 and 40 m altitude (Richards and Vita Finzi 1982). As it seems unlikely that there have been vertical tectonic displacements of over 40 m in this area since 27 000 BP, it is suggested that either the normal 'marine' salinity in previously hypersaline lagoons is the result rather of a climatic oscillation (increased rainfall) than of a marine transgression, or that the ages obtained are minimum ages that should be related to older episodes.

Similar remarks probably apply to other sediments dated about 25 000 to 35 000 BP, indicating shorelines very near or even above the present one, in areas where strong tectonic uplift movements are improbable, as for instance near Messenia (Greece) at −7 m (Kraft *et al.* 1975), Aigues-Mortes (France) near to the present sea level (Bazile *et al.* 1976), and in several other Mediterranean areas. On the other hand a marine transgression peak of −40 m off the coast of Roussillon (France) inferred at about 27 000 BP (Labeyrie *et al.* 1976), seems more consistent with what is known elsewhere. Indeed neither pollen diagrams, oceanic cores, nor weathering of loess appear to indicate a fairly important rise in temperature around 27 000 BP, sufficient to have raised the sea level to about its present altitude.

7.0   SEA LEVELS DURING THE LAST GLACIAL MAXIMUM AND THE HOLOCENE

Very few data are available indicating the minimum level reached by the Mediterranean Sea when the last glaciation was most extensive. Federici (1972) collected at a depth of 200 m off the Ligurian coast, in deposits which he attributed to a 'fossil beach', samples of cold-region fauna, *Arctica* (= *Cyprina*) *islandica* L. and *Panopaea norvegica* Lmk, which have been dated by $^{230}Th/^{238}U$ about 20 000 and 19 000 yr respectively. It is however difficult to judge how far the accumulation of these deposits is the result of eustatic factors, tectonics or slumping.

In the case of beachrock found 70 m deep in the Strait of Bonifacio between Sardinia and Corsica (Fanucci *et al.* 1974), lack of a radiometric date makes it impossible to say whether it is part of a postglacial or of a Würm interstadial shore.

Ancient submerged shorelines, more or less buried beneath sediments, are sometimes numerous on the continental platform. As many as 17 submarine platforms, between −18 and −123 m, have been reported in the Adriatic Sea (Segota 1982) and as many as 14 shorelines, between −5 and −157 m, north of Sardinia (Ulzega and Ozer 1982). The ages of these shorelines usually remain to be determined. Even though some of them may have been formed in the Pleistocene, most of them have probably been reworked and some might even have formed during the Postglacial transgression.

In the Gulf of Lions, where numerous data are available, the transgression could have begun around 19 000 BP at −100 to −110 m and the sea level started to rise towards the present level, sometimes quickly sometimes slowly, but without any marked oscillations (Labeyrie *et al.* 1976 and figure 5.5). Indeed, all the prehistoric sites located on the continental shelf were submerged (Masters and Flemming 1983). The transgressive deposits left by this rise in the Mediterranean are often called 'Versilian' resulting from the stratigraphic work of Blanc (1936) in the Versilia Plain (Italy).

In the Black Sea basin the postglacial rise in level seems to have started around 17 000–18 000 BP from −80 m (Badyukov and Kaplin 1979). Several sea-level oscillations have been reported during the Holocene, but authors disagree on their amplitude, age, and even on their existence.

In general, in the Mediterranean during the Holocene, the sea was no higher than the present level which was reached, at dates varying according to the regions, between 6000 BP (L'Homer *et al.* 1981) and the present day. Towards the end of the sea-level rise, alternating continental and marine conditions have been found in corings beneath some Mediterranean coastal plains, and palaeogeographic reconstructions indicate landscapes quite different from the present ones in some historically famous places, such as the Marathon Plain in Greece (Baeteman 1985) or the surroundings of ancient Troy at the mouth of the Dardanelles (Kraft *et al.* 1980).

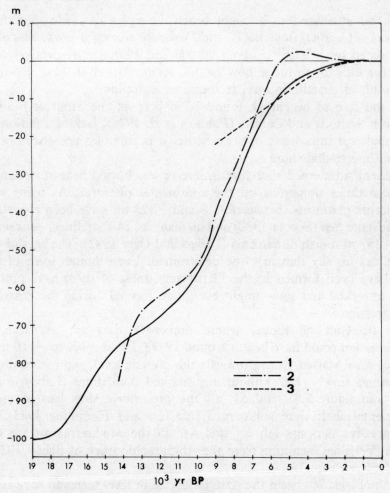

Figure 5.5 Postglacial sea-level changes in the Gulf of Lions, France (1: Labeyrie *et al* 1976; 2: Aloisi *et al* 1978) and in Messenia, Greece (Kraft 1975)

There are some areas however where the Holocene shorelines are slightly emerged. This is the case, in particular, in the Western Mediterranean, in the region of Almeria (Goy and Zazo 1986) and Cadix in Spain (Zazo and Ovejero 1976), Western Languedoc in France (+2 m about 4500–4100 BP, Aloisi *et al*. 1978), possibly in Sardinia (+2 m, not dated, Ulzega and Ozer 1982) and South Tunisia (+1 to +2 m around 5500 BP, Paskoff and Sanlaville 1983).

In the Eastern Mediterranean the present writer has made a detailed investigation of the Holocene emerged shorelines in the Hellenic Arc (Thommeret *et al*. 1981, Pirazzoli *et al*. 1982a,b). Here there is no doubt

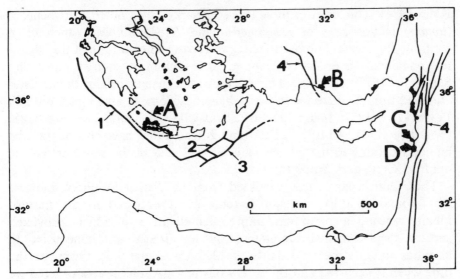

Figure 5.6 Main tectonic features (according to Le Pichon and Angelier 1979) and evidence of the 'Early Byzantine Tectonic Paroxysm', in the Eastern Mediterranean. 1: Ionian subducting trenches; 2: Pliny transform fault; 3: Strabo transform fault; 4: main strike-slip faults. Full dots: shorelines raised by the Early Byzantine Tectonic Paroxysm. A: Western Crete and Antikythira Island: a block of lithosphere approx. 200 km long was uplifted about 10 m and inclined northeastwards in a single event around 1530±40 BP (Pirazzoli *et al* 1982b); B: coastal platforms west of Alanya were uplifted 0.5 to 1.2 around 1545±40 BP (Kelletat and Kayan 1983); C: rims of Vermetidae raised at + 0.8 m, have been dated 1480±50 BP at Ile du Palmier (Sanlaville 1977); D: similar rims of Vermetidae at + 0.8 m have been dated 1635±130 BP and 1560±140 BP near Tabarja (Fevret *et al* 1967)

about the tectonic origin of the emergence. The western part of Crete, and particularly Antikythira Island, is part of a lithosphere block, 150–200 km long, which, between 4000 and 1700 BP, underwent periods of rapid subsidence in succession, leaving series of stepped shorelines in places. Later, towards 1530 BP (this date is corroborated by nine radiocarbon datings) the block of lithosphere was suddenly uplifted about 10 m and inclined north-eastwards, in a single event, resulting in the emergence of all the late Holocene shorelines and even some Pleistocene notches.

Archaeological remains and morphological features, displaced vertically by tectonics, are reported frequently from Anatolia and from the eastern border of the Mediterranean basin. In particular, emerged Holocene shorelines, sometimes multiple, have been recorded not only in the Lebanon (Fevret *et al.* 1967) but also in Syria (Sanlaville 1976), southern Turkey (Erol 1963, Dalongeville and Sanlaville 1977, Kelletat and Kayan 1983), Cyprus (Dreghorn 981) and in Israel (Flemming *et al.* 1978, Sneh and

Klein 1984). The lower of these levels is marked by a notch, surf benches (*trottoir*) and/or rims of *Dendropoma* and *Neogoniolithon*, which often continue for several kilometres along the coast. The altitude of this shore-line remains more or less constant at $+0.6/+0.8$ m, to such an extent that Sanlaville (1977) felt justified in assigning it an eustatic origin. In fact dates obtained from Vermetidae in the Lebanon (1635 ± 140 and 1560 ± 140 BP, Fevret *et al.* 1967; 1480 ± 50 yr BP, Sanlaville 1977) and calcareous algae at Alanya (1545 ± 40 BP, Kelletat and Kayan 1983) have shown that the bioherm became extinct at the same time as that of the shore before the uplift of Crete and Antikythira.

These concordant dates, obtained from far-distant localities, indicate that around 1530 BP a major tectonic event occurred in the Eastern Mediterranean, a paroxysm unprecedented in size which provoked vertical displacements, simultaneously or almost simultaneously, in localities situated over a distance of 1200 km (figure 5.6). Owing to the time when it occurred and the extent of the geographical area covered we propose to call this major event the 'Early Byzantine Tectonic Paroxysm' (Pirazzoli 1986a). Judging by the large area affected and the important crustal movements involved, this tectonic paroxysm was probably caused by junction and collision processes between the African and Eurasian plates. The apparent altitudinal variations in the sea level data suggest a jolting episode in this plate collision, consisting of a preparatory phase lasting two or three thousand years, followed by a sudden tectonic movement, which took place in the Eastern Mediterranean during historical times. It was only because the Mediterranean Sea suddenly narrowed, following a subduction thrust of the Ionian crust under the Hellenic Arc, and a readjustment of various blocks of lithosphere bordering the Eastern Mediterranean, that these two continents were able to converge.

8.0   INDICATIONS FROM ARCHAEOLOGICAL REMAINS

Archaeological remains are useful sea-level indicators when their relation to the former water levels can be established with good accuracy (Flemming 1979).

A number of types may be distinguished. Firstly, there are traces of human habitation (shell middens, etc.) which, owing to their character-istics, can only have been established in the immediate vicinity of a shoreline. These traces, rare in the Mediterranean in Greek and Roman times, but more frequent in caves inhabited in prehistoric times now submerged, indicate a minimal variation in the sea level. Man-made constructions which are now submerged, but which were meant to remain emerged (walls, paving, canalized waterways, quarries), also indicate minimal variation in the sea level. Other constuctions related to well-defined sea levels (harbour wharfs, slipways, fishery installations, fish tanks, etc.) when well-preserved, can furnish very precise details on the position of the former sea level.

Coastal archaeological remains from Roman times are especially frequent in the Mediterranean and usually indicate a slight submersion, which may be accentuated locally or be transformed into an emergence in regions which are tectonically very unstable (Flemming 1969, Pirazzoli 1976b, Flemming and Pirazzoli 1981). Vestiges of Roman fish tanks, in particular, owing to their popularity in the Mediterranean in the fairly brief period during which they were in fashion (around 100 BC to AD 100) and to the fact that they can determine the sea level position very precisely, constitute valuable indicators (Pirazzoli 1979). On the continental Tyrrhenian and Provençal coasts, for instance, if certain zones of notoriously important subsidence are eliminated (the Rhône delta, Populonia, the volcanic area of Naples) data available show a remarkable overall stability (Pirazzoli 1976a, 1979); the sea level 2000 years ago was about 0.5 m lower than today and tended to rise at an average rate of about 0.75 mm/yr. The variation in this rate of rise is discussed further in the next section.

On the whole, in the Western Mediterranean, a slight submergence seems to have been more frequent during the last 2000 years (Flemming and Webb 1986), both on the European and the African coasts; in the Eastern Mediterranean the situations appear more variable. Thus the emergence of fish tanks in the Lebanon and at Dor (Israel) contrasts with the level close to the present one at Caesarea (Israel) and Lapithos (Cyprus). In the eastern part of Crete fish tanks testify to very different situations in regions very close to each other: submergence at Khersonisos and Mocklos, slight emergence at Sitia, a definite submergence at Kato Zakros and relative stability at Hierapetra.

9.0 SEA-LEVEL TRENDS INDICATED BY TIDE GAUGE RECORDS

When the period covered is sufficiently long, tide gauges provide valuable information on present-day, local trends in the variation of mean sea level. In the Mediterranean some analyses are possible, even though the number of stations with recordings dating back to the last century is limited.

Variations in the relative sea level reported from 21 stations in the Mediterranean and the Black Sea, together with, for the sake of comparison, those of Lagos in Portugal (no. 1), and Santa Cruz in Tenerife in the Canary Islands (no. 23) are shown in figure 5.7. The values of mean sea level from each station, available in the data bank of the Permanent Service for Mean Sea Level at Bidston, Merseyside, UK (together with the values calculated by the author for Venice (no. 9)), have been grouped into five-year periods and, for each period, the value of the five-year mean sea level has been attributed to the middle year. The broken lines correspond to incomplete recordings.

Table 5.1 gives the long-term trends in variation, calculated for stations with recordings going back more than 50 years or showing sufficiently clear trends over periods just under 50 years.

The following remarks may be made concerning the tide gauge data. Firstly the few series available are unevenly distributed, being more frequent in the Western Mediterranean (France, Northern Italy, Tunisia, Algeria) than in the Eastern Mediterranean. Most of the series examined showed a tendency to increase towards the present though the rate varies from one place to another. Certain series (nos 2, 4, 5, 14, 19), on the other hand, tend to remain stable or decrease slightly. On the whole the data give no indication that the rate of sea-level rise has increased in recent years.

A certain number of fluctuations are seen to exist, some of which (e.g. the sea-level rise between 1896–1900 and 1901–05 and between 1931–35 and 1936–40) are true for all the Mediterranean stations investigated (though for the second period, an opposite tendency is observed at Lagos (no. 1). For certain relatively long periods (e.g. the last 30 years in Marseilles), variations in the relative sea level may show an opposite tendency to the longer term one. This proves how useful it is to have access to as long a series as possible when evaluating the local secular trend.

Marseilles, Genoa and Trieste all show the same mean trend (+1.3 mm/yr), whereas in Venice there is an accelerated sea-level rise of about 1.2 mm/yr greater, probably largely due to a man-induced sinking of the land. Indeed repeated levellings have revealed that the ground has

---

Figure 5.7 Average 5-yr mean sea level variations in the Mediterranean as recorded by tide gauge stations: 2-Alicante, 3-Port Vendres, 4-Sète, 5-Martigues, 6-Marseilles, 7-Villefranche, 8-Genoa, 9-Venice, 10-Trieste, 11-Bakar, 12-Split, 13-Tuapse, 14-Izmir, 15-Antalya, 16-Port Said, 17-Sfax, 18-Sousse, 19-La Goulette, 20-Bône, 21-Algiers, 22-Oran. For comparison: 1-Lagos, 23-Santa Cruz de Tenerife

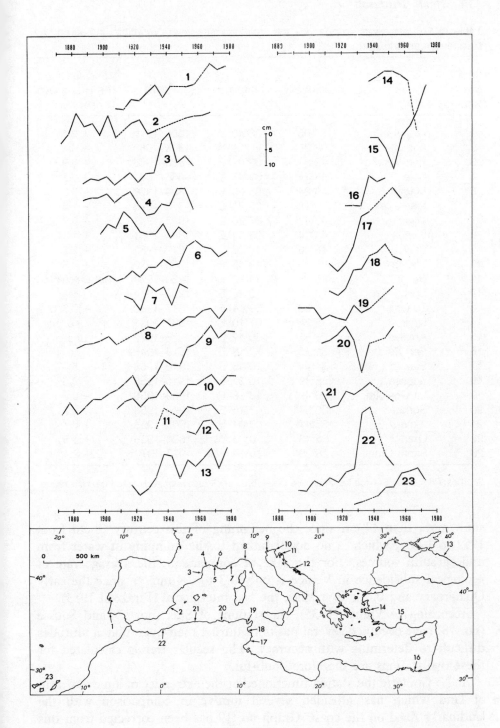

Table 5.1 Long-term trends in the relative sea-level variation indicated by Mediterranean tide gauges

Station No (see figure 5.7)	Name	Latitude N	Longitude	Period	Secular trend (+ = sea-level rise) mm/yr
1	Lagos	37°06'	08°40' W	1908–1979	+ 2.1
2	Alicante	38°20'	0°29' W	1874–1969	+ 0.4
3	Port Vendres	42°31'	03°07' E	1888–1958	+ 0.9
4	Sète	43°24'	03°42' E	1888–1961	+ 0.3
5	Martigues	43°24'	05°03' E	1894–1956	− 0.3
6	Marseilles	43°18'	05°21' E	1885–1978	+ 1.3
7	Villefranche	43°42'	07°20' E	1913–1957	+ 0.9
8	Genoa	44°24'	08°54' E	1884–1981	+ 1.3
9	Venice	45°26'	12°20' E	1872–1983	+ 2.5
10	Trieste	45°39'	13°45' E	1905–1982	+ 1.3
11	Bakar	45°18'	14°32' E	1930–1974	not calculated
12	Split	43°30'	16°26' E	1952–1974	nc
13	Tuapse	44°06'	39°04' E	1917–1980	+ 2.3
14	Izmir	38°24'	27°10' E	1937–1971	nc
15	Antalya	36°53'	30°42' E	1936–1972	nc
16	Port Saïd	31°15'	32°18' E	1923–1946	nc
17	Sfax	34°44'	10°46' E	1910–1958	+ 5.7?
18	Sousse	35°49'	10°37' E	1910–1956	+ 3.6?
19	La Goulette	36°49'	10°18' E	1889–1956	+ 0.6
20	Bône	36°54'	07°46' E	1908–1958	+ 0.7
21	Algiers	36°47'	03°04' E	1905–1958	+ 0.7
22	Oran	35°43'	0°39' W	1890–1958	+ 1.5
23	Santa Cruz	28°29'	16°14' W	1927–1974	+ 2.4

Sources: Permanent Service for Mean Sea Level, Bidston, Merseyside, U.K. and Pirazzoli, 1986b.

sunk more than 14 cm since the beginning of this century (8 cm from 1952 to 1969), which is no doubt linked to the pumping of water from underground sources. For the sake of comparison, the average rate of geological subsidence in Venice is only 0.3 to 0.4 mm/yr since the early Quaternary and 0.6 mm/yr since the last interglacial (Pirazzoli 1983).

According to Vignal (1935), the stations of Sfax (no. 17) and Sousse (no. 18) have occupied several positions during their operation at altitudes difficult to determine with accuracy. The secular trends calculated for these two stations are therefore doubtful.

At La Goulette the station functioned at the extremity of a narrow strip of land which has subsided several mm/yr in comparison with the landmarks fixed on the coast. Graph no. 19 has been corrected from this subsidence using the results of five levellings (Vignal 1935).

The strong oscillations observed at the beginning of the thirties at Bône (no. 20) and Oran (no. 22) are considered doubtful by Vignal (1935).

Lastly it is difficult to ascertain the origin of the wide variations at Izmir (no. 14) and Antalya (no. 15) which are situated in seismically active areas. Incidentally it is worthwhile recalling that the tide gauge at Messina (Sicily) recorded a sudden subsidence of 57 cm during the earthquake in 1908, followed by a relative sea-level rise of 16.5 cm between 1911 and 1920.

On the whole the series available are not sufficient, especially in the Eastern Mediterranean, to verify Rizos' model (1983), which foresees an increase in the slope of the geoid from west to east in the Mediterranean of the order of 0.5–1.0 mm/yr.

Average rates of sea level change are dependent on the timescale of observation and consideration. For example, in Marseilles, an extrapolation of the present rate of rise (1.3 mm/yr) 2000 years back would give a sea level more than 2 m lower than it really was at that time, whereas an extrapolation of the rate of rise 2000 years ago (0.75 mm/yr) up to the present would give a sea level 1 m too high. Average rates should only be applied to the time period covered by the relevant data.

10.0 CONCLUSION

Variations in the sea level in the Mediterranean depend not only on eustatic, glacio-hydro-isostatic, climatic and rheologic factors existing in the global ocean, but also on well-defined regional characteristics: fragility of the narrow strait connection with the Atlantic Ocean accompanied by an unbalanced water budget, and various tectonic and rheologic processes related to the collision between Africa and Eurasia. Each of these phenomena can have an important impact, though irregular and exceptional, which makes them difficult to predict.

Thus the possibility of the Strait of Gibraltar closing up again, due to a persistent collision process, thereby causing the Mediterranean basins to dry up, cannot be excluded. Nevertheless the likelihood of such a phenomenon, which has not happened for the last 5 million years, actually occurring remains very slight in the middle term.

Likewise, although other tectonic paroxysms are probable in the Mediterranean, the accompanying movements will no doubt be very different from those of 1530 BP. Indeed at Moni Khrisoskalitisas on the south-west coast of Crete, where the 1530 BP shoreline was raised by

7.8 m, Tyrrhenian *Strombus* deposits are found (Hearty 1984, pers. comm.), scarcely 5 m higher. This indicates that an uplift comparable to the one of 1530 BP had not occurred in this region for at least the preceding 100 000 years.

Thus, in the Mediterranean, the eustatic oscillations of the Atlantic Ocean overlie an essentially tectonic, local 'noise', which varies from one area to another, sometimes acting progressively, sometimes in jolts, and occasionally considerable. This noise tends to influence the local sea-level record even between neighbouring regions, to an extent that makes it very difficult to extrapolate local data from one area of the Mediterranean to another.

Revised typescript received 1985, December, with minor amendments 1986, December.

ACKNOWLEDGEMENTS

The author is grateful to C. Zazo for the critical reading, M. Delahaye for editing the English text and D. Maraine for typing the final version of the manuscript.

REFERENCES

Aloisi, J. C., Monaco, A., Planchais, N., Thommeret, J. and Thommeret, Y. 1978: The Holocene transgression in the Golfe du Lion, southwestern France: palaeogeographic and palaeobotanical evolution. *Geogr. Phys. Quat.*, 32, 145–62.

Angelier, J. 1979: Néotectonique de l'arc égéen. *Soc. Géol. Nord. Publ.* no. 3, Villeneuve d'Ascq.

Badyukov, D. D. and Kaplin, P. A. 1979: Sea-level changes on the coasts of the USSR during the last 15 000 years. *Proceedings of the 1978 International Symposium on coastal evolution in the Quaternary. São Paulo, Brasil, (1979)*, 135–69.

Baena, J., Goy, J. L. and Zazo, C. 1981a: *Libro-Guia Excursion – Mesa Redonda sobre el Tirreniense del litoral Mediterraneo espanol, Madrid-Lyon*, 25–44.

Baena, J., Zazo, C. and Goy, J. L. 1981b: Implicaçion del episodio con 'Strombus' en la neotectonica de la Bahia de Almeria (Espana). In *Actes Coll. Niveaux marins et tectonique quaternaires dans l'aire méditerranéenne, Paris, 1980*, CNRS and Univ. Paris I, 345–54.

Baeteman, C. 1985: Late Holocene geology of the Marathon Plain (Greece). *J. Coastal Res.*, 1, 173–85.

Barlier, F., Bernard, J., Bouiri, O. and Exertier, P. 1983: The geoid of the Mediterranean Sea deduced from Seasat data. In *Proc. 2nd Intern. Symp. Geoid in Europe and in the Mediterranean area (Rome, 1982)*, Firenze: Ist. Geogr. Mil. Ital., 14–35.

Barrier, E. 1979: Etude néotectonique des îles de Karpathos et Kassos. Thèse de 3ème cycle. Paris: Univ. Pierre et Marie Curie, Unpublished.

Bazile, F., Renault-Miskowsky, J. and Thommeret, J. 1976: Sur la présence d'un niveau littoral du Würm récent (Würm III) dans la région d'Aigues-Mortes (Gard). *C. R. Acad. Sci. Paris, D*, 282, 1149–50.

Belluomini, G., Branca, M., Delitala, L., Pecorini, G. and Spano, C. 1986: Isoleucine epimerization dating of Quaternary marine deposits in Sardinia, Italy. *Zeits. Geomorph.* Suppl.-Bd. 62, 109–117.

Bernat, M., Bousquet, J. C. and Dars, R. 1978: Io-U dating of the Ouiljian stage from Torre Garcia (southern Spain). *Nature*, 275, 302–3.

Biju-Duval, B., Dercourt, J. and Le Pichon, X. 1976: La genèse de la Méditerranée. *La Recherche*, 7, 811–22.

Blanc, A. C. 1936: La stratigraphie de la plaine côtière de la Basse Versilia (Italie) et la transgression flandrienne en Italie. *Rev. Géogr. Phys. Géol. dyn.*, 9, 129–60.

Blanc-Vernet, L., Brun, A., Morzadec-Kerfourn, M. T. and Muller, C. 1979: La mer Pélagienne. B – Evolution d'après les critères micropaléontologiques. *Géol. méditer.*, 6, 290–6.

Bloom, A. L., Broecker, W. S., Chappell, J. M. A., Matthews, R. K. and Mesolella, K. J. 1974: Quaternary sea-level fluctuations on a tetonic coast: New ^{230}Th/^{234}U dates from the Huon Peninsula, New Guinea. *Quat. Res.* 4, 185–205.

Brückner, H. 1982: Aussmass von Erosion und Akkumulation im Verlauf des Quartärs in der Basilicata (Süditalien). *Zeits. Geomorph.*, Supp.-Bd. 43, 121–37.

Brückner, H. 1986: Stratigraphy, evolution and age of Quaternary marine terraces in Morocco and Spain. *Zeits. Geomorph.*, Suppl.-Bd. 62, 83–101.

Dai Pra, G. and Stearns, C. E. 1977: Sul Tirreniano di Taranto. Datazioni su coralli con il metodo del ^{230}Th/^{234}U. *Geol. Rom.*, 16, 231–42.

Dalongeville, R. and Sanlaville, P. 1977: Témoins de lignes de rivage holocènes en Turquie méridionale. *Bull. Ass. Franç. Et. Quat.*, 53, 79–81.

Depéret, C. 1918: Essai de coordination chronologique des temps quaternaires. *C. R. Acad. Sci. Paris*, 166, 480–6.

Dreghorn, W. 1981: Recent uplift in northern Cyprus. *Geol. Mijnb.*, 60, 281–4.

Dufaure, J. J. and Zamanis, A. 1981: Styles néotectoniques et étagements de niveaux marins quaternaires sur un segment d'arc insulaire, le Péloponnèse. In *Actes Coll. Niveaux marins et tectonique quaternaires dans l'aire méditerranéenne, Paris, 1980*, CNRS and Univ. Paris I, 77–107.

Dumas, B. 1977: Succession et âges radiométriques des terrasses marines du Levant espagnol. *Bull. Ass. Française pour l'Etude du Quaternaire*, 53, 82–5.

Dumas, B. 1981: Tectonique et inscription de rivages quaternaires sur la côte du Levant espagnol. In *Actes Coll. Niveaux marins et tectonique quaternaires dans l'aire méditerranéenne, Paris, 1980*, CNRS and Univ. Paris I, 325–44.

Dumas, B., Guérémy, P., Lhénaff, R. and Raffy, J. 1981: Niveaux marins et tectonique quaternaires en Calabre méridionale (Italie). In *Actes Coll. Niveaux marins et tectonique quaternaires dans l'aire méditerranéenne, Paris, 1980*, CNRS and Univ. Paris I, 163–230.

Emiliani, C., 1978: The cause of the ice ages. *Earth Plan. Sci. Lett.*, 37, 349–54.

Erol, O. 1963: Asi Nehri deltasinin jeomorfolojisi ve dördüncü zaman deniz-akarsu sekileri – Die Geomorphologie des Orontes-Deltas und der anschliessenden pleistozänen Strand und Flussterrassen (Provinz Hatay, Türkei). (in Turkish and in German). Dil ve Tarih-Cogr. Fak. Yay. Sayi 148, Ankara.

Fanucci, F., Fierro, G., Ozer, A. and Piccazzo, M. 1974: Ritrovamento di una 'Beach-rock' a 70 metri di profondità nelle Bocche di Bonifacio. *Studi Sassaresi*, 22, 3–12.

Federici, P. R. 1972: Datation absolue de dépôts à *A. islandica* de la mer Ligurienne et reflets sur les mouvements tectoniques actuels. *Rev. Géogr. Phys. Géol. dyn.*, 14, 153–8.

Fevret, M., Picard, P. and Sanlaville, P. 1967: Sur la possibilité de datation de niveaux marins quaternaires par les Vermets. *C. R. Acad. Sci. Paris, D*, 264, 1407–9.

Flemming, N. C. 1969: Archaeological evidence for eustatic change of sea level and earth movements in the western Mediterranean during the last 2000 years. *Geol. Soc. Am., Sp. Pap.* 109.

Flemming, N. C. 1979: Archaeological indicators of sea level. In *Les Indicateurs de niveaux marins*, Paris: Oceanis, Fasc. hors-sér., 149–65.

Flemming, N. C., Raban, A. and Goetschel, C. 1978: Tectonic and eustatic changes on the Mediterranean coast of Israel in the last 9000 years. *Progr. Underw. Sci.*, 3, 33–93.

Flemming, N. C. and Pirazzoli, P. A. 1981: Archéologie des côtes de la Crète. *Hist. Archéol., les Dossiers*, 50, 66–81.

Flemming, N. C. and Webb, C. O. 1986: Tectonic and eustatic coastal changes during the last 10,000 years derived from archaeological data. *Zeits. Geomorph.* Suppl.-Bd. 62, 1–29.

Giresse, P. and Davies, O. 1980: High sea levels during the last Glaciation. One of the most puzzling problems of sea-level studies. *Quaternaria*, 22, 211–36.

Goy, J. L. and Zazo, C. 1986: Western Almeria (Spain) coastline changes since the last interglacial. *Journal of Coastal Research* Special Issue 1, 89–93.

Groupe de Recherche Néotectonique de l'Arc de Gibraltar 1977: L'histoire tectonique récente (Tortonien à Quaternaire) de l'Arc de Gibraltar et des bordures de la mer d'Alboran. *Bull. Soc. géol. France*, 19, 575–614.

Hearty, P. J. 1986: An inventory of last interglacial (sensu lato) age deposits from the Mediterranean basin. *Zeits. Geomorph.*, Suppl.-Bd. 62, 51–69.

Hearty, P. J. and Dai Pra, G. 1986: Aminostratigraphy of Quaternary marine deposits in the Lazio region, central Italy. *Zeits. Geomorph.*, Suppl.-Bd. 62, 131–40.

Hearty, P. J. and Miller, G. 1984: Aminostratigraphy of Pleistocene raised shorelines deposits in the Mediterranean basin. *Am. Quatern. Ass., Program and Abstracts*, 57, (Boulder, Colorado).

Hey, R. W. 1978: Horizontal Quaternary shorelines of the Mediterranean. *Quat. Res.* 10, 197–203.

Hey, R. W. 1984: *The INQUA Subcommission on Mediterranean and Black Sea shorelines. Newsletter* 6, 1–4. Pisa and Madrid.

Hsü, K. J. 1974: The Miocene desiccation of the Mediterranean and its climatical and zoogeographical implications. *Naturwissenschaften* 61, 137–42.

Issel, A. 1914: Lembi fossiliferi quaternari et recenti osservati nella Sardegna meridionale dal prof. D. Lovisato. *Rend. Acc. Lincei (5a)*, 23, 759–70.

Kelletat, D. and Kayan, D. 1983: Alanya batisindaki Kiyilarda ilk[14]C tarihlendirmelerinin isiginda Geç Holosen tektonik hareketleri (with English abstract). *Türkiye Geol. Kumun Bül.*, 26, 83–7.

Keraudren, B. 1970, 1971, 1972: Les formations quaternaires marines de la Grèce. *Bull. Musée Anthrop. préhist. Monaco*, no. 16, 5–148; no. 17, 87–169; no. 18, 245–82.

Kraft, J. C., Rapp, G. Jr and Aschenbrenner, S. E. 1975: Late Holocene palaeogeography of the coastal plain of the Gulf of Messenia, Greece, and its relationships to archaeological settings and coastal change. *Geol. Soc. Am. Bull.*, 86, 1191–208.

Kraft, J. C., Kayan, I. and Erol, O. 1980: Geomorphic reconstructions in the environs of ancient Troy. *Science*, 209, 776–82.

Labeyrie, J., Lalou, C., Monaco, A. and Thommeret, J. 1976: Chronologie des niveaux eustatiques sur la côte du Roussillon de −33 000 ans BP à nos jours. *C. R. Acad. Sci. Paris, D*, 282, 349–52.

Le Pichon, X. and Angelier, J. 1979: The Hellenic arc and trench system: a key to the neotectonic evolution of the Eastern Mediterranean area. *Tectonophys.*, 60, 1–42.

L'Homer, A., Bazile, F., Thommeret, J. and Thommeret, Y. 1981: Principales étapes de l'édification du delta du Rhone de 7000 BP à nos jours: variations du niveau marin. *Oceanis*, 7, 389–408.

Lisitzin, E. 1965: The mean sea level of the world ocean. *Soc. Sci. Fenn., Comm. Phys.-Math.* 30, 7, 5–35.

Lisitzin, E. 1974: *Sea-level Changes.* Elsevier Oceanography Series 8. Amsterdam: Elsevier.

Masters, P. M. and Flemming, N. C. (eds) 1983: *Quaternary Coastlines and Marine Archaeology.* London: Academic Press.

Meco, J. 1977: *Los* Strombus *neogenos y cuaternarios del Atlantico Euroafricano.* Cabildo Insular de Gran Canaria: Ediciones del Excmo.

Mesolella, K. J., Matthews, R. K., Broecker, W. S. and Thurber, D. L. 1969: Astronomical theory of climatic changes, Barbados data. *J. Geol.*, 77, 250–74.

Paskoff, R. and Sanlaville, P. 1982: Sur les dépôts tyrrhéniens et würmiens des littoraux de la Méditerranée occidentale. *C. R. Acad. Sci. Paris, II*, 294, 737–40.

Paskoff, R. and Sanlaville, P. 1983: *Les côtes de la Tunisie*. Lyon: Maison de l'Orient.

Pirazzoli, P. A. 1976a: *Les variations du niveau marin depuis 2000 ans*. Dinard: Lab. Géomorph. EPHE, Mém. 30.

Pirazzoli, P. A. 1976b: Sea-level variations in the Northwest Mediterranean during Roman times. *Science*, 194, 519–21.

Pirazzoli, P. A. 1979: Les viviers à poissons romains en Méditerranée. In Les indicateurs de niveaux marins, Paris: *Oceanis*, Fasc. hors-sér., 5, 191–201.

Pirazzoli, P. A., Montaggioni, L. F., Thommeret, J., Thommeret, Y. and Laborel, J. 1982a: Sur les lignes de rivage et la néotectonique à Rhodes (Grèce) à l'Holocène. *Ann. Inst. Océanogr.* 58, 89–102.

Pirazzoli, P. A., Thommeret, J., Thommeret, Y., Laborel, J. and Montaggioni, L. F. 1982b: Crustal block movements from Holocene shorelines: Crete and Antikythira (Greece). *Tectonophys.*, 86, 27–43.

Pirazzoli, P. A. 1983: Flooding ('Acqua alta') in Venice (Italy): a worsening phenomenon. In E. C. F. Bird and P. Fabbri (eds), *Coastal Problems in the Mediterranean Sea* Bologna: IGU Comm. Coastal Envir., 23–31.

Pirazzoli, P. A. 1986a: The Early Byzantine tectonic paroxysm. *Zeitsch. für Geomorph.*, Suppl.-Bd. 62, 31–49.

Pirazzoli, P. A. 1986b: Secular trends of relative sea-level (RSL) changes indicated by tide-gauge records. *Journal of Coastal Research*, Special Issue No. 1, 1–26.

Radtke, U. 1986: Value and risks of radiometric dating of shorelines – Geomorphological and geochronological investigations in central Italy, Eolian Islands and Ustica (Sicily). *Zeits. Geomorph.* Suppl.-Bd. 62, 167–181.

Richards, G. W. and Vita Finzi, C. 1982: Marine deposits 35 000–25 000 years old in the Chott of Djerid, southern Tunisia. *Nature*, 295, 54–5.

Rizos, C. 1983: Plate tectonics in the Mediterranean area and implications for the long term stability of the geoid. In *Proc. 2nd Intern. Symp. Geoid in Europe and Mediterranean area* (*Rome, 1982*), Firenze: Ist. Geogr. Mil. Ital., 303–31.

Sanlaville, P. 1976: Sur l'existence en Syrie de lignes de rivages holocènes supérieures à l'actuelle. *Bull. Lab. Rhodanien Géomorph.* 1, 45–52.

Sanlaville, P. 1977: *Etude géomorphologique de la région littorale du Liban*. 2 vols. Beyrouth: Univ. Libanaise.

Sanlaville, P. 1981: Niveaux marins et tectonique littorale quaternaires au Liban. In *Actes Coll. Niveaux marins et tectonique quaternaires dans l'aire méditerranéenne, Paris, 1980*, CNRS and Univ. Paris I, 27–38.

Segota, T. 1982: Razina mora i vertikalno gibanje dna Jadranskog mora od ris-virmoskog interglacijala do danas (with English abstract). *Geol. vjesnik* 35, 93–109.

Shackleton, N. J. and Opdyke, N. D. 1973: Oxygen isotope and palaeomagnetic stratigraphy of equatorial Pacific Core V 28–238: Oxygen isotope temperature and ice volumes on a 10^5 year and 10^6 year scale. *Quat. Res.*, 3, 39–55.

Sneh, Y. and Klein, M. 1984: Holocene sea-level changes at the coast of Dor, Southeast Mediterranean. *Science*, 226, 831–2.

Stanley, D. J. and Blanpied, C. 1980: Late Quaternary water exchange between the eastern Mediterranean and the Black Sea. *Nature*, 285, 537–41.

Stearns, C. E. 1981: A molluscan revival? In *Actes Coll. Niveaux marins et tectonique quaternaires dans l'aire méditerranéenne, Paris 1980*, CNRS and Univ. Paris I, 15–26.

Stearns, C. E. and Thurber, D. L. 1965: $^{230}Th/^{234}U$ dates of late Pleistocene marine fossils from the Mediterranean and Moroccan littorals. *Quaternaria*, 7, 29–42.

Thommeret, Y., Thommeret, J., Laborel, J., Montaggioni, L. F. and Pirazzoli, P. A. 1981: Late Holocene shoreline changes and seismo-tectonic displacements in western Crete (Greece). *Z. Geomorph.*, Suppl.-Bd. 40, 127–49.

Thunell, R. C. 1979: Eastern Mediterranean sea during the last glacial maximum; an 18 000 years BP reconstruction. *Quat. Res.* 11, 353–372.

Ulzega, A. and Ozer, A. 1982: *Comptes-rendus de l'Excursion-Table ronde sur le Tyrrhenian de Sardaigne, INQUA, 1980*. Univ. Cagliari.

Vignal, J. 1935: Le changement du niveau moyen des mers, *Ann. Ponts et Chaussées*, Mém. Doc., Paris.

Weisrock, A. L. E. 1980: Géomorphologie et paléo-environnements de l'Atlas Atlantique (Maroc). Thèse Doctorat d'Etat ès-Lettres, Paris: University of Paris I, unpublished.

Zazo, C., Goy, J. L. and Aguirre, E. 1984: Did *Strombus* survive the Last Interglacial in the Western Mediterranean Sea? *Mediterranea*, 3, 131–7.

Zazo, C., Goy, J. L., Hoyos, M., Dumas, B., Porta, J., Martinell, J., Baena, J. and Aguirre, E. 1981: Ensayo de sintesis sobre el Tirrenniense peninsular espanol. *Est. Geol.*, 37, 257–62.

Zazo, C. and Ovejero, G. 1976: Niveles marinos cuaternarios en el litoral de la Provincia de Cadiz. In M. T. Alberdi and E. Aguirre (eds), *Miscelanea Neogena*, 5, 141–5.

6

Quaternary sea-level changes in Japan

Yoko Ota and Hiroshi Machida

1.0 BACKGROUND FOR SEA-LEVEL STUDY IN JAPAN

Based on an environmental setting of the Japanese Islands (figure 6.1), the following characteristics serve as a background for study of Quaternary sea-levels in Japan.

The Japanese Islands are located along trenches and troughs marginal to the plate boundaries, and belong to a young mobile belt, where various types of tectonic deformation have continued through the Quaternary under the compressive stress field caused by the subduction of oceanic plates. For example, former shoreline heights preserved on marine terraces show a considerable local difference in altitude due to vertical deformation. The maximum height of the last interglacial shoreline of $c.125\ 000$ BP and that of the postglacial of $c.6000$ BP reaches about 200 m and 30 m respectively. The Pacific coast of central and south-western Japan has been especially active. Here a landward tilt of marine terraces and subdivision of the Holocene marine terraces are characteristic features associated with great earthquakes that occurred in the subduction zone between the Philippine Sea plate and Asian plate (e.g. Yonekura 1975, Ota and Yoshikawa 1978).

Such a rapid uplift causes a difficulty for reconstruction of palaeo-sea-level heights and regional eustatic sea-level curve. On the other hand, an uplifting coast is thought to be a favourable place for the study of sea levels, because each former sea-level stand should remain as successive terraces on land owing to continuous uplift. In fact, a flight of well-defined marine terraces is preserved on the coast where the uplift rate is 0.3 m/1000 yr or more.

Despite the small area of the Japanese Islands, their latitudinal extent is great, covering various climatic zones from Hokkaido where a periglacial

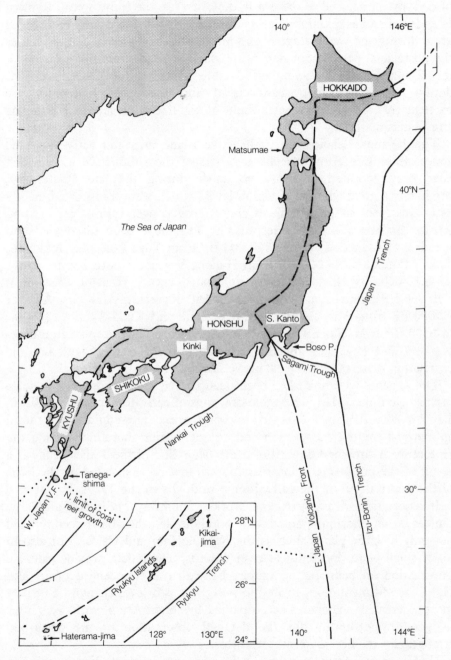

Figure 6.1 A map showing the regional setting of the Japanese Islands

condition prevailed in the glacial period and former shorelines are often buried by periglacial slope wash deposits, to the subtropical Ryukyu Islands defined as a marginal area for coral growth. Here coral reefs could grow during the warm stage of the interglacial and interstadial as well as the postglacial period, but not in the glacial period. Raised coral reefs of the Ryukyus provide abundant datable materials for U-series or ^{14}C dating. Several former sea-levels during the late Quaternary are particularly well preserved as a flight of coral reef terraces in Kikai-jima and Hateruma-jima.

The Japanese Islands are both active island arcs and active volcanic zones. Explosive eruptions characteristic of the subductive mobile belt have been repeated at many volcanoes during the late Quaternary, producing a great amount of tephra layers which were transported mainly eastwards from source volcanoes and deposited over various pre-existing terrace surfaces. Several widespread tephras have been discovered and dated; for instance, Toya of *c.*110 000 BP from Toya Volcano, Hokkaido, Tokyo Pumice of 49 000 BP from Hakone Volcano, south Kanto, Pm–1 of *c.*80 000 BP from Ontake Volcano, central Honshu, Aso–4 of *c.*70 000 BP from Aso Volcano, central Kyushu, Aira-Tn (AT) of 22 000 BP from Aira Caldera, south Kyushu and Kikai-Akahoya (K-Ah) of 6300 BP from Kikai Caldera, south Kyushu. They are valuable time-markers and key beds for the determination of terrace ages and the correlation of terraces over extensive areas.

The Japanese Islands have been occupied by dense populations since prehistoric times. Many archaeological sites of early Jomon (*c.*6000 BP) to Yayoi (*c.*2000 BP) age are located in coastal areas. These middens are used as material for the recognition and age of former shorelines during the Holocene. A drowned dendritic former shoreline of the Kanto Plain as a result of the postglacial transgression, was first reconstructed on the basis of the distribution of the early Jomon middens in the 1920s.

In association with construction works of highways, railroads, and large buildings, an enormous amount of borehole data has been accumulated not only in large plains such as the Kanto, Nobi and Osaka, but also in many small plains located near river mouths. These data provide valuable information on bedrock topography beneath the Holocene deposits and Holocene sedimentation, related to postglacial sea-level changes. Furthermore, increasing exposures accompanied by construction works also offer us good opportunities for the detailed observation of the cover-bed stratigraphy of the Quaternary terraces.

Under these circumstances, Quaternary sea-level studies have been carried out in many places in Japan, although the reconstruction of an eustatic sea-level curve itself is still problematical. As a part of IGCP project 61 and 200, sea-level studies have progressed. In addition to intensive studies in local areas, several reviews or comprehensive papers on this topic have been published (e.g. Moriwaki 1978, Omoto 1979, Machida 1981, Ota *et al.* 1982a, Ota 1982, Naruse and Ota 1984).

In this paper, the recent study of sea-level since the middle Quaternary in Japan will be summarized and discussed.

2.0 MARINE-TERRESTRIAL SEQUENCES IN THE MIDDLE PLEISTOCENE

In Japan, the Shimosa-Kazusa groups around Tokyo Bay in south Kanto and the upper part of the Osaka group in Kinki both represent the standard early to middle Quaternary sequences and have been studied in detail. These groups are characterized by the cyclic sedimentation caused by transgression and regression corresponding to climatic changes. By the middle 1970s chronological study in both areas was independently carried out on the basis of stratigraphy together with palaeomagnetism, radiometric dating, tephrochronology and changes in floral and faunal assemblages. At the end of 1970s, several important datum planes of volcanic ash layers were found resulting in the correlation of both stratigraphic sequences (Machida *et al.* 1980).

These marker ashes are the Azuki-Kokumoto 6c (Ku6c, *c.*870 000 BP), Imakuma 1–Kokumoto 1 and Sakura–Kasamori 11 (Ks–11) ashes (*c.*450 000 BP). Two ashes from them are dated by the fission-track method on zircon crystals included in the ash and the underlying ash. From this information it can be indicated that the three major transgressive-regressive cycles were recorded during the period from Brunhes–Matuyama geomagnetic boundary (*c.*700 000 BP) to the Sakura–Kasamori 11 horizon (*c.*450 000 BP) in both districts (figures 6.2 and 6.3). Also, at least five major cycles can be seen during the next 300 000 yr from the Sakura–Kasumi 11 horizon to the Shimosueyoshi (*c.*130 000 BP) in south Kanto (figure 6.2).

In order to evaluate the magnitude of repeated high sea-levels during the past 700 000 yr, it is necessary to obtain as much information as possible and to synthesize it. First, for the section in the northern part of Yokohama where marine terraces are typically developed, Machida (1975) determined the elevation of older sea levels at each of the higher sea-level periods by applying the average uplift rate of 0.3 m/1000 yr from the difference between the present and the estimated elevation of the original palaeo-sea-level at Shimosueyoshi terrace (*c.*130 000 BP). This was

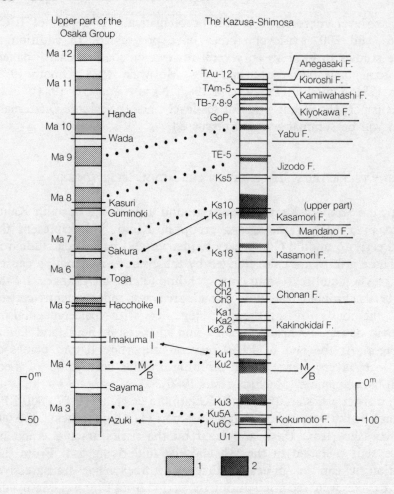

Figure 6.2 A diagram showing the correlation between the Osaka Group, Kinki and the Kazusa Group, south Kanto (Machida *et al.* 1980). I, marine clay; 2, marine deposits with faunal assemblages indicating warm, sea surface temperatures. Handa, TAu-12, etc. are marker tephras. M/B is the Matuyama-Brunhes geomagnetic boundary. Solid arrowlines are identified marker tephras. Localities are shown in Figure 6.1

assumed to be +7 m, and that of the Holocene transgressive peak (*c.*6000 BP) was taken as +2 m. The results show that the Shimosueyoshi peak was the highest (figure 6.3).

There is a problem, however, if an assumption of constant uplift rate is applied to the middle Pleistocene by extrapolation. Accordingly, as the second criterion for the evaluation, information on palaeo-temperatures

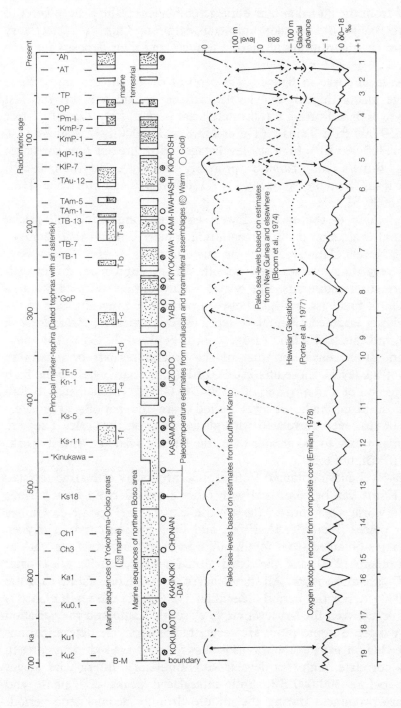

Figure 6.3 Climatic and sea-level changes in the Brunhes epoch with special reference to the marine sequence in south Kanto analysed by tephrochronology (Machida and Arai 1980)

estimated from the faunal and/or floral assemblages on the eastern coast of the Tokyo Bay should be taken into consideration. Third, it is necessary to compare the distribution of marine terraces and their deposits for each period.

The sea-level curve in figure 6.3 is a result of the integration of these data. Five major higher sea levels can be recognized for the last 450 000 yr, each indicating a full interglacial period, i.e., Tama-f (T-f or Ma 7, *c*.450 000 BP); Tama-e (T-e or Ma 8, *c*.370 000 BP); Tama-c (T-c or Ma 9, *c*.300 000 BP); high sea-level stages with three or four substages including Tama-a and Tama-b (probably Ma 10, *c*.240–180 000 BP); Shimosueyoshi (S or probably Ma 11, *c*.130 000 BP) and Holocene (H or Ma 12, *c*.6000 BP).

Determination of the ages of lower sea levels, indicating full glacial periods, and evaluation of their magnitude is more difficult than those of higher sea levels. However, on the eastern coast of the Tokyo Bay, problems regarding low sea-level periods can be approached by investigating terrestrial sediments and buried valley bottoms. In addition, a comparison of fossil assemblages between periods and investigation of the strata yielding large continental vertebrates (in particular, *Palaeoloxodon naumani*), indicate that a land bridge existed between the Asian continent and Japan. It is considered that of the several periods of maximum lowering of sea levels, those of *c*.250 000 BP (immediately before the high sea-level period of Tama-b) and of *c*.150–140 000 BP (immediately before the Shimosueyoshi high sea-level period), are the periods of greatest lowering of sea level (correlated with glacial ages) on the scale. They are equal in magnitude to, or greater than, the latest glacial age with its peak, *c*.20 000 BP (figure 6.3).

The sea-level curve obtained from tephrochronology of marine terraces in south Kanto can be compared with other curves derived from various parts of the world. On figure 6.3 the sea-level curve from Papua-New Guinea and other places (Bloom *et al*. 1974), and the variation curve of oxygen isotopic ratios obtained from foraminifera in deep sea cores from various places (Emiliani 1978), and the dated glacial advances in Hawaii (Porter *et al*. 1977) are also shown. All these curves resemble one another for the last 150 000 yr. For the period older than 150 000 yr, the resemblance is also notable between the sea-level curve of south Kanto and the variation curve of oxygen isotopic ratio. However, radiometric age determinations will be needed for marker-tephras as well as for deep sea sediment cores in order to correlate high sea levels with Emiliani's interglacial stages especially before 300 000 BP. Both interglacial peaks of Tama-e and Tama-c are prominent during the middle Brunhes geomagnetic period.

Consequently, tentative correlations of Tama-e and Tama-c with undated Emiliani's stages 11 and 9 could be possible as indicated by broken arrows in figure 6.3. During the last 300 000 yr principal high sea-level stages and the numbered oxygen isotopic ones could be correlated as follows: Tama-b and Tama-a to the peaks among stage 7; S to stage 5.

3.0 SEA LEVEL CHANGES IN THE LATE PLEISTOCENE

3.1 An approach from tephrochronology in south Kanto

The most prominent marine terrace in the environs of Tokyo and Yokohama, south Kanto (figure 6.4), the Shimosueyoshi terrace, has a lot of evidence that it was formed in the interglacial stage. The marine formation which constitutes this terrace was brought about by a marked transgression and it bears an abundant faunal and floral assemblage of interglacial affinity. These aspects closely resemble those of the Holocene formation, so that the transgression is supposed to have been caused by a glacio-eustatic change in sea level.

However, there were some discussions on the age of Shimosueyoshi transgression: whether it can be assigned to the last interglacial or penultimate one, and how old it is. In 1971, a solution to this problem was provided by tephrochronological studies (Machida and Suzuki 1971). In this district there is a continuous mantle of thick Pleistocene tephra formation originating from the Fuji and Hakone volcanoes to the west. The higher terrace surfaces are covered by thicker layers than the lower ones, implying that tephra was showered down more or less continuously throughout the Quaternary. Hence, correlation of terraces by means of tephra is regarded as indispensible.

As a result of precise examination, many of the marker-tephras have been traced from the source volcanoes to the environs of Yokohama and Tokyo and further eastward to the Boso Peninsula. Several marker-tephras can be well-dated by radiocarbon, obsidian hydration and fission-track methods. Nearly all the dates available are summarized in the second column of figure 6.5. From the stratigraphic relation with the dated tephra, the age of each marine terrace can be estimated (Machida and Suzuki 1971). Of particular interest are the ages of the Shimosueyoshi and younger marine terraces.

The Shimosueyoshi transgression seems to have attained its peak *c.*130 000 BP, because TAu-12 pumice of Hakone origin dated to 145 000±10 000 BP occurs within the marine formation of this stage and

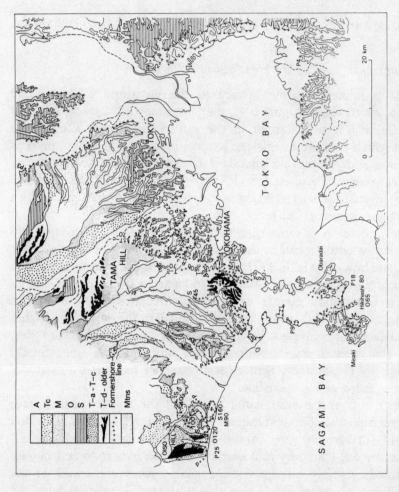

Figure 6.4 The terraces of south Kanto (Machida 1975). A, alluvial plains; Tc, Tachikawa river terrace; M, Misaki marine and river terrace; O, Obaradai marine and river terrace; S, Shimosueyoshi marine and river terrace; T-a ~ T-c, Tama-a to Tama-c marine and river terraces; T-d ~ older, Tama-d and older terraces; the heights of former shorelines are shown in metres above sea-level; Mtns, mountains; P, postglacial shoreline

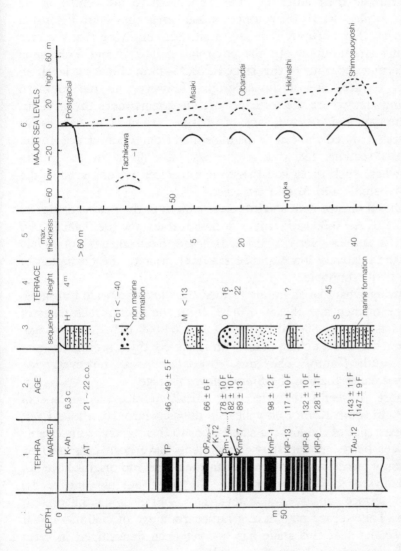

Figure 6.5 A framework for dated tephra and marine terrace sequences in south Kanto and major sea-level changes (from Machida 1975, modified). 1, stratigraphic column of dated tephra; 2, age in ka: c, radiocarbon age, O, obsidian hydration age, F, fission track age for obsidian and zircon; 3, H, Holocene, Tc, Tachikawal, M, Misaki, O, Obaradai, H, Hikihashi; S, Shimosueyoshi; 4, the height of former shoreline in metres above sea-level in the northern part of Yokohama; 5, the maximum thickness of sediments

K1P-6 pumice of Hakone with an age of 128 000±11 000 BP covered the palaeo-shoreline of the Shimosueyoshi terrace.

The former shoreline and terrace surface of the Shimosueyoshi stage gradually decrease their altitudes from Yokohama to the centre of the Kanto Plain, while towards the southern coastal area, the Miura Peninsula and Oiso coast, they abruptly increase in altitude, implying that the area is undergoing strong uplift. In the environs of Tokyo and Yokohama where the former shoreline of this stage lies *c*.35–40 m above sea level, all the younger terraces are of fluvial origin. However, in the southern actively rising area where the former shoreline attains more than 100 m, most of the younger terraces are of marine origin. The successive shorelines are separated and can be distinguished from other terraces there. The standard sections for younger terraces are given in the Miura Peninsula, where such three late Pleistocene terraces are observed as the Hikihashi, Obaradai and Misaki terraces.

The Hikihashi terrace with an altitude of *c*.80 m in the peninsula has an estimated age of *c*.100 000 BP from the fission-track age (98 000±12 000 BP) of KmP-1 pumice overlying on it. Because this terrace is not widely developed, the relatively low stand of sea-level prior to the formation of this terrace is questionable.

The following Obaradai shoreline formed by a less extensive transgression has an estimated age of *c*.80 000 BP from the fission-track dates of such tephras as Pm-1 (*c*.80 000 BP) and OP (*c*.66 000 BP). At this stage, extensive benches and a deltaic plain with relatively thick sediments were formed in south Kanto. The area covered by sea, however, was considerably smaller than in the Shimosueyoshi stage.

Furthermore, it seems that the next Misaki terrace has an age of *c*.60 000 BP. In south Kanto, no valley fill deposits have been found yet, so that the existence of the low sea stand prior to this terrace is uncertain.

The terraces buried under alluvial sediments have been examined by drilling in many places in south Kanto, but their ages and origins have not yet been analysed in detail. However, the most notable one is the Tachikawa-1 terrace, observed at a level of *c*.−40 m along the present river mouth. This terrace may have a radiocarbon age of *c*.30 000 BP or more. The sea-level of this stage has not yet been determined in great detail, but is presumably lower than −40 m.

The elimination of the effects of tectonic movement is necessary to produce a real eustatic curve. Hence the sea-level curve drawn as the solid line in figure 6.5 is based on the assumption of a uniform rate of uplift and the assignment of probable altitudes to original sea levels for 130 000 BP and 6000 BP. In the northern part of Yokohama, here

adopted as a standard section, the Shimoseuyoshi shoreline stands at
c.45 m above sea level, that of Obaradai (80 000 BP) at 16–22 m, that of
Misaki (60 000 BP) at less than 13 m and that of the postglacial
transgression peak (6000 BP), at *c*.4 m.

Many studies place the sea level of *c*.130–125 000 BP at 2–10 m higher
than it is at present (e.g. Veeh 1966, Veeh and Chappell 1970, Bloom
et al. 1974) and that of *c*.6000 BP at 0–4 m higher than at present. If these
values are adopted, the mean uplift rate of this area during the last
130 000 yr is calculated to be a little less than 0.3 m/1000 yr in good
agreement with that inferred from the postglacial. Adjusting for this uplift
rate, changes in sea level around the stages of several high stands are
tentatively inferred as in figure 6.5. The 100 000 BP sea level may have
been similar to that of 80 000 BP, because the difference of altitude
between the Hikihashi and the Obaradai is not so large in the strongly
uplifted Miura Peninsula.

3.2 *Extensive correlation of marine terraces by using widespread tephras*

In the coastal area of Japan, there are many places where a flight of
marine terraces is developed. The ages of terraces, however, are usually
not known except for the above-mentioned south Kanto, the Ryukyus,
composed of datable coral reefs and Holocene terraces which contain
abundant material for radiocarbon dating. Accordingly, relative correlation
and age estimation of terraces have been done tentatively based on
geological and geomorphological characteristics of terraces and their
deposits such as the presence of either the transgressive marine deposits or
only thin beach deposits overlying a wave-cut surface, degree of
weathering of terrace deposits, thickness of tephra layers, and continuity
and degree of dissection of terrace surfaces.

With the recent discovery of several widespread ash layers (Machida
and Arai 1983) age determination of terraces has started. A list of six
widespread tephras, important time-markers for late Quaternary chronology, is shown in table 6.1. Only the Toya ash originated from Hokkaido
and the other five from Kyushu. All of them are favourable not only for
analysing the nature of large scale eruptions but also for establishing the
chronological framework for late Quaternary chronology of Japan.

When distal ashes need to be identified, petrographic and chemical
characterizations are indispensible. As shown in table 6.1, accurate
determinations of refractive indices of glass and phenocrysts are used as
the first and most efficient parameter for quick characterization of distal
ashes, together with crystal assemblages and micrographic features of
glass shards (Arai 1972). The chemical composition of glass and crystal is

Table 6.1   A list of widespread ashes (tephras) occurring in and around the Japanese islands

Source and tephra*	Age (1000 yr) and dating method	Bulk volume (km³)	Volcanic glass		Phenocrystal minerals
			Type	Refractive index	
Kikai – Akahoya (K – Ah)	6.3 ^{14}C	150	bw≥pm	1.508–1.514	pl; opx, cpx opx γ = 1.709–1.712
Aira – Tn (AT)	21–22 ^{14}C	300	bw>pm	1.498–1.501	pl; opx, cpx, (ho, qt) opx γ = 1.728–1.734
Aso – 4	c.70 FT, S	300+	bw>pm	1.506–1.514	pl; ho, opx, cpx opx γ = 1.699–1.701 ho n_2 = 1.685–1.691
Kikai – Tozurahara (K – Tz)	c.75 FT, S	150+	bw>pm	1.497–1.500	pl, qt; opx, cpx opx γ = 1.705–1.709
Ata	c.85 FT, S	200+	bw>pm	1.508–1.513	pl; opx, cpx, (ho) opx γ = 1.704–1.708
Toya	c.100–130 FT, S	100+	pm>bw	1.494–1.498	pl, qt; opx, cpx opx γ = 1.756–1.761

* Including pyroclastic-flow deposits.
pm = pumiceous shard; bw = bubble-walled shard; pl = plagioclase; qt = quartz;
opx = orthopyroxene; cpx = clinopyroxene; ho = hornblende. FT = Fission track method;
S = stratigraphy. ^{14}C = radiocarbon.
n_2 and γ are refractive indices.

also used for identification of tephras.

The radiocarbon age determinations for the younger tephras, K-Ah and AT, are successful; however, for other tephras they are not, because these occur in lower stratigraphic horizons beyond the time-range of the radiocarbon dating method. New data on the stratigraphic position in a standard tephra sequence of south Kanto show that the three Kyushuan tephras occur between tephras which have already been dated by fission-track methods on obsidian and zircon crystals from the tephras (Machida and Suzuki 1971): Aso-4 and the underlying K-Tz ashes both occur below Obaradai pumice (c.66 000 BP) and above Pm-1 (c.80 000 BP), hence the former was produced c.70 000 BP and the latter c.75 000 BP; Ata ash is found below Pm-1 and above KmP-7 (c.89 000 BP), hence presumably occurred c.85 000 BP.

Toya has not been found in a tephra sequence of south Kanto, but is estimated to have been produced between 110 000 BP and 130 000 BP, because the Toya pyroclastic flow deposits simultaneously erupted with Toya ash have a fission-track age of c.130 000 BP (Okumura and Sangawa 1984) and they occurred in a regressive stage after the last interglacial culmination of transgression.

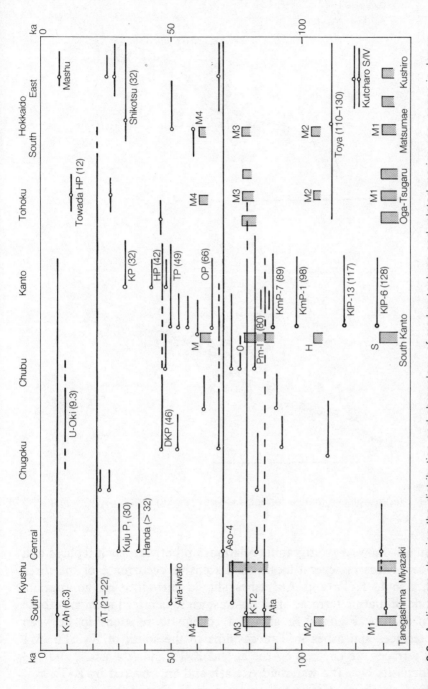

Figure 6.6 A diagram showing the distribution and chronology of marker tephras and related marine sequences in Japan. The horizontal lines show the extent of each marker tephra with radiometric ages (× 1000) in parenthesis. Shaded columns indicate the position of the marine sequences. Abbreviations are the same as on Figure 6.4 and 6.5.

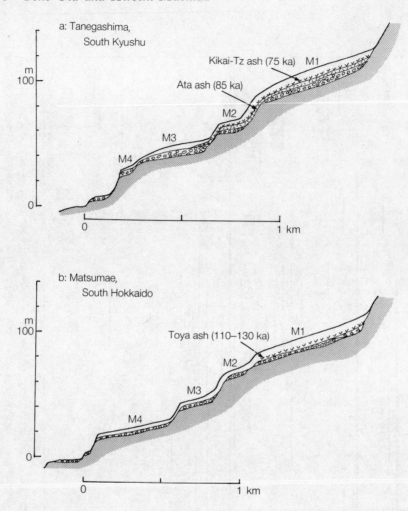

Figure 6.7 Representative marine terrace profiles showing relation with widespread tephras

Figure 6.6 shows a stratigraphic relationship between such tephras and marine sequences in several localities. Extensive occurrence of the three tephras, Aso-4, K-Tz and Ata ashes should introduce an appropriate correlation of marine terraces of south-western to central Japan with those of south Kanto. Figure 6.7a shows a schematic relationship between marine terraces and ashes in Tanegashima to the south of Kyushu. M1 and M2 terraces are covered by the airlaid K-Tz and Ata ashes, and M3 terrace deposits bear the waterlaid Ata ash and are covered by K-Tz ash. M4 terrace was formed after the eruption of K-Tz and Aso-4.

Such stratigraphic features in Tanegashima indicate the possibility that the M1 terrace, the most prominent one, is assigned to the last interglacial Shimosueyoshi terrace, and M2, M3 and M4 are respectively correlated with the Hikihashi, Obaradai and Misaki terraces of south Kanto.

Marine terraces in northern Japan can be readily identified by direct tephrostratigraphic control. Principal time-marker-tephras are Aso-4 (*c*.70 000 BP), Toya (*c*.110–130 000 BP) and Kutcharo ashes (*c*.130 000 BP). Figure 6.7b shows the marine terrace profile with the stratigraphic position of the Toya ashes at Matsumae, south-western Hokkaido, where strong uplift is recorded. The M1 terrace should be assigned to the last interglacial: Shimosueyoshi terrace and M2, M3 and M4 terraces possibly to the Hikihashi, Obaradai and Misaki terraces respectively.

Marine terraces which have hitherto been correlated and dated by such tephrochronological methods are mainly shown in figure 6.6. Generally, marine terraces formed during the last 130 000 yr increase in number with increasing uplift rate.

3.3 Age of high sea levels deduced from coral reef terraces of the Ryukyu Islands

Of many coral reef terraces in the Ryukyu Islands, a flight of dated terraces, which record successive high sea levels in the late Quaternary, is known from two islands, Kikai-jima to the north and Hateruma-jima to the south (figure 6.1).

Despite the great distance apart of these islands, they are very similar in terms of their location to the Ryukyu trench and geologic history. First, they are the nearest islands to the trench; second, they are composed of a raised table reef, which unconformably overlies the Neogene sedimentary rocks and consists of the highest part of the island, accompanied by lower groups of terraces of fringing reef origin. Thirdly, these coral reef terraces have been dislocated by active faults.

In Kikai, the easternmost of the Ryukyus, the highest terrace, *c*.200 m high at the eastern margin, tilts westwards. Pleistocene coral reefs can be divided into five groups, down to about 20 m at the lowest. Holocene raised coral reefs of four steps entirely surround the Pleistocene terraces, separated by steep postglacial sea-cliffs (figure 6.8). The ^{230}Th and ^{231}Pa ages of corals from a locality of 170 m high belonging to the highest terrace, are 122 000±2000 BP and 124 000±5000 BP. Successive younger radiometric ages are obtained as follows: 99 000±8000 BP (140 m), 81 000±3000 BP and 86 000±4000 BP (120 and 65 m), 50 000±1000 BP to 59 000±5000 BP (less than 50 m) and 36 000±2000 BP to 45 000±2000

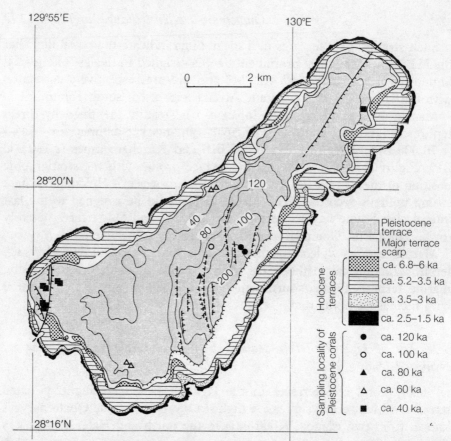

Figure 6.8 Map of Kikai-jima, northern Ryukyu showing the ages of Pleistocene corals and of the Holocene tephras (compiled from Konishi *et al.* 1974 and Ota *et al.* 1978). More than 70 radiocarbon dates have been obtained from a series of Holocene coral reefs (Ota *et al.* 1978, Nakata *et al.* 1978). The sampling localities have been omitted

BP (19–28 m) (Konishi *et al.* 1974). Those radiometric ages exactly coincide with coral reefs of New Guinea, characterized by a high uplift rate, *c.* 2.5 m/1000 yr (Chappell 1974). These ages are also comparable with the higher sea-level stages obtained from south Kanto (Machida 1975) and Barbados (Broecker *et al.* 1968; James *et al.* 1971), except that no terrace of *c.*60 000 BP is found in these two areas with relatively low uplift rate. However, owing to a displacement of coral reef terraces by active faults, a typical circular arrangement of successive terraces cannot be observed in Kikai and a question remains on the terrace correlation of the various parts of the island, except well-defined and dated Holocene reefs (e.g. Ota *et al.* 1978).

In contrast to Kikai, Hateruma-jima shows an excellent circular arrangement of a flight of coral reef terraces as shown in figure 6.9.

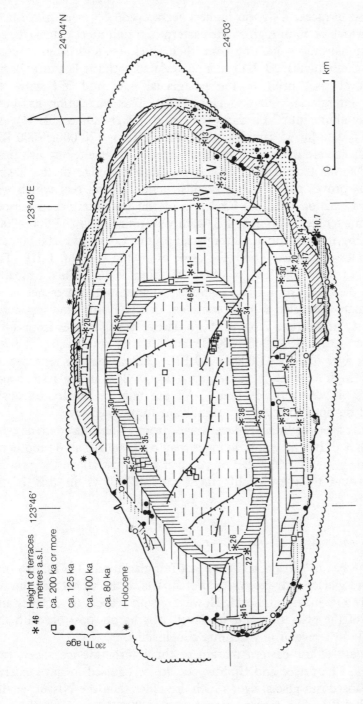

Figure 6.9 Map of Hateruma-jima, southern Ryukyu showing the ages of the coral reef terraces (compiled from Ota and Hori 1980, Omura 1984)

Among these terraces, T-I, the highest terrace and 58 m at maximum, and T-III, which is 40 m high at the eastern part and most extensive, are of constructional origin, judging from their thickness and facies of coral limestones. Consequently, T-III can be correlated with the last interglacial major sea-level rise, prior to the postglacial one, and T-I with the penultimate interglacial (Ota and Hori 1980). This correlation has been confirmed by abundant ^{230}Th dates (Ota *et al.* 1982b, Omura 1984). An average ^{230}Th date for 35 samples taken from T-III is 128 000±7000 BP. Corals of this age are discovered not only from T-III itself, but also from the terraces lower than T-III, even from the outer edge of the lowest terrace. This proves that T-III is a constructional coral reef which was formed in association with sea-level rise of the last interglacial period. Similarly, an average ^{230}Th age of 23 samples from T-I is 207 000±3000 BP, confirming its penultimate interglacial origin. Corals of *c*.200 000 are found from lower terraces than T-I also, as in the case of T-III. The oldest date of *c*.300 000 BP is obtained from T-III. This probably represents a basal part of T-I reef complex, suggesting the presence of an antepenultimate interglacial reef complex in Hateruma and erosional origin of T-II. An average value of ^{230}Th dates for six samples from T-IV and lower terraces is 103 000±1000 BP and that for seven samples from T-V and younger ones is 81 000±3000 BP. These dates are regarded as evidence of high sea levels subsequent to the last interglacial major transgression. Lower terraces than T-VI are only secondary erosional features and do not represent any significant former sea level.

Radiometric ages for high sea-level stages from Hateruma coincide with those from Kikai, but no corals younger than *c*.80 000 BP are found here, and Holocene reefs of *c*.6000 BP or younger exist just above the present sea level, owing to a low uplift rate, *c*.0.3 m/1000 yr in this Island (figure 6.10).

3.4   *Lower sea levels in the last glaciation*

Early stage of the last glaciation. In the last full glaciation, it is known that ice sheets and glaciers advanced in various parts of the world and the sea was lowered to its maximum level. However, with respect to the ages and magnitudes of the glaciation and sea level, it is hardly possible with the data available to arrive at any definite conclusions.

In the region of the eastern margin of the Laurentide ice sheet, two glacial stades, Cherrytree and Guildwood, are recognised to have existed during the Wisconsin glacial age, which are older than the Nissuri stade, around 20 000 BP. The former, dated at *c*.35 000 BP, was a relatively

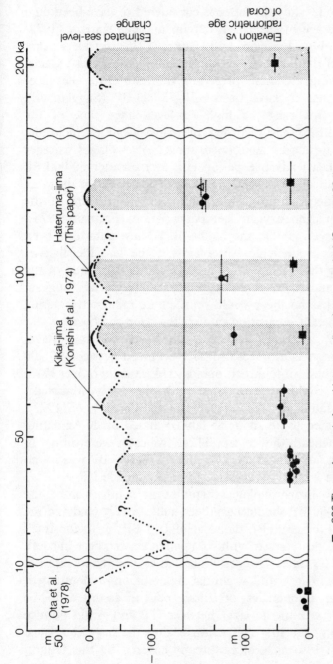

Figure 6.10 A time/altitude graph to show the relation of heights and radiometric ages of corals from Kikai-jima and Hateruma-jima, together with an estimated sea-level curve compiled and modified from Konishi *et al.* 1974, Ota *et al.* 1978 and Omura 1984

small scale glacial period, while the latter is considered to have been on a large scale. As for the age of the latter, Dreimanis and Karrow (1972) estimated *c*.55 000 BP, but Dreimanis and Raukas (1975) considered that it was *c*.70 000 BP. On the South Island of New Zealand, the last glacial advance period, Early Otira Glacial, preceding the Late Otira Glacial of *c*.20 000 BP, is estimated to have been *c*.50–75 000 BP (Suggate and Moar 1970). During this range, a high sea-level stage (one of the interstadials), *c*.60 000 BP, was recorded in many localities including south Kanto and Kikai-jima as mentioned above. Accordingly whether the early Wisconsin glacial advance period is before or after 60 000 BP constitutes an important chronological problem. The record of deep-sea cores has not yet provided significant information on this problem. In the generalised curve of marine oxygen isotope variation (Emiliani 1978), stage 4 should fall between 70 000 and 75 000 BP. These data have been used in discussing the chronological problems of the late Pleistocene, providing the basis for the discussion of the age of the beginning of the Wisconsin glaciation and/or the end of the last interglacial (Suggate 1974). Moreover, this has not been based on accurate radiometric dating but on assuming a constant deposition rate on the deep-sea floor.

In the Japan Alps, a glacial advance, called the Murodo stage, preceding the last stage, was estimated to have occurred between 60 000 and 50 000 BP, on the basis of tephrochronology (Machida and Arai 1978, Machida 1980). This could be correlated with the Early Makanaka advance recorded in Mauna Kea Volcano in Hawaii (Porter *et al.* 1977). The latter was determined to be about 55 000 BP based on K-Ar dating on a lava from a vent beneath the ice cap. These two cases were similar in that the scale of glacial advance that occurred *c*.55–50 000 BP was by no means smaller than the last event which happened *c*.20 000 BP.

According to the tephrochronological studies in south Kanto, the climate around 55–50 000 BP should have been substantially cold and the sea level low. Tokyo Pumice (TP), dated at 49 000 BP by fission-track method, directly covers peaty layers with cold pollen assemblages in south Kanto. Palynological studies suggest that the cool-temperate to subarctic or subalpine climate with low annual precipitation predominated, on the basis of high frequencies of *Picea* pollen, assumed to be *P. maximowiczii*, and *Larix* in the layer between TP and Anjin pumice (*c*.60 000 BP), indicating the first cold climate after the last interglacial age (Tsuji *et al.* 1984). Fluvial terraces directly covered by this tephra, along with Sagami and Tama Rivers in south Kanto, are considered to have been formed at a low sea-level period because of their steep longitudinal profiles. In addition, in the southern part of the Miura

Peninsula, where uplift is rapid, airfall TP covers the scarp of Misaki marine terrace to an elevation at least 5 m above sea-level. This terrace has an age of *c.*60 000 BP and the present elevation of the former shorelines is 35 m. Since the average uplift rate in the locality during the past 60 000 yr is estimated to be about 1 m/1000 yr, sea level at the time of eruption of TP must have been at a lower position than −55 m. Thus, evidence is obtained that there was a prominent low sea-level period at the time of the post-Misaki terrace. However, during the interim period between 80 000 BP and 60 000 BP, no evidence has been obtained to show substantial lowering of sea level. On the other hand, the sea-level curve obtained from New Guinea (Bloom *et al.* 1974) is different in part from the information from south Kanto or from deep-sea cores, which presents a clearly indented shape (figure 6.3). Almost all of the interim periods between times of high sea level had significantly low sea levels.

Problems still remain concerning the age and scale of glacial substages and low sea-level periods in the chronology of the late Pleistocene. There is still a possibility of finding glacial substages older than 55–50 000 BP and later than the interglacial stage of 130–125 000 BP. Because the scales are different in various districts, more data will be needed from each area. Nevertheless, it can be said that the data concerning the glacial substage of 55–50 000 BP suggest a possibility of modifying the peak of stage 4 of marine oxygen isotope variation to having occurred 55–50 000 BP, rather than 75–70 000 BP.

Late stage of the last glaciation. The last glacial advances in the Japanese high mountains occurred after an interstadial of *c.*40–30 000 BP. The extension of glaciers, however, was much more limited than in the earlier stade. Ages of maximum extensions have not yet been fully dated except for the following cases: the Akakurazawa advance in the northern Japanese Alps was reported to have occurred *c.*25 000 BP (Koaze *et al.* 1974); the Awasuno accumulation terracing immediately before 22 000 BP (Machida 1980); the Tottabetsu advance in the Hidaka mountains, Hokkaido, before 13 000 BP (Ono and Hirakawa 1975).

Compared with such data on glaciation, there are a number of studies on reconstruction of palaeoclimate in the period between 25 000 BP and 10 000 BP on the basis of pollen analytical examinations. According to Tsukada (1983), northern Hokkaido was distinguished by coniferous parkland and tundra vegetation during the last glacial maximum around 20 000 BP, while southern Hokkaido and northernmost Honshu were covered by northern boreal coniferous forests. Central Honshu and the mountains of southwestern Japan supported subalpine coniferous forests. Temperate coniferous forests existed principally in the western and southern Honshu, Shikoku and Kyushu.

A pollen analytical study from the Ozegahara moor, in central Honshu, indicated the coldest stage in the last glaciation to have been around 21 000 BP (Sakaguchi 1978). Data from Lake Mikata, located in the northern Kinki district facing the Sea of Japan, suggest that two stages of severely cold and dry condition existed: *c*.24–20 000 BP and 18–15 000 BP (Yasuda 1982).

A low stand of sea level in the latest glaciation has been discussed by many authors. The submarine topography and buried valleys around river mouths supply material for the resolution of this problem. Detailed seismic profiling surveys revealed buried channels and sand bars developing on the submarine terraces, suggesting the palaeo-shoreline, traced to deeper than 90–110 m in the surroundings of the Tsushima Strait where the Japanese Islands connected with the Asian continent (e.g. Mogi 1981, Sato and Mogi 1982). Also, several submarine terraces were found at higher levels: −90 to −110 m, −60 to −70 m, and −20 to −35 m, indicating the intermittent rise in sea level. One problem is that few radiometric dates of these submarine deposits have been obtained as yet.

The problem, closely related with such low stands of sea level, should be whether the Sea of Japan was open to the adjacent seas or not by the formation of land bridges between Kyushu and Korea and between Honshu and Hokkaido, and if they were formed, when? On this problem, Arai *et al*. (1981) reported oceanographical changes of the Sea of Japan in the last glaciation on the basis of changes in palaeosalinity and palaeotemperature, which were calculated from the $\delta^{18}O$ values of the benthonic and planktonic foraminiferal tests in the piston cores. Vertical changes in the lithological, foraminiferal and oxygen isotope characteristics of the tephrochronologically dated ones from the southern part of the sea occur at *c*.93–63 000, 13 000 and 23 000 BP.

Figures 6.11 (a–d) show palaeogeographical changes deduced from these data. The water of the Sea of Japan seems to have been of relatively constant salinity (33–34‰) and low temperature (8–10°C) in the period before 23 000 BP (figure 6.11a). A continuous decrease in the salinity of the sea water took place in the period from 23 000 to 13 000 BP. It seems probable that the inflow of water from the open sea was checked by some palaeogeographical changes at the strait, caused by lowering of sea level (figure 6.11b). The $S^{18}O$ value of the planktonic foraminifera tests increased suddenly and the benthonic foraminiferal fauna which live today in the shallow water of the northwest Pacific coast appeared at *c*.13 000 BP, suggesting a probable inflow of a cold current through the Tsugaru Strait into the Sea of Japan (figure 6.11c). The coiling direction

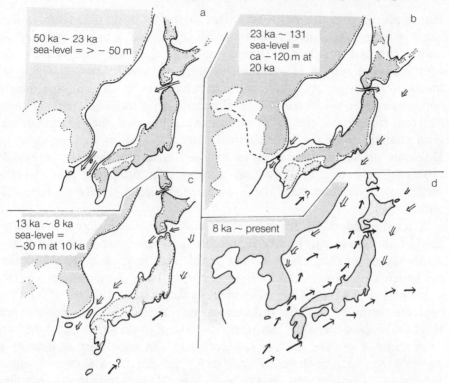

Figure 6.11 Palaeogeographical and oceanographical maps of the Japanese Islands and adjacent seas in the past 50 000 years. Solid arrows indicate a warm current: open arrows indicate a cold current.

of *Globigerina pachyderma* changed from sinistral to dextral at *c.*8000 BP. The warm water planktonic foraminifera appeared in the cores, and the surface water temperature increased abruptly by 7–8°C, indicating that an abundant inflow of the Tsushima warm current into the Sea of Japan began *c.*8000 BP (figure 6.11d).

4.0 HOLOCENE SEA-LEVEL CHANGES

4.1 *Characteristics of the holocene sea-level curves*

The Japanese working group of IGCP Project 61 compiled and published an *Atlas of Holocene Sea-level Records in Japan* in 1981, in which 39 Holocene sea-level curves published since 1960 were included (Ota *et al.* 1981). Since then, seven more curves have been published. However, as some curves prepared in the early stage were drawn by using data from various areas, which have different tectonic histories, and some were based on only a limited number of dated samples, they are not suitable for comparison. Figure 6.12 summarizes selected reliable curves which are based on intensive study of some particular areas in terms of age, height and environmental control of the Holocene deposits. They usually cover different time spans: that is, those from uplifting areas mainly discuss sea-level changes since the hypsithermal stage, because in such an area the Holocene marine sequence can be exposed as terrace deposits and easily observable. In contrast, sea-level curves from subsiding areas usually include periods older than the hypsithermal, based chiefly on bore-hole data.

A considerable local difference exists in the curves in figure 6.12. This implies that each curve only represents a 'relative sea-level curve' as a combination of an eustatic change of sea level and local vertical movements of various types. It is true that there is no single sea-level curve and all the curves are more or less relative ones. It is still difficult to separate tectonic, isostatic and eustatic effects from a given relative sea-level curve quantitatively. An important thing to do at the moment is to reconstruct a precise relative sea-level curve in each area as exactly as possible, considering the number of dated samples, their ages and heights together with stratigraphic and palaeontological characteristics of sampling horizons. A geomorphological examination of the Holocene terrace is, of course, necessary. Moreover it should be noted that there is some limitation in accuracy in the discussion of Holocene sea-level change, that is an order of 10^{-1}m in magnitude of sea-level fluctuation and 100 yr in an age.

Examining the sixteen curves in figure 6.12, the following tendencies can be recognized.

Sea level rose very rapidly from c.15 000 to c.6000 BP. This sea-level rise, correlated with the postglacial transgression, is called the 'Jomon transgression' in Japan, after the presence of early Jomon middens in the vicinity of the estimated shoreline of this transgression. During this transgression, a regression at c.10 000 BP is observed rather commonly, which is regarded as corresponding to a marked cold climate, recognized by palynological and micro-fossil analysis on deep-sea cores taken from the Pacific Ocean off Kanto (Chinzei *et al.* 1984).

All the relative sea-level curves except of 1–B and 1–C from the Sendai Plain (Omoto 1979), reached to a slightly higher level than the present one at about 6000 BP of the hypsithermal stage, even in relatively stable or slightly subsiding areas. In the following, this high sea level is described

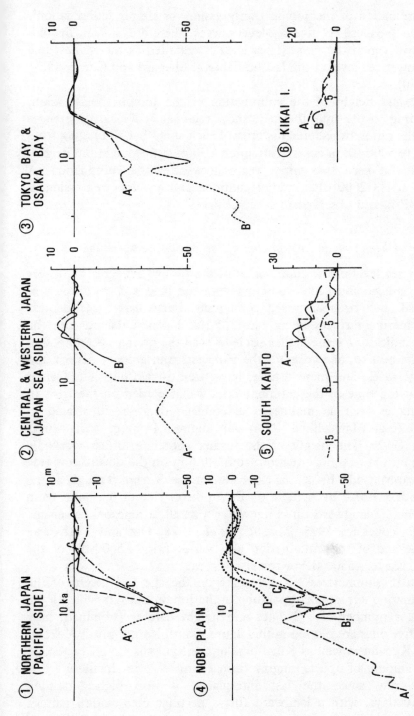

Figure 6.12 Relative Holocene sea-level curves from the Japanese Islands (modified from Ota et al. 1982b). 1: A, Tohoku Nosei-Kyoku 1979; B, Omoto 1979; C, Chida et al. 1984. 2: A, Fujii and Fujii 1981; B, Toyoshima 1978. 3: A, Maeda 1976; B, Kaizuka et al. 1977. 4: A, Furukawa 1972; B, Umitsu 1979; C, Iskeki and Moriyama 1981; D, Maeda et al. 1983. 5: A, Nakata et al. 1978; B, Yokota 1978; C, Moriwaki 1979. 6: A, Ota et al. 1978; B, Nakata et al. 1978. The zero horizontal axis datum is mean sea level

as the 'culmination of the Jomon transgression' or simply 'culmination'. Most of the Japanese relative sea-level curves, therefore, do not fit with the curves in which the present sea level is regarded as the highest one since the lower sea level of the last glacial (e.g. Shepard and Curray 1967, Bloom 1970).

The age and height of the culmination of the Jomon transgression, corresponding to the hypsithermal, show regional and local differences reflecting the different tectonic histories of each area, that is, ranging from c.7000 BP to 5000 BP in age and attaining c.30 m at the maximum height.

There are at least two minor regressions after the culmination. A regression of c.3–2000 BP is rather common and an older regression of c.5–4000 BP is also observed in several curves.

4.2   *Age and height of the culmination of the Jomon transgression*

The higher sea level of the culmination of the Jomon transgression leaves abundant geologic and geomorphic evidences on land such as raised sea-caves, fossil shell beds or raised coral reefs. Particularly, well-defined Holocene marine terraces along most of the Japanese Islands are the significant indicator for the higher sea level than the present. South Kanto is one of the best studied areas for the Holocene transgressive history and Holocene terraces, and many studies have been carried out. The former shoreline at the time of the culmination is well recorded on the basis of terrace data as well as molluscan assemblage data, as illustrated in figure 6.13 (e.g. Matsushima 1984) and figure 6.14 (e.g. Matsushima 1984, Ota 1982). The height of the former shoreline differs markedly depending on the tectonic situation from −0.6 m on the downthrow side of the Kozu-Matsuda Fault, an extension of the Sagami Trough at the plate boundary, to 22 m or more on the upthrow side of the fault, or in the area where a landward tilt is known as a result of repeated co-seismic uplift (*e.g.* Yonekura 1975, Matsuda *et al.* 1978, Ota and Yoshikawa 1978). The age of the culmination also varies from c.5000 BP of the subsiding area to c.6800 BP of the rising area.

Figure 6.15 summarizes available data on the age and height of the Holocene marine terrace corresponding to the Jomon transgression. In the area where a number of ^{14}C dates and height data are obtained, only representative ones are plotted in this figure. South Kanto, south Shikoku and south Kyushu as well as Kikai-jima of the Ryukyus are characterized by a high amount of uplift, ranging from c.8 m to 25 m. In these areas, the uplift rate since the last interglacial is also high, attaining 1–1.5 m/1000 yr, with a landward tilt, a peculiar deformation pattern

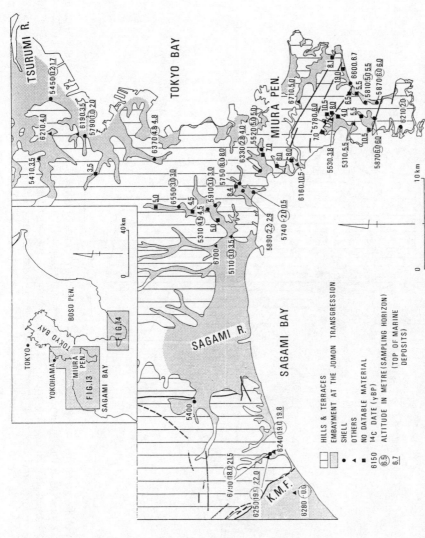

Figure 6.13 A map of the western part of south Kanto to show the altitude and age of the culmination of the Jomon transgression (compiled from Matsushima 1984). The inset map shows the locations of figure 6.13 (= fig. 13) and figure 6.14 (= fig. 14) in relation to Tokyo Bay and Sagami Bay

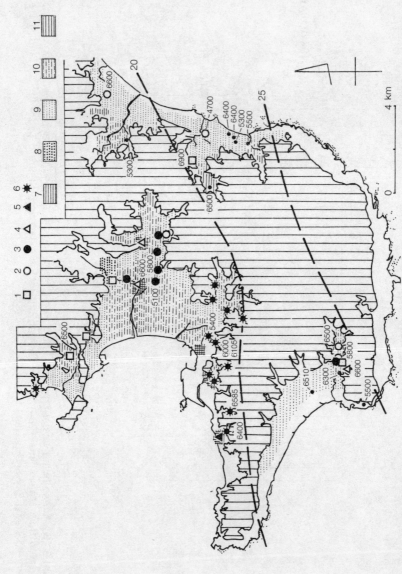

Figure 6.14 A map of the southern part of the Boso peninsula, south Kanto, to show the palaeoenvironment, radiocarbon dates and isobases of the shoreline at the maximum of the Jomon transgression (Matsushima 1984, supplemented by Ota 1982). The location of the Boso Peninsula is shown on figure 6.13. Key: symbols 1–6 are types of molluscan assemblages: 1, ntertidal; 2, sandy embayment; 3, muddy embayment; 4, rocky embayment; 5, rocky open coast; 6, coral. Symbols 7–11 are sediment or land form types: 7, mud; 8, silt; 9, sand; 10, sand and gravel; 11, wave-cut platform. Dashed lines are isobase contours in metres

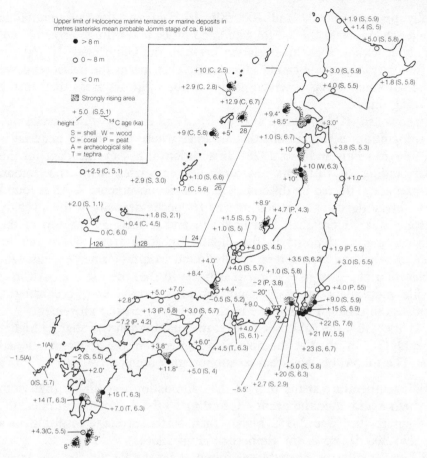

Figure 6.15 A map of the Japanese Islands to show the altitude and age of the former sea level at the culmination of the Jomon transgression

close to the northern limit of the Philippine Sea plate. Along the western coast of northern Honshu the height of the culmination of the former shoreline is also high, reaching a maximum of *c*.11 m. A new plate boundary off western Honshu, proposed by Nakamura (1983) and others may be responsible for such a high uplift rate. On the other hand, the height of the former shoreline at the culmination is *c*.5 m or slightly lower in Hokkaido and some other places. In addition, an apparent subsidence can be seen in the Seto Inland Sea coast and in north Kyushu, where a submergence of early Jomon archaeological sites is known (e.g. Tachibana and Sakaguchi 1971).

In the uplifting area above mentioned, ^{14}C dates of the culmination are usually between *c*.6000 and 7000 BP. In contrast, the culmination is younger than *c*.6000 BP in Hokkaido and other low altitude areas. Thus, roughly speaking, a positive relation between the height and ^{14}C date of the Jomon transgression can be elucidated. That means the palaeosea-level of the culmination has emerged earlier in the uplifting areas than in the subsiding ones.

Atahoya ash (K-Ah), dated at 6300 BP, is an excellent time-marker for the recognition of the culmination in areas where no datable material is available (Machida and Arai 1978). In addition, it has a critical age for the understanding of different environments associated with the Jomon transgression, affected by difference in tectonic movement. K-Ah is found in the fluvial deposits overlying marine Holocene deposits in the strongly uplifting areas (more than 3 m/1000 yr), and it rests on the top of the Holocene marine deposits in the slightly uplifting areas, whilst on the stable or subsiding coasts, it is usually found within marine deposits with an elevation of −2 m to −40 m. It is believed that the use of K-Ah may provide more data on stable and subsiding coasts and, accordingly, elucidate the regional difference in the Holocene crustal movement.

It is likely that the palaeosea-level at the culmination was slightly higher (probably 2–3 m) than at the present, judging from the above-mentioned facts. The following data seem to support this opinion:

1   The temperature at the time of the culmination was higher than both before and after the event. According to the palynological data, the temperature was 2–3°C higher than at the present, resulting in a 200–300 m rise of the timberline (Fuji 1966).
2   Littoral molluscan assemblages found along the Pacific coast of Japan suggest that the water temperature was at most *c*.5°C higher than at the present. This means that the water condition of that time seems to correspond to that of 1–6° lower in latitude (Matsushima and Oshima 1974).

4.3   Sea-level fluctuations after the culmination of the Jomon transgression

As already stated, minor regressions and transgressions after the culmination of the Jomon transgression are recognized in the Japanese sea-level curves (figure 6.12). The younger regression at *c*.3–2000 BP was first pointed out in the Nobi Plain based on the finding of shallow buried channels beneath the Holocene marine deposits (Iseki 1972, Furukawa 1972). Since then, this regression has been reported from 20 areas of Japan, based on the presence of submerged trees or dropping of waterlevel of a coastal lagoon, regardless of the nature of the tectonic setting, implying a probable eustatic origin for this regression, named as the 'Yayoi' regression.

In 1978, another regression at *c*.5–4000 BP and a subsequent transgression, prior to the Yayoi regression, was discovered from several areas such as the southern part of the Boso Peninsula (Yokota 1978), Kikai Island of the northern Ryukyus (Ota *et al*. 1978), the San'in coast of southwestern Honshu (Toyoshima 1978). In the south Boso and Kikai, the Holocene marine terrace or raised coral reef is composed of four well-defined steps, the highest of which was formed in association with the Jomon transgression. The second higher terrace of the Boso Peninsula is composed of a relatively thick marine deposit at *c*.4700–3600 BP, unconformably overlying the older Holocene transgressive marine deposits. The second higher raised coral reef of Kikai, dated at *c*.5000–3800 BP, is the widest among the four Holocene coral reefs and it consisted of a very flat lagoonal surface fringed by higher reef edges. No fossil corals of *c*.5800–5000 BP were found in Kikai Island.

The above mentioned facts suggest that these second higher terraces were formed accompanied by a minor transgression, subsequent to a minor regression, which followed the culmination of the Jomon transgression. This regression is reported from several areas of different tectonic settings and the possibility of an eustatic origin for this regression is suggested. This is called the 'middle-Jomon minor regression' (Ota *et al*. 1982a). However, the age of the regression is somewhat different, slightly older in the uplifting areas such as the Boso and Kikai than in rather stable areas.

A probable sea-level lowering responsible for these two regressions seems to be supported from the following facts which indicate the presence of cold climate corresponding to the age of these regressions.

For the middle-Jomon regression;

1 Warm water species of shallow water molluscan assemblage began to decrease in number *c*.5000 BP and disappeared around 4500 BP in the embayment in south Kanto (Matsushima 1979).

2 The $\delta^{18}O$ values of *Meretrix lamarcki* shells which occur at prehistoric shell middens in south Kanto indicate that the sea water temperature continued to fall since *c*.7000 BP and reached its minimum about 4500 BP (Chinzei *et al*. 1980).

3 Microfossil analysis and $\delta^{18}O$ values in deep-sea cores taken from eastern and southern Kanto indicate the presence of a weak but rather long cold episode between *c*.5000 and 4000 BP (Chinzei *et al*. 1984).

4 A detailed palynological analysis of the Ozegahara peat, northern Kanto, shows the presence of a remarkable cold period of 2267 BC (4217 BP) to 2446 BC (4396 BP) which is called 'mid/late Jomon cold stage' (Sakaguchi 1983).

For the Yayoi regression;

1 Palynological data mainly from the northern coast of central Honshu indicate a cooler climate of 1–2°C less than today between *c*.4000 and 1500 BP (Fuji 1966).
2 A cold stage of *c*.2000 BP is known from the microfossil analysis of deep-sea cores mentioned above (Chinzei *et al.* 1984).
3 The latest cold stage of 865 BC (2815 BP) to 398 BC (2348 BP) is demonstrated by pollen analysis of the Ozegahara peat and this cold stage is reported world wide (Sakaguchi 1983).

Thus the period of two regressions approximately coincides to the cold climate, although the suggested age for each cold period is slightly different, depending on number and spacing of sampling horizons and the accuracy of analysis. Whether these cold periods resulted from minor glacial advances since the culmination of the postglacial transgression or not, is, however, still open to question. An exact amount of sea-level fluctuation is also not yet determined.

Some of the subdivided Holocene marine terraces can be interpreted as a result of repeated co-seismic uplift (e.g. Matsuda *et al.* 1978, Ota *et al.* 1976). Therefore, the formation of the subdivided marine terraces cannot be attributed to sea-level change only, but one which superposed on continuous land uplift; and the possibility of co-seismic uplift should be taken into consideration for the interpretation of complicated relative sea-level curves.

5.0 LATE QUATERNARY VERTICAL DEFORMATION OF THE CRUST AS DEDUCED FROM FORMER SHORELINE DATA

The former shorelines preserved on marine terracs are the best references for detecting the late Quaternary vertical deformation of the Earth's crust in coastal areas. Detailed measurement of former shoreline heights of the last interglacial marine terraces (Shimosueyoshi terrace and its correlatives, *c*.125 000 BP), together with younger or older ones, have been carried out in many localities. The height of the last interglacial terraces ranges from *c*.10 to 200 m above sea level and that of the Holocene terraces (*c.*6000 BP) ranges from *c.*1 to 30 m above sea level. Four types of deformation pattern, which show a particular regional distribution, are recognized on the Japanese coast. Regional differences of deformation patterns are regarded as having resulted from different responses of the area to island arc tectonics. In addition, it is considered that these regional patterns have been maintained throughout the late Quaternary, judged by progressive deformation of shoreline heights (Ota 1975, Ota and Yoshikawa 1978).

5.1 Landward tilting

The Pacific coast of central and southwest Japan is characterised by a noticeable landward tilting related to the co-seismic deformation associated with great earthquakes occurring along the Nankai, Suruga and Sagami troughs at a plate boundary. Tectonic deformation in this region is closely related to the subduction of the Philippine Sea plate beneath the Eurasian plate (Ota 1975, Yonekura 1975, Ota and Yoshikawa 1978, Matsuda *et al.* 1978). In this region, the uplift rate is the largest in Japan reaching up to 1.5 m/1000 yr for the last interglacial terrace (e.g. southern Shikoku and Kikai Island), and 3–4 m/1000 yr for the Holocene terrace (e.g. southern part of the Kanto plain).

One of the characteristic features in these areas is the subdivision of the Holocene marine terrace. For example, Holocene marine terraces in the southern Boso Peninsula located close to the Sagami trough, the northern margin of the Philippine Sea plate, can be subdivided into four levels and they are named Numa I–IV in decending order. The region experienced sudden uplifts of about 2 m and 6 m maximum associated with the 1923 and 1703 earthquakes, respectively. The highest former shoreline of Numa I terrace attains *c.*30 m above sea level. Historical documents indicate that the lowest Numa IV terrace emerged at the time of the 1703 earthquake. The upper three terraces are considered to have emerged due to co-seismic uplifts, as in the case of the 1703 earthquake (Matsuda *et al.* 1978), and they show progressive deformation (Ota 1982). Many radiocarbon dates indicate that great earthquakes resulting in sudden uplift should have occurred at *c.*6200 BP, 4400 BP and 2900 BP (Nakata *et al.* 1979, 1980). Consequently, great earthquakes such as the 1703 one are considered to occur repeatedly with a recurrence interval of about 2800 to 1500 years.

The height distribution of the Holocene marine terraces around Sagami Bay was firstly related to co-seismic deformation associated with great earthquakes such as the 1923 event (Sugimura and Naruse 1954). Later, it is attributed to a combination of the crustal deformations of both the 1923 and 1703 events and local faulting (Yonekura 1975, Matsuda *et al.* 1978), based on the difference in the amount and areal extent of uplift between these two events. Recently, Kayanne and Yoshikawa (1986) re-examined present and emerged coastal landforms on the south-east coast of the Boso Peninsula. They found that emergent geomorphic systems of bench-nip-abrasion platform were developed at four different levels and that each system consisted of 2–4 steps of benches, a nip and an abrasion platform. They concluded that the region experienced intermittently four major uplifts and two or four minor uplifts intercalated between two consecutive major uplifts, which were probably associated with earthquakes similar in magnitude of displacement to the 1703 and 1923 seismic events, respectively.

5.2   Tilting of small blocks

The tilting of small blocks with a length of 10–30 km is observed in the coastal area of central Honshu along the Sea of Japan. The uplift rate of this area attains 1 m/1000 yr for the last interglacial terrace and 2 m/1000 yr for the Holocene terrace (e.g. Sado Island). Co-seismic uplift associated with historical earthquakes and its accumulated character are also recorded in this area (e.g. the Niigata earthquake of 1964 in Awashima Island, Nakamura *et al.* 1964 and the Ogi earthquake of 1802 in Sado Island, Ota *et al.* 1976).

5.3   Warping of small wave-length

The coastal area of northern Honshu along the Sea of Japan, including the western part of Hokkaido, is deformed by a warping with small wave-length of 20–40 km. Such a warping corresponds to the present pattern of major landforms such as mountains, hilly land or plains. Maximum uplift rate of this region is equivalent to the area characterized by tilting of small blocks.

As mentioned above the uplift rate in the coastal area of northern and central Japan along the Sea of Japan is very high, regardless of its deformation pattern. Recently, a new plate boundary between the Eurasian plate and the North American plate (or the North-east Japan microplate) has been proposed off the Sea of Japan coast, on the basis of recent seismic activity and tectonic landforms (e.g. Nakamura 1983). This high rate of uplift may reflect an activity along a possible trench. Tectonic deformation in the eastern part of the Sea of Japan should be re-examined within the framework of the newly proposed plate boundary. Tilting and warping probably resulted from the different response of the area to the stress field, related to different thicknesses of Neogene sedimentary rocks in the two regions.

5.4 Gentle undulation

The Pacific coast of northern Honshu which is parallel to, but rather far away from, the Japan trench, is accompanied by very gentle undulation with a wave-length larger than 100 km. The uplift rate is relatively small, usually less than 0.3–0.4 m/1000 yr.

6.0 DISCUSSIONS AND CONCLUSIONS

1 Marine sequences between the Osaka group, Kinki and the Kazusa group, South Kanto, can be correlated by using dated widespread tephras. Nine major cycles of transgressions and regressions are recognized in both areas since c.700 000 BP of Brunhes-Matuyama geomagnetic boundary. The peaks of the transgressions are c.690 000, 610 000, 500 000, 430 000, 370 000, 290 000, 230 000, 130 000 and 6000 BP respectively.

2 Recently there has been an interesting discussion on the cause of climatic changes in the Quaternary, relating to seasonal and latitudinal distribution of solar radiation, due to variation in relation to the Earth's orbit (e.g. Emiliani 1978). One of the problems in testing this theory is the uncertainty in geological chronology. For the past 150 000 years however, considerably more accurate ages have been determined and it can be said that a chronology has almost been established. For older ages, the chronology is still insufficient. Even for the oxygen isotope ratio curve by Emiliani (1978), there were only three fixed points, i.e. the present, 125 000 BP and 700 000 BP. The curve was drawn by interpolation between these fixed points. Under such circumstances, the tephrochronology of south Kanto, where several dates were determined between 140 000 and 450 000 BP, has great significance. However, radiometric dating of marker-tephras between 300 000 and 400 000 BP, which is missing, must be supplied and important marker-tephras should be dated by various methods for cross-checking.

3 There is a good agreement on the age of high sea levels since the last interglacial, between south Kanto where marine terraces are dated tephrochronologically, and Kikai-jima and Hateruma-jima where U-series

dates are obtained from a series of coral reef terraces. The following common ages for high sea-level periods are obtained from these three areas, that is, *c*.130–125 000 BP, corresponding to the major transgression of the last interglacial, *c*.100 000 BP and 80 000 BP. These ages coincide with the high sea-level stages from New Guinea or Barbados, indicating their glacial eustatic origin. The transgression of *c*.60 000 BP is observed in south Kanto and Kikai-jima, and that of *c*.40 000 BP is only from Kikai-jima, where the uplift rate is estimated at more than 1.5 m/1000 yr. Only three high sea levels are known in Hateruma-jima with an uplift rate of *c*.0.3 m/1000 yr. Thus it can be said that the number of terraces recording previous high sea levels varies locally depending on the uplift rate of the area. It is certain that the actively rising coast is the favourable place for sea-level study.

4   These three areas are the same in terms of the lower sea level at *c*.100 000 BP and 80 000 BP than the present level and the last interglacial of *c*.130–125 000 BP. The height of palaeo-sea levels, however, are different; that of *c*.100 000 BP is −11 m in south Kanto, −10 m in Kikai and −1 m in Hateruma, and that of *c*.80 000 BP is −7 m, −15 m and −2 m, respectively.

Such a different may raise a question on the assumption of a constant rate of uplift which has been used as the fundamental premise for the calculation of palaeosea-level height. Actually, an assumption of constant rate of uplift seems to be probable from some examples in the Japanese study. However, if we compare the uplift rate over a long term (since *c*.130 000 BP) and that of a short term (postglacial), an accelerated uplift can be recognized in many areas (Ota and Yoshikawa 1978), although the Holocene may be too short in time span to discuss the uplift rate. It is important to know an exact age of terraces for discussion of the temporal sequence of uplift rate in any case.

5   Four particular deformation patterns, that is, landward tilting, tilting of small blocks, warping of small wave-length and gentle undulation, are recognised on the Japanese coast, based on former shoreline data. Regional characteristics of deformation patterns are also discussed. Uplift rates vary regionally and locally depending on the different tectonic history of each area. It is highest in the area characterised by the landward tilting associated with great earthquakes, located near the northern margin of the Philippine Sea plate. There, the maximum uplift rate is 1.5 m/1000 yr for the last interglacial and 4 m/1000 yr for the Holocene. Co-seismic uplift also has resulted in the formation of subdivided Holocene marine terraces.

6   The height of low sea level between transgressions is more difficult

to determine, except for that of the low sea level of the last glacial at *c.*20 000 BP, when the Japanese Islands were connected with the Asian continent by land-bridges. Even in this case, there is an argument about the exact height of the palaeo-sea-level. Further studies on submarine topography are both necessary and indispensable.

7   An examination of Holocene relative sea-level curves reveals that most of the former shoreline at the culmination of the Jomon transgression was higher than at the present by at least 2–3 m. It is very likely that the sea level of that time was slightly higher than at the present, although a possibility of tectonic uplift may still remain for the interpretation of this phenomenon.

8   Two minor regressions after the culmination of the Jomon transgression are recognized, that is the middle-Jomon regression at *c.*5–4000 BP and Yayoi regression at *c.*3–2000 BP. The amount of these regressions is uncertain, but probably very small. These regressions correspond to the cold climate periods deduced from analysis of molluscan assemblages, micro-fossils and palynological data as well as $\delta^{18}O$ values. However, a relation between the cold climate and glacial advance is not known.

9   Concerning a discussion of sea-level change in a short time span like the Holocene, an exact determination of the date of the transgression and of the present height of former sea level are necessary. The former sea level is recognized by the shoreline angle at the inner edge of terraces in rocky coasts or as the upper limit of marine deposits in depositional areas such as embayments. However, a problem remains about the kind of flat marine surface which really represents a former mean sea level on an open coast. Similarly, in depositional environments, it is important to investigate if the marine limit of deposits determined by palaeontological analysis and facies analysis represents a mean sea level, or a level lower than that.

Revised typescript received 1986, April.

REFERENCES

 * in Japanese
** in Japanese with English abstract

Arai, F. 1972: Identification of particular tephras by means of refractive indices of orthopyroxenes and hornblendes – a fundamental study of tephrochronology. *Quat. Res. Japan*, 11, 254–69.**
Arai, F., Oba, T., Kitazato, H., Horibe, S. and Machida, H. 1981: Late Quaternary tephrochronology and palaeo-oceanography of the sediments of the Japan Sea. *Quat. Res. Japan*, 20, 209–30.**

Bloom, A. L. 1970: Holocene submergence in Micronesia as the standard for eustatic sea-level changes. *Quaternaria*, 12, 145–54.

Bloom, A. L., Broecker, W. S., Chappell, J. M. A., Matthews, R. K. and Mesolella, K. J. 1974: Quaternary sea level fluctuations on a tectonic coast: new ^{230}Th/^{234}U dates from the Huon Peninsula, New Guinea. *Quat. Res.*, 4, 185–205.

Broecker, W. S., Thurber, D. L., Goddard, J., Teh-Lung Ku, Matthews, R. K. and Mesolella, K. J. 1968: Milankovitch hypothesis supported by precise dating of coral reefs and deep-sea sediments. *Science*, 159, 297–300.

Chappell, J. 1974: Geology of coral terraces, Huon Peninsula, New Guinea: a study of Quaternary tectonic movements and sea-level changes. *Geol. Soc. Am. Bull.*, 85, 553–70.

Chida, N., Matsumoto, H. and Obara, S. 1984: Recent Alluvial deposit and Holocene sea-level change on Rikuzentakata Coastal Plain, Northeast Japan. *Ann. Tohoku Geogr. Assoc.*, 36, 232–9.**

Chinzei, K., Oba, T., Koike, Y., Matsushima, Y. and Kitazato, H. 1980: In N. Egami (ed.), *Researches on archeological sites, cultural properties and so on by natural scientific methods*, Tokyo: Report to the Ministry of Education, Science and Culture, 103–17.*

Chinzei, K., Okada, H., Oda, M., Oba, T., Kitazato, H., Koizumi, I., Sakai, T., Tanimura, Y., Fujioka, K. and Matsushima, Y. 1984: In N. Watanabe (ed.), *Comprehensive report of scientific researches on preservation of cultural properties.* Kyoto: Doho-Sha, 103–17.*

Dreimanis, A. and Karrow, P. F. 1972: Glacial history of the Great Lakes – St. Lawrence region, the classification of the Wisconsin (an) stage and its correlatives. *Intern. Geol. Congr. 24th Sess.* Montreal, sec. 12, 5–15.

Dreimanis, A. and Raukas, A. 1975: Did Middle Wisconsin, Middle Weichselian, and their equivalents represent an interglacial or an interstadial complex in the Northern Hemisphere. In R. P. Suggate and M. M. Cresswell (eds), *Quaternary studies*, The Royal Society of New Zealand, Bulletin 13, 109–20.

Emiliani, C. 1978: The cause of the ice ages. *Earth, Planet. Sci. Lett.*, 37, 349–59.

Fuji, N. 1966: Climatic changes of Postglacial Age in Japan. *Quat. Res. Japan*, 5, 149–56.**

Fujii, S. and Fuji, N. 1981: Sea-level curve in Hokuriku district during the last 20,000 years. In Ota *et al.* (eds.) 1981, *Atlas of Holocene sea level records in Japan*, 43–4.

Furukawa, H. 1972: Alluvial deposits of the Nohbi Plain, Central Japan. *Mem. Geol. Soc. Japan*, 7, 39–59.**

Iseki, H. 1972: Changes on the deltaic plains in Japan. *Quat. Res. Japan*, 11, 117–23.**

Iseki, H. and Moriyama, A. 1981: Sea-level changes in the Nōbi Plain and adjacent areas. In Ota *et al.* 1981, 67–8.

James, N. P., Mountjoy, E. W. and Omura, A. 1971: An early Wisconsin reef terrace at Barbados, West Indies and its climatic implications. *Geol. Soc. Am. Bull.*, 82, 2011–18.

Kayanne, H. and Yoshikawa, T. 1986: Comparative study between present and emerged erosional land forms on the southeast coast of Boso Peninsula, Central Japan. *Geogr. Rev. Japan*, A.59, 18–36.★★

Kaizuka, S., Naruse, Y. and Matsuda, I. 1977: Recent formations and their basal topography in and around Tokyo Bay, Central Japan. *Quat. Res.*, 8 32–50.

Koaze, H., Sugihara, S., Shimizu, F., Utsunomiya, Y., Iwata, S. and Okazawa, S. 1974: Geomorphological study of Mt. Shirouma, Central Japan. *Sundai-Shigaku*, 35, 1–86.★

Konishi, K., Omura, A. and Nakamichi, O. (1974): Radiometric coral ages and sea-level records from the late Quaternary reef complexes of the Ryukyu Islands. *Proc. 2nd Intern. Coral Reef Sympo.* 595–613.

Machida, H. 1975: Pleistocene sea level of South Kanto, Japan, analysed by tephrochronology. In R. P. Suggate and M. M. Cresswell (eds.), *Quaternary Studies*, The Royal Society of New Zealand Bulletin, 13, 215–22.

Machida, H. and Arai, F. 1978: Akahoya ash – a Holocene widespread tephra erupted from the Kikai Caldera, South Kyushu, Japan. *Quat. Res. Japan*, 17, 143–63.★★

Machida, H. and Arai, F. 1983: Extensive ash falls in and around the Sea of Japan from large late Quaternary eruptions. *J. Volcanol. Geotherm. Res.*, 18, 151–64.

Machida, H. and Suzuki, M. 1971: A chronology of the late Quaternary period as estimated by fission-track dating. *Kagaku*, 41, 263–70.★

Machida, H., Arai, F. and Sugihara, S. 1980: Tephrochronological study on the middle Pleistocene deposits in the Kanto and Kinki districts, Japan. *Quat. Res. Japan*, 19, 233–61.★★

Maeda, Y. 1976: The sea level changes of Osaka Bay from 12 000 BP to 6000 BP – environmental changes in the Osaka Bay area during the Holocene (Part I). *J. Geosci., Osaka City Univ.*, 20, 43–59.

Maeda, Y., Yamashita, K., Matsushima, Y. and Watanabe, M. 1983: Marine transgression over Mazukari shell mound on the Chita Peninsula, Aichi Prefecture, Central Japan. *Quat. Res. Japan*, 22, 213–22.★★

Matsuda, T., Ota, Y., Ando, M. and Yonekura, N. 1978: Fault mechanism and recurrence time of major earthquakes in Southern Kanto district, Japan, as deduced from coastal terrace data. *Geol. Soc. Am. Bull.*, 89, 1610–18.

Matsushima, Y. 1979: Littoral molluscan assemblages during the post-glacial Jomon transgression in the Southern Kanto, Japan. *Quat. Res. Japan*, 17, 243–65.★★

Matsushima, Y. 1984: Shallow marine molluscan assemblages of Postglacial Period in the Japanese Islands – its historical and geographical changes induced by the environmental changes. *Bull. Kanagawa Prefectural Museum*, 15, 37–109.★★

Matsushima, Y. and Oshima, K. 1974: Littoral molluscan fauna of the Holocene climatic Optimum (5000–6000 BP) in Japan. *Quat. Res. Japan*, 13, 135–59.★★

Mogi, A. 1981: Geomorphological evolution of continental shelves of Tsushima

Strait with reference to the Tsushima land bridge. *Quat. Res. Japan*, 20, 243–56.**

Moriwaki, H. 1978: Problems concerning Holocene sea-level changes. *Geogr. Rep. Tokyo Metropol. Univ.*, 13, 49–64.

Moriwaki, H. 1979: The Landform evolution of the Kujukuri Coastal Plain, Central Japan. *Quat. Res. Japan*, 18, 1–16.**

Nakamura, K. 1983: Possible nascent trench along the eastern Japan Sea as the convergent boundary between Eurasian and North American Plates. *Bull. Earthq. Res. Inst.*, 58, 207–42.**

Nakamura, K., Kasahara, K. and Matsuda, T. 1964: Tilting and uplift of an island, Awashima, near the epicenter of the Niigata earthquake in 1964. *Jour. Geodetic. Soc. Japan* 10, 172–179.

Nakata, T., Takahashi, T. and Koba, M. 1978: Holocene emerged coral reefs and sea-level changes in the Ryukyu Islands. *Geogr. Rev. Japan*, 51, 87–108.**

Nakata, T., Koba, M., Jo, W., Imaizumi, T., Matsumoto, H. and Suganuma, T. 1979: Holocene marine terraces and seismic crustal movement. *Sei. Rep. Tohoku Univ. 7th Ser. (Geogr.)*, 29, 195–204.

Nakata, T., Koba, M., Imaizumi, T., Jo, W. R., Matsumoto, H. and Suganuma, T. 1980: Holocene marine terraces and seismic crustal movements in the southern part of Boso Peninsula, Kanto, Japan. *Geogr. Rev. Japan*, 53, 29–44.**

Naruse, Y. and Ota, Y. 1984: Sea-level changes in the Quaternary in Japan. In S. Horie, (ed.), *Lake Biwa*, Otsu, Japan: Kyoto University, 461–73.

Okumura, K. and Sangawa, A. 1984: Age and distributon of Toya pyroclastic flow. *Bull. Volcanol. Soc. Japan*, 29, 338.*

Omoto, K. 1979: Holocene sea-level change: a critical review. *Sci. Rep. Tohoku Univ. 7th Ser. (Geogr.)*, 29, 205–22.

Omura, A. 1984: Uranium-series age of the Rinkin limestone on Hateruma Island, southwestern Ryukyus. *Trans. Proc. Palaeont. Soc. Japan, N. S.*, 135, 415–26.

Ono, Y. and Hirakawa, K. 1975: Geological significance of the discovery of the Eniwa-a pumice-fall deposits in the Hidaka Range, Hokkaido. *J. Geol. Soc. Japan*, 81, 333–4.*

Ota, Y. 1975: Late Quaternary vertical movement in Japan estimated from deformed shorelines. In R. P. Suggate and M. M. Creswell (eds.), *Quaternary Studies*, The Royal Society of New Zealand, Bulletin 13, 231–40.

Ota, Y. 1982: Holocene marine terraces of uplifting areas in Japan. In D. J. Colquhoun (ed.), *Holocene sea level fluctuations, magnitude and causes*, Columbia, SC: University of South Carolina, 118–34.

Ota, Y. and Hori, N. 1980: Late Quaternary tectonic movement of the Ryukyu Islands, Japan. *Quat. Res. Japan*, 18, 221–40.**

Ota, Y., Hori, N. and Omura, A. 1982b: Age and deformation of marine terraces of Hateruma Island, Ryukyu Islands, Southwest Japan. *Abstr. XI INQUA Congress, Moscow* 2, 232.

Ota, Y., Machida, H., Hori, N., Konishi, K. and Omura, A. 1978: Holocene raised coral reefs of Kikai-jima (Ryukyu Islands) – An approach to Holocene sea level study. *Geogr. Rev. Japan*, 51, 109–30.★★

Ota, Y., Matsuda, T. and Naganuma, K. 1976: Tilted marine terraces of the Ogi Peninsula, Sato Island, Central Japan, related to the Ogi Earthquake of 1802. *Zishin, II*, 29, 55–70.★★

Ota, Y., Matsushima, Y. and Moriwaki, H. (eds.) 1981: *Atlas of Holocene sea-level records in Japan*. Yokohama: Japanese working group of IGCP Project 61.

Ota, Y., Matsushima, Y. and Moriwaki, H. 1982a: Notes on the Holocene sea-level study in Japan on the basis of *Atlas of Holocene Sea-level Records in Japan*. *Quat. Res. Japan*, 21, 133–43.★★

Ota, Y. and Yoshikawa, T. 1978: Regional characteristics and their geodynamic implications of late Quaternary tectonic movement deduced from deformed former shorelines in Japan. *J. Phys. Earth Suppl.*, 26, s379–89.

Porter, S. C., Stuiver, M. and Yang, I. C. 1977: Chronology of Hawaiian glaciations. *Science*, 195, 61–3.

Sakaguchi, Y. 1978: Climatic changes in Central Japan since 38,400 BP – viewed from palynological study on Ozegahara deposits. *Bull. Dept. Geogr. Univ. Tokyo*, 10, 1–10.

Sakaguchi, Y. 1983: Warm and cold stages in the past 7600 Years in Japan and their global correlation – Especially on climatic impacts to the global sea-level changes and the ancient Japanese history. *Bull. Dept. Geogr. Univ. Tokyo* 15, 1–31.

Sato, T. and Mogi, A. 1982: Sea-level change in the Japan Sea deduced from submarine terraces and buried shelf channels. *Quat. Res. Japan*, 21, 203–10.★★

Shepard, F. P. and Curray, J. R. 1967: Carbon-14 determination of sea level changes in stable areas. In M. Sears (ed.), *Progress in Oceanography*, 4, 283–91. Oxford: Pergamon Press.

Suggate, R. P. 1974: When did the last interglacial end? *Quat. Res.*, 4, 246–52.

Suggate, R. P. and Moar, N. T. 1970: Revision of the chronology of the Late Otira Glacial. *N. Z. J. Geol. Geophys.*, 13, 742–6.

Sugimura, A. and Naruse, Y. 1954: Changes in sea level, seismic upheavals, and coastal terraces in the southern Kantô region, Japan (I). *Japan. Jour. Geol. Geogr.*, 24, 101–13.

Tachibana, K. and Sakaguchi, K. 1971: Age of beachrock containing the Jômon pottery in the Gotô Islands – Beachrock of the Gotô Island (Part 2). *Quat. Res. Japan*, 10, 54–9.★★

Tohoku Nosei-kyoku (Regional Agricultural Administration Office) 1979: *Report on the earth surface submergence at Haramachi district, Fukushima prefecture, north Japan*.★

Toyoshima, Y. 1978: Postglacial sea level change along San'in district, Japan. *Geogr. Rev. Japan*, 51, 147–57.★★

Tsuji, S., Minaki, M. and Osawa, S. 1984: Palaeobotany and palaeoenvironment of the late Pleistocene in the Sagami Region, Central Japan. *Quat. Res. Japan*, 22, 279–96.★★

Tsukada, M. 1983: Vegetation and climate during the last glacial maximum in Japan. *Quat. Res.*, 19, 212–35.

Umitsu, M. 1979: Geomorphological evolution of the Noki Plain, Central Japan since the latest Pleistocene. *Geogr. Rev. Japan*, 52, 199–208.★★

Veeh, H. H. 1966: ^{230}Th/^{238}U and ^{234}U/^{238}U ages of Pleistocene high sea-level stand. *J. Geophys. Res.*, 71, 14.

Veeh, H. H. and Chappell, J. 1970: Astronomical theory of climatic change: support from New Guinea, *Sci.* 167, 862–5.

Yasuda, Y. 1982: Pollen analytical study of the sediment from the Lake Mikata in Fukui Prefecture, Central Japan – Especially on the fluctuation of precipitation since the Last Glacial Age on the side of Sea of Japan. *Quat. Res. Japan*, 21, 255–71.★★

Yokota, K. 1978: Holocene coastal terraces on the southeast coast of the Boso Peninsula. *Geogr. Rev. Japan*, 51, 349–64.★★

Yonekura, N. 1975: Quaternary tectonic movements in the Outer Arc of southwest Japan with special reference to seismic crustal deformations. *Bull. Dept. Geogr. Univ. Tokyo*, 7, 19–71.

7

Quaternary sea-level studies in the Eastern United States of America: a methodological perspective

Thomas M. Cronin

1.0 INTRODUCTION

This paper is a highly selective history of sea-level studies of the Eastern United States of America, a region which includes glacio-isostatically uplifted postglacial and glacial deposits in the north-east, emerged interglacial marine deposits in the Atlantic Coastal Plain, and carbonate reefs in Florida. Figure 7.1 shows the region discussed in this paper and lists localities mentioned in the text. No single regional sea-level curve adequately portrays the diversity of local factors contributing to the observed record and a review of the entire history of study would be too extensive for this volume. Consequently, this paper focuses on the methodology for determining and dating the postglacial sea-level curve and the stratigraphic record of the last interglacial period in the Eastern United States of America. Two themes pervade the sea-level literature of this region. First, the need to extract eustatic changes in ocean level from isostatic and tectonic movements of the land has always clouded the interpretation of observed sea-level patterns. Second, the reliability of sea-level indicators, particularly various biological lines of evidence, has been vigorously researched in Eastern USA.

2.0 SEA-LEVEL CHANGES SINCE THE LATE WISCONSIN GLACIAL MAXIMUM

2.1 Holocene sea-level changes

The Eastern USA sea-level record was at the heart of early disputes about the shape of the Holocene sea-level curve. Did global sea level oscillate

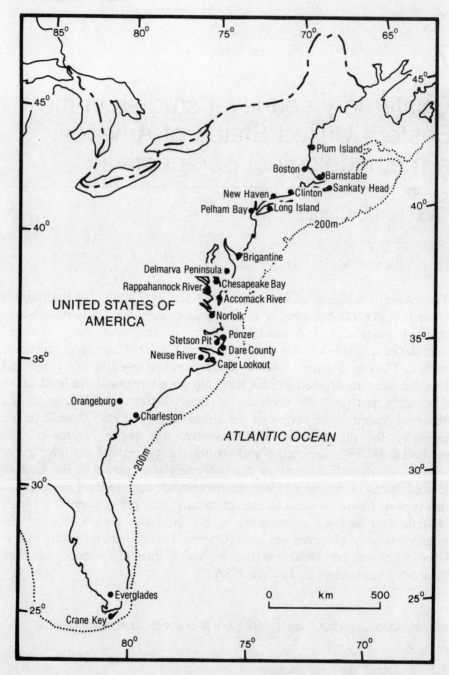

Figure 7.1   A map of the eastern seaboard of the United States of America, showing the localities mentioned in the text

frequently and rise above its present level by up to several metres since 5000 years ago (BP) (Fairbridge 1961) or did it rise gradually, without oscillation, and without exceeding its present level (Shepard 1963). Richards (1971), in a useful summary of early studies, suggested the Fairbridge and Shepard curves differed because the former was based on data from Europe, South America and Australia and the latter from North America. While generally true, Fairbridge (1961) cited examples of radiocarbon dated material from many eastern North America locations to support his sea level hypothesis.

Both the Shepard and Fairbridge curves were constructed relatively soon after radiocarbon dating was applied to sea-level studies. During the 1960s, many studies of the eastern USA were published and discussed in terms of the rate of eustatic sea level rise and the contribution of eustatic, tectonic and isostatic factors to the local record of submergence. In one paper on post-glacial sea levels near New Haven, Connecticut, Upson *et al.* (1964, p. 132) concluded: 'The individual contributions of eustatic rise of sea-level and subsidence of the land which gave the relative change of sea level observed at New Haven can not be separated by the data presented in this paper.' This statement suggests a cautionary tone that has characterized most studies since.

One key paper differed in approach from the typical local sea-level curve papers and, in some ways, led the way to a new generation of sea-level studies. Bloom (1967) gave a critical assessment of five published eastern US submergence curves: Plum Island, Massachusetts; Barnstable, Massachusetts; Brigantine, New Jersey; Clinton, Connecticut; and the Florida Everglades. In proposing the use of sea-level records to test the theory of isostasy, Bloom emphasized the significance of the transfer of mass between oceans and glaciated regions during glacial-interglacial cycles. Bloom (1967, p. 1491) found that 'The postglacial submergence histories of five eastern United States coastal sites support the hypothesis that the load of water added to the continental margins by the post-glacial rise of sea level has been sufficient to isostatically deform coastal areas in proportion to the average depth of water in the vicinity. . . . It is therefore reasonable to hypothesize that the entire ocean floor deforms in response to changes of sea level of the magnitude of the glacial-interglacial cycle.'

The apparent influence on future research of this simple but convincing explanation of seemingly discrepant sea-level curves was significant in two separate areas. Bloom specifically identified the Pleistocene sea-level record of oceanic islands as a primary means of testing the theory of isostasy: 'Thus, oceanic islands, like a dipstick thrust into the ocean floor, record only the true magnitude of glacially controlled sea-level changes' (Bloom 1967, p. 1490). Here in this early study of eastern USA post-glacial sea levels is an important statement on the most enduring model of Pleistocene eustatic sea-level changes – that developed using Bloom's dipstick approach on emerged reef tracts on Barbados (Broecker *et al.* 1968, Matthews 1973) and New Guinea (Bloom *et al.* 1974).

The second area of research that Bloom's 1967 paper foreshadowed was the quantitative analysis of global sea level through numerical models of the Earth's response to shifts in mass and its effect on observed sea-level records. Most notable was the paper by Clark *et al.* (1978) who concluded: 'There are no "stable" regions where eustatic sea level can be measured, because deglaciation and the addition of water to the ocean basins deform the earth and change the observer's point of reference.' (p. 286). By comparing sea-level records predicted by their numerical model to observed records of submergence, an overall close agreement was found, leading to the conclusion that no net change in ocean volume occurred during the last 5000 years. Clark *et al.* (1978) designated the collapsing forebulge region of the eastern United States as a discrete area and found that their predicted submergence exceeded observed submergence by a factor of two. They suggested the lithosphere may have played a role in causing this difference.

Newman *et al.* (1980) collated extensive sea level, tide gauge and levelling data from the eastern United States and suggested that glacio-isostatic rebound alone does not account for the observed patterns. They offered several mechanisms to account for the data including hydro-isostasy, peripheral bulge movements, geosynclinal subsidence, and sediment loading. Newman *et al.* (1981) analyzed several thousand radiocarbon dates and concluded that the relation of ice volume to sea level remains a riddle because the Holocene geoid has been very unstable and that mass redistribution within the earth has changed during the past 12 000 years.

Where do we stand today with respect to the eastern USA Holocene sea level record? In general, most east coast empirical data still fit a generalized Shepard curve better than the oscillating curve of Fairbridge. Glacio-eustasy explains most coastal submergence and the hypothesis that hydro-isostatic movement has altered the eustatic picture still remains a plausible explanation for many aspects of local sea-level curves. However, recent studies show that the evidence for the middle to late Holocene record is sometimes contradictory. Colquhoun *et al.* (1981) presented archaeological evidence from the south-eastern USA and stated that 'sea level generally rose in the manner of the Shepard curve, but through a series of fluctuations similar to the Fairbridge curve.' (p. 147). The frequency of the oscillations is about 400 to 500 years and they attribute them to a glacio-eustatic mechanism. Rampino and Sanders (1981a) showed that the development of coastal marshes during the Holocene submergence in the north-eastern US has been episodic. They proposed that the initiation of marsh growth coincides with slowing in the rate of submergence and cite evidence from radiocarbon dates that this happened about 4700, 5600, 6600, 7700, 8200 and 8600 BP. They postulated a glacio-eustatic mechanism to account for these oscillations and suggest the controlling climatic cycles may reflect an astronomical cycle having an approximate 1000 year cycle. Some authors working in the eastern United States do not even attempt to decouple eustatic, glacio-eustatic and hydro-isostatic components of the local record (Rampino and Sanders 1980). We may be just beginning to understand the Holocene record of this area.

2.2 Criteria for identifying ancient sea level

The east coast has also been the site of critical assessment of criteria used to identify a former sea level. Two lines of evidence are noteworthy: basal peats and *in situ* molluscs, of which the latter are discussed in the next section. Many authors have discussed the significance of the origin of peats for sea level studies (eg Upson *et al.* 1964). Redfield and Rubin (1962) were among the first to recognize the importance of salt marsh peat accretion in sea level studies. They pointed out that the vertical range of *Spartina alterniflora* is between high marsh and just below mean sea level, a total of about 2 metres in most eastern USA areas and suggested that vertical accretion during the high marsh stage is controlled by sea level rise. The classic paper by Kaye and Barghoorn (1964) on the autocompaction of peat provided quantitative data on peat formation and described the importance of radiocarbon dating of rootlet contamination and wood intrusion during compaction. Through an understanding of autocompaction, a process known in engineering and soil mechanics, Kaye and Barghoorn demonstrated that only salt-marsh peats taken from the basal part of a section should be dated and used as criteria for a former sea level. They applied the results to construct a late Holocene relative sea-level record from the Boston area showing sea level at $c. -21$ m about 10 000 BP and $c. -0.6$ m at 3000 BP. The importance of understanding the relationship between peat formation, salt-marsh growth and sea-level change continues to play an important role in many east coast studies (Rampino and Sanders 1981a, Belknap and Kraft 1977, Field *et al.* 1979).

2.0   Sea level during the Late Wisconsin glacial maximum

The position of sea level during the Late Wisconsin glacial maximum is an elusive and still unknown datum and has received considerable attention in the Eastern USA. Molluscs preserved in late Pleistocene sediments on the Atlantic Continental Shelf have been radiocarbon dated and used by various authors to reconstruct sea-level history during early postglacial times between 18 000 and 10 000 BP (see Emery and Merrill 1979 and references therein). However, the reliability of certain molluscs as indicators of former shoreline positions has been questioned on two accounts (MacIntyre *et al.* 1978, 1979). First, some species (*Placopecten magellanicus* and *Mesoderma artactum*) are considered unreliable palaeo-depth indicators, having a wider range of depth habitats than just the shore zone. Second, oyster shells can undergo landward transport by sediment action on the continental shelf so that dated shells do not always represent *in situ* material. Emery and Merrill (1979) contend that sea level about 15 000 BP was between −100 and −130 metres depth whereas MacIntyre *et al.* (1979) believe these estimates are based on unreliable data and that sea level between 16 000 and 12 000 BP was higher.

The resolution of questions about the reliability of dated shells on the continental shelf is significant for obtaining a more accurate estimate of sea level during the glacial maximum and rates of sea-level rise during the initial phases of deglaciation. It is noteworthy that this debate centred on the biologic criteria and the taphonomy of fossil assemblages used to identify sea-level positions. The geochronology, that is, the accuracy of the dating method itself, has been of less concern than the reliability of the datable material as a sea-level indicator. This contrasts with the continuing debate about mid-Wisconsin radiocarbon dates purportedly documenting a 30 000 BP marine high stand (Bloom 1983) and uranium series and amino acid dating of interglacial sea levels (see below) where the precision of the dating method as a geochronologic tool has highlighted discussions about the east coast sea level record.

Recently, Bloom (1983, p. 219) stated: 'Perhaps the current range of estimates of 120±60 m for the late Wisconsin sea-level change is an accurate expression of the extreme complexity of a variable that earth scientists previously and naively expected to be unique and easily measured.' Conflicting data from the Eastern USA have contributed to recognizing the difficulty in studying submerged material in sea-level studies. Even more important is that the lesson learned from the postglacial record be applied to the rest of the Pleistocene: observed sea-level records from different regions should not match one another because of crustal movements and consequently correlation by elevation is unwarranted.

It is almost axiomatic in Quaternary studies that global sea level exceeded its present level only once during the last interglacial interval, about 125 000 BP. This model was developed from studies of many reef tracts, including those from Barbados and New Guinea that were dated by the uranium series method, and from the oxygen-isotope record of deep-sea cores. Originally, one major high stand was recognized about 120 000 BP. Then Broecker (1966) placed increasing emphasis on a second, less prominent, high stand about 80 000 BP. Broecker *et al.* (1968) added the 103 000 BP high stand from Barbados data and suggested that the 103 000 and 80 000 BP high stands were about 13 metres below present day sea level, while the 120 000 BP high stand was assumed to be +6 metres. Recent reviews have concluded that there were probably four high stands during the last interglacial (Moore 1982, Stearns 1984), about 135 000, 120 000, 105 000 and 80 000 BP, although all did not necessarily reach present sea level.

Sea-level data from Eastern USA late Pleistocene deposits have frequently been studied in light of these eustatic models. Given the uncertainty about isostatic and tectonic crustal movements during the past 140 000 years, the east coast record of the last interglacial is not so anomalous in light of the New Guinea and Barbados records. It is, however, characterized by a complex of minor sea-level events that took place near or slightly below present sea level during an interglacial between about 140 000 and 70 000 yr BP. Absolute dating and correlation methods in the east coast interglacial sea-level studies will be reviewed. Selected regional stratigraphic studies and associated climatologic and palaeontologic lines of evidence which, independent of radiometric dating, document multiple sea-level and palaeoclimatic changes during the last major interglacial will also be discussed.

3.1 Absolute age and correlation methods

Critics of the Eastern USA as a source of valid sea-level data have focused on two issues – the reliability of dating techniques (uranium series dates and amino acid racemization) and whether or not the stratigraphic record supports evidence from radiometric-dating for multiple high stands. This section emphasizes correlation methods and absolute dating whereas the next section focuses on physical stratigraphy. Cronin *et al.* (1981) outlined the late Pleistocene climatic and sea-level record for the Eastern USA and provided new uranium series dates on corals for exposed interglacial deposits. With respect to the results given in that paper, Stearns (1984, p. 61) stated: 'Thus, [230]Th ages alone, from two separate areas, provide neither a firm basis for correlation with a standard sea-level history nor support for the suggestion that sea level was at the same elevation at three different times.' In that paper, it was not intended to suggest that a single sea-level record characterized the entire region for it is well-known that different parts of the coast have unique tectonic and isostatic histories. These topics were touched upon in the paper and were amplified in Cronin (1981). Nor did the paper imply that correlations should be made on the basis of uranium-series dates alone. Indeed, six references of that paper cited numerous studies of the local and regional stratigraphic framework into which the palaeontologic and uranium-series data fit. In addition, the maximum age of many deposits can be constrained by palaeontologic or palaeomagnetic data (Cronin *et al.* 1984). Cronin *et al.* (1981) clearly stated that sea-level data represented a relative sea-level record and that crustal movements probably affected it to an unknown extent. The major emphasis was on the combined continental (pollen) and marine (ostracods) palaeoclimatic signal in late Pleistocene deposits. Direct evidence for palaeoclimatic conditions is rarely obtained in sea-level studies despite its relevance to the interpretation of sea-level history (Cronin 1983).

Concern that Coastal Plain corals yield incorrect ages because they are open geochemical systems are so far unsubstantiated, although further interlaboratory analysis is warranted to determine the limits of the technique (Ku 1982). Szabo (1985) recently published a summary of uranium-series data from Coastal Plain corals. With respect to the cluster of ages around 75 000 BP from the south-eastern Virginia and eastern North Carolina area, Szabo (1985) has performed repeated analyses, including analysis of [231]Pa (see regional stratigraphy below). It is clear that most corals meet the geochemical criteria necessary to yield reliable age estimates. Not only are most corals geochemically 'clean', but their taphonomy supports their use in regional correlations. They usually are associated with highly fossiliferous molluscan beds and are very common in most sections where they are present. They are most abundant in *Mercenaria*-rich sands in the Norfolk Formation in south-eastern Virginia, can be collected *in situ* from the outcrop, and have been observed attached to shells of articulated *Mercenaria* preserved in living position. In many cases, the corals were part of the life assemblage and reworking of specimens can be ruled out.

Thus the patchy geographic distribution of datable corals should not detract from their significance in providing one means of estimating the age of lithostratigraphic units of demonstrable marine origin. Both uranium ages (Cronin *et al.* 1981, Szabo 1985) and physical stratigraphic evidence (see below) indicate that marine deposits younger than isotope substage 5e provide evidence for relative high stands often containing evidence for cool climatic conditions (see below).

Besides controversy over absolute age, distinct methodological approaches have also been an integral part of correlating east coast Quaternary deposits and interpretations for sea-level history. Ward (1985) attempted to correlate shorelines from South Carolina with Gippsland and south-east Queensland, Australia, Morocco and New Zealand by means of their elevation above sea level. Ward strongly criticized Eastern USA studies that applied uranium-series dating of corals from coastal outcrops to problems of late Pleistocene correlation. His paper exemplifies a return to the geomorphic approach to correlation. The method of correlation by shoreline elevation has had a long and controversial history in the Atlantic Coastal Plain (Oaks and DuBar 1974, Cronin 1981, for reviews). Its major proponent, C. W. Cooke (1930), tried to correlate over the entire Coastal Plain and even to other continents on the basis of elevation. He assumed that glacio-eustasy was the most important mechanism accounting for the observed record and that tectonic movements did not affect the record. Among the many problems with this approach, the premise that only a geomorphic expression of a shoreline is relevant in sea-level studies is unwarranted. This notion is antiquated by the fact that since no coasts are stable, it is less important to identify the precise position of an ancient shoreline – for that shoreline has surely been uplifted, has subsided or both. Rather, it is more important to establish that a marine transgression or regression occurred using any kind of data – sedimentologic, geomorphic or biologic. Sea-level studies that do not use palaeo-shorelines, but which emphasize palaeoenvironmental reconstructions based on fossil assemblages, sedimentologic and geophysical criteria are standard practice in geology – witness the success of the 'Vail model' for Phanerozoic onlap-offlap cycles (Payton 1977) and its implications for global sea level.

The geomorphic approach, coupled with assumed correlations to deep-sea isotope stage age estimates, also assumes that the deep-sea cores always contain a more complete record of late Pleistocene interglacial periods and ignores the fact that some emerged stratigraphic sequences on continental and island margins, particularly thick Quaternary sections in regions of rapid sedimentation, might actually contain more information of the fine scale details of interglacials, although the record may require more integrated approaches to unravel (Chappell 1981, Cronin 1983).

Finally, should one 'date' coastal shorelines by accepting the ages of deep sea core warm intervals (as does Ward, 1985) rather than actual radiometric and palaeontologic data from associated marine deposits? For two reasons, I think not. First, the ages of deep-sea isotope stages were themselves originally derived from uranium-series dates on deep sea carbonate sediments (Rosholt *et al.* 1961, Ku and Broecker 1966, Broecker *et al.* 1968). Broecker and Van Donk (1970) gave an excellent discussion of the history of these early studies in which they postulated correlations between Emiliani's ^{18}O stages and uranium series-dated reefs on Barbados based on results from Caribbean cores. At the time of those early studies, a serious discrepancy existed between the dates of Rosholt *et al.* (1961) and Rona and Emiliani (1969) and those of Broecker *et al.* (1968) for the ages of interglacials. The discrepancy was resolved by Broecker and Ku (1969) in part because they recalibrated the $^{230}Th/^{231}Pa$ ratios and they also noted the correspondence of the ages of uplifted Barbados reefs with warm intervals in the cores (see Broecker and Ku 1969). The dating of deep-sea isotope stages has had, therefore, a complex history, closely tied to dating of emerged corals. Should the accuracy of absolute age determinations of deep sea warm intervals made on deep sea sediments be greater than those made on emerged marine deposits? Of course, questions of absolute age do not detract from the use of isotope curves as 'scales' representing 'series of alternating or continuously varying parameters that form a distinctive pattern in marine sequences' (Berggren *et al.* 1980, p. 279). As pointed out by Berggren, scales are intrinsically elastic and ages are not fixed.

Second, it is known that the hydrologic, glaciologic and biologic factors that determine the isotopic composition of foraminifera vary in the modern ocean and in different oxygen stages. For example, the contribution of ice volume change and bottom-water temperature change to oxygen-isotope values is still not clear (Dodge *et al.* 1983, Fillon and Williams 1983). Further, vital effects among different foraminiferal taxa are known to complicate the isotopic signal. Andrews (1982) calculated that, contrary to the opinion of many workers, a large discrepancy exists between sea-level records calculated from uplifted Barbados and New Guinea terraces and those from the marine stable isotope record: 'Given the differences between the ^{18}O and coral reef records I would claim that we do not know what global sea level variations there have been over the last 125 000 to within ± 30 m.' (Andrews 1982, p. 25). Chappell (1981,

p. 424) states: 'I conclude that the deep sea core records are seriously smoothed, for events shorter than 10^4 years and that relative sea level curves derived from well dated flights of raised coral reefs constitute the best available records of ice/ocean water volume changes, in the 10^4 to 10^5 year time frame, while the cores provide the best records in the 10^5 to 10^6 year frame.'

Most researchers now favour an integrated approach to the Coastal Plain in which they apply lithostratigraphy, biostratigraphy and modern geochronologic dating methods to understand geologic history (e.g., Oaks and DuBar 1974). For example, in the Eastern USA Cronin *et al.* (1981) used sedimentologic, trace fossil (*Callianassa* burrows), palaeontologic (*in situ Crassostrea virginica*) and brackish water ostracod evidence to estimate relative sea levels. The sea-level estimates in Cronin (1980) and Cronin *et al.* (1981) are based on richly fossiliferous marine deposits that are unequivocal evidence of marine transgressions for which the elevation of the fossiliferous deposits was given with respect to present sea level. The values 6 m to about 7.5 m above present sea level cited in Cronin *et al.* (1981) for late Pleistocene sea levels represent ranges of maximum sea levels for each stratigraphic section studied. This does not imply (a) they should necessarily signify the maximum high stand for a particular interglacial, (b) any association with particular regional geomorphic features, or (c) that these estimates were anything but *relative* sea level estimates. Palaeoclimatic data in these studies were derived from marine ostracods and pollen assemblages.

With reference to the east coast, it is important to stress the critical approach that has been adopted by numerous research groups and the testability of the multiple working hypotheses generated in the last decade of research. Further, there are few regions where uranium series and amino acid dates have been so critically scrutinized as they have for the Eastern US. Cronin *et al.* (1981, p. 238) state: 'as the first uranium series study of this region, our composite chronology must be considered a first approximation.' With regard to a single date of 120 000 BP, it was stated (p. 238) 'We hesitate to rely on a single date.' The detailed papers by McCartan *et al.* (1982), Wehmiller and Belknap (1982) and Szabo (1985) clearly exemplify the scrutiny virtually every date and every important dated outcrop has gone through, including revisiting dated sections, reanalysis of corals and molluscs using new material, and interlaboratory calibration of geochemical data. The following section outlines physical stratigraphic evidence from several regions that constitutes strong field evidence for the hypothesis that the last interglacial is represented by a complex of sea-level events.

4.0   REGIONAL STRATIGRAPHY OF LATE PLEISTOCENE INTERGLACIAL
DEPOSITS

The following summaries were abstracted from selected detailed surface
and subsurface stratigraphic and mapping studies that document the late
Pleistocene history of parts of the Eastern United States. To appreciate
their detail as well as points of uncertainty, the reader should refer to
original publications, many of which also contain geologic maps and cross-
sections constructed from subsurface data. Primary emphasis here will be
on the physical stratigraphy which constitutes evidence for multiple sea-
level fluctuations during the last interglacial. Second, the palaeoclimatic
evidence for climatic change during this interval will be mentioned.
Finally, problematic absolute age determinations of many lithostratigraphic
units are discussed briefly.

4.1   North-eastern United States of America

At Sankaty Head on the island of Nantucket, Massachusetts, Oldale *et al.*
(1982) have documented the following stratigraphic sequence: a lower
glacial drift unconformably overlain by a conformable marine sequence
that includes the lower part of the Sankaty Sand, in turn overlain
unconformably by an upper marine unit including the upper part of the
Sankaty Sand, which is capped by a ventificated pebble layer and overlain
by an upper drift. The stratigraphy therefore indicates two distinct marine
units. The palaeoclimates indicated by molluscs and ostracods were
interglacial and slightly warmer than at present during deposition of the
lower part of the Sankaty Sand and slightly cooler during deposition of
the upper part. This climatic reconstruction is similar to that derived from
the Gardiners Clay and Wantagh Formation (Rampino and Sanders
1981b) sequence of Long Island but the correlation between the two areas
is tentative (see below). The Sankaty section has been dated using
uranium series, radiocarbon dates and amino acid racemization and
suggests approximate ages between 140 000 and 120 000 BP for the
marine units.

Rampino and Sanders (1981b) summarized the local subsurface
stratigraphy of south-western Long Island and proposed regional
correlations with late Pleistocene deposits of northern Long Island and
Massachusetts. They showed that the Wantagh Formation stratigraphically
overlies the Merrick Formation of Rampino and Sanders (1981b), which
in turn overlies the stratigraphic equivalent of the Gardiners Clay in the

western part of their study area. The Wantagh Formation represents a shallow water, nearshore marine to lagoonal environment and shows evidence for temperate palaeoclimatic conditions somewhat cooler than those of today. The sands and gravels of the Merrick Formation are interpreted as fluvioglacial outwash and the Gardiners Clay is an interglacial marine deposit. A radiocarbon age of 28 150 BP for the Wantagh Formation is considered by Rampino and Sanders (1981b) very tentative and in discussing this age and the general problem of a mid-Wisconsin high sea level, they conclude (pp. 123–124): 'At present, we can only point to the record from Long Island as a suggestion that sea level may have been near its present height about 30 000 radiocarbon years ago, although we are well aware of the problems of radiocarbon dating. . . . However, there is an alternative explanation: If the radiocarbon age determinations are in error, then the Wantagh deposits of Long Island and the underlying glacial drift (Montauk-Merrick) may well be much older than 30 000 yr BP. The nearshore marine Wantagh deposits may correlate with one of the well-documented high stands of the sea associated with the Eemian Interglacial and its equivalents, which took place around 120 000 years ago, or the somewhat later high stands of the sea indicated by marine terraces dated by U-Th methods of about 105 000 and 80 000 yr BP . . . and which are well-documented in the oxygen-isotope records in deep-sea cores . . . '. There remains an alternative hypothesis that the Wantagh Formation represents the last interglacial, the Merrick Formation a full glacial interval and the 15 metre clay beneath the Merrick a previous interglacial about 200 000 BP corresponding to oxygen isotope stage 7.

While the age and palaeoenvironmental origin of Long Island late Pleistocene deposits and their correlation with those in Massachusetts remain unclear, the stratigraphic record suggests a history involving several marine events and different palaeoclimatic conditions.

4.2 Norfolk, Virginia, Chesapeake Bay region

Oaks and Coch (1973) described the stratigraphy of the Norfolk Virginia area and Mixon *et al.* (1982) have re-examined this area, provided uranium-series dates for several stratigraphic units, and proposed tentative correlations to other parts of the Chesapeake Bay area. While not all stratigraphic relationships are resolved, Mixon *et al.* (1982, p. E2) state the following: 'We are in basic agreement with Oak's interpretation of the stratigraphy of the Norfolk and Kempsville Formations in the type area of these units south of Norfolk. . . . Oak's detailed geologic section through the Fentress rise and Hickory scarp area shows two superposed rock-stratigraphic units of marginal marine origin (Norfolk and Kempsville Formations) that are traceable across the Hickory scarp and two younger units (Sand Bridge and Londonbridge Formations of Oaks and Coch, 1973) that underlie a relict marine plain (Mount Pleasant flat) east of the scarp'. In proposing a tentative rock-stratigraphy for Norfolk and the Delmarva Peninsula area, Mixon *et al.* (1982) summarize the geology as follows: 'These lithic units may be grouped into three, or possibly four, depositional sequences, including, from oldest to youngest: (1) the Accomack and Rappahannock River beds and "Norfolk" Formation beds *west* of the Suffolk scarp; (2) the type beds of the Norfolk Formation of Oaks and Coch and equivalent strata *east* of the Suffolk scarp; (3) the Kempsville Formation of Oaks and Coch and the Sedgefield[2] and Occohannock beds; and (4) the Sand Bridge Formation, Kent Island Formation, and Lynnhaven[2]–Poquoson beds. . . . If the Norfolk beds and the Kempsville Formation should represent transgressive and regressive phases, respectively, of the same depositional cycle, the low-lying terrace deposits in the southern Chesapeake region would include only three mappable sequences.' (p. E4).

Palaeoclimatologic studies of the late Pleistocene of the Norfolk area have been performed on ostracods (Valentine 1971, Cronin 1979, Cronin *et al.* 1981) and molluscs (Spencer and Campbell, in press). The results generally show interglacial warm climatic conditions in the Great Bridge and parts of the Norfolk and cooler climatic conditions in the Kempsville.

Based on uranium-series data, Mixon *et al.* (1982) lumped the type Norfolk beds, and the Kempsville and Sand Bridge Formations as post-140 000 BP and the Norfolk west of the Suffolk scarp and the Rappahannock River beds as pre-140 000 BP Pleistocene. Mixon *et al.* (1982) thought the three uranium series-dated corals from the Norfolk and Kempsville Formations that indicated a 72 000 BP age might have suffered post-depositional loss of thorium causing ages to appear too young. They imply an age possibly corresponding to oxygen substage 5e. Because a 125 000 BP age was anticipated, Szabo (1985) further analyzed additional corals from the late Pleistocene of the Norfolk and surrounding areas, including ^{231}Pa growth towards equilibrium with ^{235}U for three of them. Szabo stated (pp. 400–1): 'The ^{231}Pa dates are concordant with those derived from the ^{230}Th growth. It is unlikely that all of these samples independently lost equivalent amounts of thorium and protactinium to produce concordant apparent dates. In addition, uranium-trend dating of the sediment enclosing the three corals at 3 localities . . . yielded an average uranium-trend date of 76 000±28 000 BP (Rosholt and Szabo

1982, J. N. Rosholt 1983, written communication). Concordant [230]Th, [231]Pa, and uranium-trend results support a late Pleistocene oxygen isotope substage 5a age for the depositional event of the Norfolk-Kempsville.'

In the central and southern Delmarva Peninsula, Mixon (1985) has mapped the surface and subsurface stratigraphy and found the following sequence: The Accomack Member of the Omar Formation is overlain by the Nassawadox Formation, which consists of three members – the Stumptown, the Butlers Bluff and the Occohannock. Overlying the Nassawadox is the Kent Island Formation. In the region bordering the east side of the central upland of Delmarva, Mixon (1985) described the Joynes Neck Sand and the overlying Wachapreague Formation; these deposits are assigned to one or more late Pleistocene interglacial periods. According to Mixon (1985), the precise stratigraphic relationship between the Wachapreague and underlying beds is unclear. In some places the Wachapreague beds 'appear to truncate the Butlers Bluff Member of the Nassawadox Formation' (p. G45), whereas elsewhere, they 'appear to overlie the Stumptown Member (?) of the Nassawadox Formation with little or no indication of an erosional unconformity. . . . A truncating relationship between the Wachapreague Formation and the older Joynes Neck Sand is suggested by the apparent inset of both the depositional surface at the top of the Wachapreague and the surface of unconformity at the base of the unit below surfaces of the Joynes Neck Sand.' (p. G45).

The palaeoclimatic conditions during deposition of the Accomack Member of the Omar Formation and the Nassawadox Formation were determined by faunal and floral (pollen) analysis and indicate that warm temperate interglacial climates prevailed. The Kent Island also shows relatively warm climates; however the correlative Wachapreague Formation shows a more complex situation: 'The pollen assemblages from the type section of the Wachapreague Formation (W–1), from the shelly beds at Piggen (W–2) and Bell Neck (Ex–24), and from equivalent nonshelly strata to the northwest in the Nassawadox and Townsend quadrangles (N–3, T–16) indicate a progressive change from warm–temperate climatic conditions in the earliest Wachapreague time to cool– or cold–temperate conditions in middle and late Wachapreague time.' (Mixon 1985, pp. G44–5). This progressive cooling matches that recorded from the Norfolk area.

4.3   Eastern North Carolina

The stratigraphy of Pleistocene beds of Eastern North Carolina was described by DuBar and Solliday (1963), 'Fallaw and Wheeler (1969),

DuBar *et al.* (1974), Mixon and Pilkey (1976) and Miller (1982, 1985). In a detailed stratigraphic study of the Flanner Beach Formation and related Pleistocene deposits, Miller (1985, p. 111) stated: 'In the Quaternary section of the Neuse River area, four major transgressive–regressive depositional cycles are preserved as unconformity–bounded sequences. These are, from oldest to youngest: (1) James City Formation (early Pleistocene); (2) Flanner Beach Formation (middle Pleistocene); (3) Core Creek sand (late Pleistocene); and (4) Diamond City Clay–Atlantic sand (also late Pleistocene). . . . Each depositional cycle should correspond to *at least* [italics mine] one period of global warming, diminution of continental ice sheets, and rise in world sea-level.'

The palaeoclimatology of the Flanner Beach Formation, Core Creek, and Diamond City Clay of Susman and Heron (1979) in the vicinity of Dare County, North Carolina is being studied in detail by myself and T. A. Ager (US Geological Survey) (Cronin *et al.* 1984). At present, the data indicate warm interglacial conditions for the Flanner Beach and most of the Core Creek sand but significant cooling in the equivalent of the Diamond City Clay. The best evidence for cool climatic conditions comes from the Stetson borrow pit, east-central Dare County (Miller 1982), where cool temperate marine ostracods and pollen assemblages 'transitional between interglacial (pine, oak, hickory) and glacial (pine, spruce) floras' have been recorded (Cronin *et al.* 1984, p. 28). Szabo (1985) dated a coral from this pit using $^{230}Th/^{234}U$ at 72 000±4000 BP and the ^{231}Pa method at 69 000±11 000 BP. The age of the Flanner Beach Formation is about 250 000 to 200 000 BP based on two uranium-series ages on corals from Ponzer averaging 221 000 BP (Cronin *et al.* 1981, Szabo 1985) and supporting amino acid ratios suggesting an age between 250 000 and 200 000 BP (Wehmiller and Belknap 1982). The greater than 500 000 BP date given in Cronin *et al.* (1981) came from a coral that was reworked from the James City Formation into the overlying Flanner Beach Formation (McCartan *et al.* 1982).

4.4   Charleston area, South Carolina

The middle and lower Coastal Plain of the Charleston, South Carolina region has been the site of intensive surface and subsurface studies resulting in a proliferation of geomorphic and lithostratigraphic names. Using 'physical, chemical and biotic parameters preserved in cyclic formations' Colquhoun (1971, p. 21) was one of the early workers to adopt an integrated approach in the recognition of former sea-level fluctuations. Colquhoun recognized four major Pleistocene cycles: the

Wicomico (including the Penholoway Formation), the Talbot (including the Pamlico Formation), the Princess Anne and the Silver Bluff. The nature of the contacts between cycles is complex (see Colquhoun 1971, p. 31) but generally is represented by extended periods of emergence.

McCartan *et al.* (1984) published a 1:250 000 scale geologic map of the region between Charleston, SC and the Orangeburg Scarp and recognized five Pleistocene and one Holocene stratigraphic marine units. They correlated these units, to which they assigned informal numerical symbols, to the those of Colquhoun (1965) and the general correspondance is good except that McCartan *et al.* (1984) lumped the Silver Bluff Formation with Holocene sediments into unit Q1. With respect to the nature of the six depositional units, McCartan *et al.* (1984) stated: 'Several still stands have been recorded for the regressive phase of each transgressive-regressive cycle in the Quaternary of South Carolina.'

The ages of the Charleston area units have been the source of much controversy. Ward *et al.* (1971) and Ward (1985) estimated the ages of South Carolina shorelines using an equation that calculates 'altimetric age' based on shoreline elevation and the rate of uplift and compared this age to the estimated ages of deep-sea core warm stages. Scattered uranium-series ages from New Zealand shorelines were used to calibrate Australian and South Carolina shorelines and correlate them with deep sea isotope stages.

McCartan *et al.* (1982) discussed the stratigraphy and absolute age of Charleston area Pleistocene deposits emphasizing uranium series and amino acid racemization data. Uranium series-dated corals from the Socastee Formation gives an age of about 230 000 and 202 000 BP (see also Szabo, 1985). The stratigraphically younger Wando Formation (McCartan *et al.* 1980) is the youngest Pleistocene unit in the area; Szabo (1985) summarized the uranium series ages for the Wando: 'Dating of these fossils yielded two age groupings. The uncorrected ^{230}Th dates of one group range between 83 000 and 93 000 yr; two samples from Mark Clark Pit and Detyens Shipyard localities yielded dates of 120 000±6000 and 133 000±10 000 yr, respectively . . . the two groups of ages therefore suggest two depositional episodes within the Wando . . . (p. 401). Szabo (1985) believed the old and young Wando deposits appear to correspond with oxygen isotope substages 5e and 5c respectively.

The palaeoclimatic conditions during late Pleistocene interglacial deposits in the Charleston area consistently show evidence for climates as warm as or slightly warmer than those of today (Cronin 1979, Cronin *et al.* 1981, Lyon, in press).

5.0   SUMMARY AND CONCLUSIONS

Studies of the Holocene sea-level record discussed in the first section of this paper reveal two points: (1) The present elevation of a marine deposit reflects post-depositional processes such as peat autocompaction and sedimentary processes on the continental shelf; radiocarbon-dated material should be viewed cautiously when interpreting sea level data. (2) The fine structure of the Holocene sea-level record may be complex and involve frequent rapid fluctuations, although the bulk of the evidence still indicates a tangential curve. We are thus still testing models of the postglacial record. It should not be surprising, therefore, that the record of the last interglacial on the continental margin of eastern North America is so difficult to unravel. With this in mind it is useful to summarize several meaningful patterns that emerge when one carefully assesses the physical stratigraphy, palaeontology, palaeoclimatology and age dating of Eastern United States interglacial deposits.

Whereas each region has a distinct history and the precise meaning of the data is subject to different interpretations, it is worthwhile to point out several features that are apparent and deserve further testing. They fall into three categories.

(1) Physical stratigraphy.   In most field and mapping investigations of deposits of the last interglacial, complex depositional events probably related to relatively rapid (10^4 to 10^5 yr) sea-level fluctuations have been found. Numerous stratigraphic units have been given formation or member rank and have been described as mappable physical units. The contacts between units are variably described as unconformable, truncated, conformable but lithologically distinct, conformable in one region but disconformable in another, gradational or unknown. These results have been interpreted as evidence of either multiple high stands or minor pulses of sea level, or successive still stands occurring within an extended interval of high sea level. All dating points to the interval between about 140 000 and 70 000 BP as the age range for these events. Regardless of whether one accepts the various radiometric dating techniques that have been applied to these units, the stratigraphic history of each region speaks for itself and must be accounted for when interpreting the relative sea level history of the Eastern USA.

(2) Palaeoclimates.   Climatic reconstructions in regions from Cape Hatteras and north consistently show a pattern of relatively warm continental and nearshore marine palaeoclimates in the lower (stratigraphically) deposits from the last interglacial, grading (progressively?)

into relatively cool climates in the upper parts of the interglacial. In most cases these cool climates signify conditions somewhat cooler than the present interglacial, even approaching an interstadial and are correlated with oxygen isotope substages 5c and/or 5a. The predominance in the Charleston area of warm interglacial conditions throughout the entire interglacial record is attributed to its southern location in a region continuously influenced by warm Gulf Stream water, even as the Wisconsin glaciation approached.

(3) Absolute age. Many deposits that previously have been assigned to a middle Wisconsin high sea level are probably correlative with deposits now dated by uranium-series on corals at 80 000 to 70 000 BP. These represent the youngest, i.e., the stratigraphically highest, pre-Holocene marine deposits in many areas. It is as yet difficult to say whether there are three or four relative high stands represented within deposits of the last interglacial of the east coast but existing evidence for marine deposits in at least some areas dating about 140 000 to 120 000, 105 000 to 90 000 and 80 000 to 70 000 BP is strong. Ku (1982) has discussed the uncertainty as to whether there were four or three high stands between 140 000 and 70 000 BP. It is none the less encouraging that east coast radiometric dates generally support the physical stratigraphic evidence described in numerous published sources which indicate a late Pleistocene relative sea-level history far more complicated than a single brief high stand at 125 000 BP. The strictly geomorphic approach of Ward (1985) rejects the stratigraphic and geochronologic evidence and accepts the deep-sea isotope record as faithfully recording all intervals of warm climate and high sea level. This is reminiscent of Cooke's acceptance of the four glacial periods documented in the mid-continent and his interpretation of Coastal Plain shorelines in the light of this model. This approach cannot lead to reasonable models of sea-level change and crustal movement that are testable by independent evidence from stratigraphy and geochronology. Given tectonic and isostatic movements and the difficulty in determining a eustatic sea level curve, it appears unwarranted to assume the Coastal Plain record should necessarily match in detail the deep sea climatic isotopic record or the relative sea-level record of other coastal areas.

ACKNOWLEDGEMENTS

I would like to thank Dr. Byron Stone, Dr. Meyer Rubin, and Dr. Robert Mixon (US Geological Survey) for helpful insights on eastern United

States sea levels and comments on earlier drafts of the manuscript. Laurel Bybell (US Geological Survey) provided a helpful review of the manuscript. I have also benefited greatly from discussions over the last few years with Professor David Bowen (University of London, Royal Holloway and Bedford New College) Dr John Wehmiller (University of Delaware), Dr Walter Newman (Queen's College), Drs Thomas Ager and B. J. Szabo (US Geological Survey), and Dr Arthur Bloom (Cornell University). I am grateful to Dr William Miller (Humboldt State University) for initially pointing out the Dare County, NC late Pleistocene deposits.

Typescript received 1986, April.

REFERENCES

Andrews, J. T. 1982: On the reconstruction of Pleistocene ice sheets: A review. *Quat. Sci. Rev.*, 1, 1–30.
Belknap, D. F. and Kraft, J. C. 1977: Holocene relative sea-level changes and coastal stratigraphic units on the northwest flank of the Baltimore Canyon Trough geosyncline. *J. of Sedimen. Petr.*, 47, 610–29.
Berggren, W. A., Burckle, L. H., Cita, M. B., Cooke, H. B. S., Funnell, B. M., Gartner, S., Hays, J. D., Kennett, J. P., Opdyke, N. D., Pastouret, L., Shackleton, N. J. and Takayanagi, Y. 1980: Towards a Quaternary time scale, *Quat. Res.* 13, 277–302.
Bloom, A. L. 1967: Pleistocene shorelines: A new test of isostasy. *Geol. Soc. Am. Bull.*, 78, 1477–94.
Bloom, A. L. 1983: Sea level and coastal geomorphology of the United States through the late Wisconsin glacial maximum. In S. C. Porter (ed.), *Late Quaternary Environments of the United States*, vol. 1, Minneapolis: University of Minnesota Press, 215–29.
Bloom, A. L., Broecker, W. S., Chappell, J. M. A., Matthews, R. K. and Mesolella, K. J. 1974: Quaternary sea-level fluctuations on a tectonic coast: New $^{230}Th/^{234}U$ dates from the Huon Peninsula, New Guinea. *Quat. Res.*, 4, 185–205.
Broecker, W. S. 1966: Absolute dating and the astronomical theory of glaciation. *Science*, 151, 299–304.
Broecker, W. S. and Ku, T.-L. 1969: Caribbean cores P6304–8 and P6304–9: New analysis of absolute chronology. *Science*, 166, 404–6.
Broecker, W. S., Thurber, D. L., Goddard, J., Ku, T.-L., Matthews, R. K. and Mesolella, K. J. 1968: Milankovitch hypothesis supported by precise dating of coral reefs and deep sea sediments. *Science*, 159, 297–300.
Broecker, W. S. and Van Donk, J. 1970: Insolation changes, ice volumes, and the ^{18}O record in deep-sea cores, *Rev. of Geophys. and Space Physics*, 8, 169–98.

Chappell, J. 1981: Relative and average sea level changes, and endo-, epi-, and exogenic processes on Earth. In I. Allison (ed.), *Sea Level, Ice and Climatic Change*, International Association of Hydrological Sciences, 131, 411–30.

Clark, J. A., Farrell, W. E. and Peltier, W. R. 1978: Global changes in postglacial sea level: A numerical calculation. *Quat. Res.*, 9, 265–87.

Colquhoun, D. J. 1965: Terrace sediment complexes in central South Carolina. *Atlantic Coastal Plain Geological Association Field Conference Guidebook*, Columbia, South Carolina.

Colquhoun, D. J. 1971: Glacio-eustatic sea level fluctuation of the middle and lower Coastal Plain, South Carolina. *Quaternaria*, 15, 19–34.

Colquhoun, D. J., Brooks, M. J., Michie, J., Abbott, W. B., Stapor, F. W., Newman, W. and Pardi, R. R. 1981: Location of archaeological sites with respect to sea level in the southeastern United States. *Striae*, 14, 144–50.

Cooke, C. W. 1930: Correlation of coastal terraces *J. Geology*, 38, 577–89.

Cronin, T. M. 1979: Late Pleistocene marginal marine ostracods from the southeastern Atlantic Coastal Plain. *Geogr. Phys. et Quat.*, 33, 121–73.

Cronin, T. M. 1980: Biostratigraphic correlation of Pleistocene marine deposits and sea levels, Atlantic Coastal Plain of the southeastern United States. *Quat. Res.*, 13, 213–29.

Cronin, T. M. 1981: Rates and possible causes of neotectonic vertical crustal movements of the emerged southeastern United States Atlantic Coastal Plain. *Geol. Soc. Am. Bull.*, 92, 812–33.

Cronin, T. M. 1983: Rapid sea-level and climate change: Evidence from continental and island margins. *Quat. Sci. Rev.*, 1, 177–214.

Cronin, T. M., Ager, T. A., Szabo, B. J., Rosholt, J. and Shaw, E. G. 1984: Cool climates – high sea level: Interglacial deposits of the North Carolina Coastal Plain. In *American Quaternary Association 8th Biennial Meeting, Program and Abstracts*, 28.

Cronin, T. M., Szabo, B. J., Ager, T. A., Hazel, J. E. and Owens, J. P. 1981: Quaternary climates and sea levels of the U.S. Atlantic Coastal Plain. *Science*, 211, 233–40.

Dodge, R. E., Fairbanks, R. G., Benninger, L. K. and Maurrasse, F. 1983: Pleistocene sea levels from raised coral reefs of Haiti. *Science*, 219, 1423–5.

DuBar, J. R. and Solliday, J. R. 1963: Stratigraphy of Neogene deposits, lower Neuse Estuary, North Carolina. *Southeast. Geol.*, 4, 213–33.

DuBar, J. R., Solliday, J. R. and Howard, J. F. 1974: Stratigraphy and morphology of Neogene deposits, Neuse River Estuary, North Carolina. In R. Q. Oaks, Jr and J. R. DuBar (eds), *Post-Miocene Stratigraphy, Central and Southern Atlantic Coastal Plain*. Logan, Utah: Utah State Univ. Press, 102–22.

Emery, K. O. and Merrill, A. S. 1979: Relict oysters on the United States Atlantic continental shelf: A reconsideration of their usefulness in understanding late Quaternary sea-level history: Discussion and reply. *Geol. Soc. Am. Bull.*, 90, 689–92.

Fairbridge, R. W. 1961: Eustatic changes in sea level: In L. H. Ahrens *et al.*

(eds.), *Physics and Chemistry of the Earth* 4, London: Pergamon Press, 99–185.

Fallaw, W. C. and Wheeler, W. H. 1969: Marine fossiliferous Pleistocene deposits in southeastern North Carolina. *Southeast. Geol.*, 10, 35–54.

Field, M. E., Meisburger, E. P., Stanley, E. A. and Williams, S. J. 1979: Upper Quaternary peat deposits on the Atlantic inner shelf of the United States. *Geol. Soc. Am. Bull.*, 90, 618–28.

Fillon, R. H. and Williams, D. F. 1983: Glacial evolution of the Plio-Pleistocene: Role of continental and arctic ocean ice sheets. *Palaeogeogr., Palaeoclimatol., Palaeoecol.*, 42, 7–33.

Kaye, C. A. and Barghoorn, E. S. 1964: Late Quaternary sea-level change and crustal rise at Boston, Massachusetts, with notes on the autocompaction of peat. *Geol. Soc. Am. Bull.*, 75, 63–80.

Ku, T.-L. 1982: Progress and perspectives. In M. Ivanovich and R. S. Harmon (eds.), *Uranium Series Disequilibrium: Applications to Environmental Problems*, Oxford: Clarendon Press, 497–506.

Ku, T.-L. and Broecker, W. S. 1966: Atlantic deep-sea stratigraphy: Extension of absolute chronology to 320,000 years. *Science*, 149, 448–50.

Lyon, S. K. In press: Biostratigraphic and palaeoenvironmental interpretations from late Pleistocene Ostracoda, Charleston, South Carolina: Studies related to the Charleston, South Carolina earthquake of 1886 – Neogene and Quaternary lithostratigraphy and biostratigraphy. *US Geological Survey Professional Paper* 1362.

MacIntyre, I. G., Pilkey, O. H. and Struckenrath, R. 1978: Relict oysters on the United States Atlantic Continental Shelf. *Geol. Soc. Am. Bull.*, 89, 277–82.

MacIntyre, I. G., Pilkey, O. H. and Struckenrath, R. 1979: Reply to Emery and Merrill, 1979. *Geol. Soc. Am. Bull.*, 90, 692–4.

Matthews, R. K. 1973: Relative elevation of late Pleistocene high sea level stands: Barbados uplift rates and their implications. *Quat. Res.*, 3, 147–53.

McCartan, L., Owens, J. P., Blackwelder, B. W., Szabo, B. J., Belknap, D. F., Kriausakul, N., Mitterer, R. M. and Wehmiller, J. F. 1982: Comparison of amino acid racemization geochronometry with lithostratigraphy, biostratigraphy, uranium-series coral dating, and magnetostratigraphy in the Atlantic Coastal Plain of the southeastern United States. *Quat. Res.*, 18, 337–59.

McCartan, L., Weems, R. E., Lemon, E. M. Jr 1980: The Wando Formation (upper Pleistocene) in the Charleston, South Carolina area. *US Geological Survey Bull.*, 1502–A, 110–17.

McCartan, L., Weems, R. W., Lemon, E. M. Jr 1984: Geologic map of the area between Charleston and Orangeburg, South Carolina. *US Geological Survey Miscellaneous Investigations*, Map I–1472.

Miller, W. III 1982: The paleoecologic history of late Pleistocene estuarine and marine fossil deposits in Dare County, North Carolina *Southeast. Geol.*, 23, 1–13.

Miller, W. III 1985: The Flanner Beach Formation (middle Pleistocene) in eastern North Carolina. *Tulane Studies in Geol. and Paleontol.*, 18, 93–122.

Mixon, R. B. 1985: Stratigraphic and geomorphic framework of uppermost Cenozoic deposits in the southern Delmarva Peninsula, Virginia and Maryland. *US Geological Survey Professional Paper* 1067-G.

Mixon, R. B. and Pilkey, O. H. 1976: Reconnaissance geology of the submerged and emerged Coastal Plain Province, Cape Lookout area, North Carolina. *US Geological Survey Professional Paper* 859.

Mixon, R.B., Szabo, B. J. and Owens, J. P. 1982: Uranium-series dating of mollusks and corals and age of Pleistocene deposits, Chesapeake Bay area, Virginia and Maryland. *US Geological Survey Professional Paper* 1067-E.

Moore, W. S. 1982: Late Pleistocene sea-level history. In M. Ivanovich and R. S. Harmon (eds.), *Uranium Series Disequilibrium: Applications to Environmental Problems*, Oxford: Clarendon Press, 481–96.

Newman, W. S., Cinquemani, L. J., Pardi, R. R. and Marcus, L. F. 1980: Holocene deleveling of the United States' east coast. In N.-A. Mörner (ed.), *Earth Rheology, Isostasy and Eustasy*, Chichester: John Wiley, 449–63.

Newman, W. S., Marcus, L. F. and Pardi, R. R. 1981: Palaeogeodesy: late Quaternary geoidal configurations as determined by ancient sea levels in I. Allison (ed.), *Sea Level, Ice and Climatic Change*, International Association Hydrological Sciences 131, 263–75.

Oaks, R. Q. Jr and Coch, N. K. 1973: Post-Miocene stratigraphy and *morphology, southeastern Virginia. Virginia Division of Mineral Resources Bulletin* 82.

Oaks, R. W. Jr and DuBar, J. R. 1974: Tentative correlation of Post-Miocene units, central and southern Atlantic Coastal Plain. In R. Q. Oaks and J. R. DuBar (eds.), *Post-Miocene Stratigraphy, central and southern Atlantic coastal plain*, Logan, Utah: Utah State University Press, 232–46.

Oldale, R. N., Valentine, P. C., Cronin, T. M., Spiker, E. C., Blackwelder, B. W., Belknap, D. F., Wehmiller, J. F. and Szabo, B. J. 1982: Stratigraphy, structure, absolute age, and paleontology of the upper Pleistocene deposits at Sankaty Head, Nantucket Island, Massachusetts *Geology*, 10, 246–52.

Payton, C. E. (ed.) 1977: *Seismic stratigraphy – applications to hydrocarbon exploration*. American Association of Petroleum Geologists, Memoir 26. Tulsa, Okl.

Rampino, M. R. and Sanders, J. E. 1980: Holocene transgression in south-central Long Island, New York. *J. Sediment. Petrol.*, 50, 1063–80.

Rampino, M. R. and Sanders, J. E. 1981a: Episodic growth of Holocene tidal marshes in the northwestern United States: A possible indicator of eustatic sea-level fluctuations. *Geology*, 9, 63–7.

Rampino, M. R. and Sanders, J. E. 1981b: Upper Quaternary stratigraphy of southern Long Island, New York. *Northeast. Geol.*, 3, 116–28.

Redfield, A. C. and Rubin, M. 1962: The age of salt marsh peat and its relation to recent changes in sea level at Barnstable, Massachusetts. *Proc. Nat. Acad. Sci.*, 48, 1728–35.

Richards, H. G. 1971: Sea level during the past 11,000 years as indicated by data from North and South America. *Quaternaria*, 14, 7–15.

Rona, E. and Emiliani, C. 1969: Absolute dating of Caribbean cores P6304–8 and P6304–9. *Science*, 163, 66–8.

Rosholt, J. N., Emiliani, C., Geiss, J., Koczy, F. F. and Wangersky, P. J. 1961. Absolute dating of deep-sea cores by the $^{231}Pa/^{230}Th$ method. *J. Geology*, 69, 162.

Rosholt, J. N. and Szabo, B. J. 1982: Comparison of uranium-series dating of coral and uranium-trend dating of coral-bearing terraces of the U.S. Atlantic Coastal Plain. *Geol. Soc. Am. Abstr. with Program*, 14, 603.

Shepard, F. P. 1963: Thirty-five thousand years of sea level. In T. Clements (ed.) *Essays in Marine Geology in honor of K. O. Emery*. Los Angeles: University of Southern California Press, 1–10.

Spencer, R. S. and Campbell, L. D. in press: The fauna and paleoecology of the late Pleistocene marine sediments of southeastern Virginia. *Bull. Am. Paleontol.*

Stearns, C. E. 1984: Uranium-series dating and the history of sea level. In W. C. Mahaney (ed.), *Quaternary Dating Methods, Developments in Palaeontology and Stratigraphy*, 7, 53–66.

Susman, K. R. and Heron, S. D. Jr 1979: Evolution of a barrier island, Shakleford banks, Carteret County, North Carolina. *Geol. Soc. Am. Bull.*, 90, 205–15.

Szabo, B. J. 1985: Uranium-series dating of fossil corals from marine sediments of southeastern United States Atlantic Coastal Plain. *Geol. Soc. Am. Bull.*, 96, 398–406.

Upson, J. E., Leopold, E. B. and Rubin, M. 1964: Postglacial change of sea-level in New Haven Harbor, Connecticut. *Am. J. Sci.*, 262, 121–32.

Valentine, P. C. 1971: Climatic implications of a late Pleistocene ostracode assemblage from southeastern Virginia. *US Geological Survey Professional Paper* 683–D.

Ward, W. T. 1985: Correlation of east Australian Pleistocene shorelines with deep-sea core stages: A basis for coastal chronology. *Geol. Soc. Am. Bull.*, 96, 1156–66.

Ward, W. T., Ross, P. J. and Colquhoun, D. J. 1971: Interglacial high sea levels – an absolute chronology derived from shoreline elevations. *Palaeogeogr., Palaeoclimatol., Palaeoecol.*, 9, 77–99.

Wehmiller, J. F. and Belknap, D. F. 1982: Amino acid age estimates, Quaternary Atlantic Coastal Plain: Comparison with U-series dates, biostratigraphy, and paleomagnetic control. *Quat. Res.*, 18, 311–36.

8

Quaternary sea-level changes on the Atlantic coast of Africa

Pierre Giresse

1.0 INTRODUCTION

The map of World Quaternary shorelines, which was published in 1981, indicates on the West African coast the existence of evidence of emergence during the Holocene (between 2500 and 6000 BP) and the Eemian (at about 120 000 BP). In fact, the data provided by this map appear to be of rather uneven value now. The definition of the Holocene raised shorelines has largely been verified in several areas, e.g. Mauritania, Senegal, the Ivory Coast, Benin, Nigeria, Gabon, Congo and Angola, where detailed analyses have, in several cases, permitted the production of regional relative sea-level curves. In these cases, observations from the environment immediately inland or from the offshore zone often provide valuable complementary evidence for the definition of regional factors. On the other hand, the significance of many Pleistocene terraces attributed to a marine origin is now being questioned: certain topographic surfaces presumed to be marine result from one or several continental morpho-genetic episodes controlled by the renewed effect of old pre-Cambrian structural lines; in other cases, the marine materials have been man-modified or else result from the colluvial reworking of older materials, in some cases of Pliocene age. Only in the coastal sectors, where repeated radiometric measurements have been made, can the terraces be confirmed as of marine origin and they are relatively small in extent. They are found in Morocco, Western Sahara, Mauritania and Angola. These are sites of positive epeirogenic movements the cause and amplitude of which have been more or less completely analysed. This contrasts with the Atlantic coast between southern Senegal and northern Angola where the absence of dated evidence of raised Pleistocene sea levels would indicate, relatively a greater stability, but this inference is contradicted by recent seismic evidence from several coastal locations in West Africa.

The basins of the Taoudeni, Chad, Nile, Congo, Zambeze and Karoo (figure 8.1) constitute sedimentation zones on the shield . which are separated by uplifted shield zones. To the north and south of the continent, recent folding is attributed to the Alpine orogeny. Finally, the peri-shield sedimentation zones correspond to the basins of the Atlantic and Indian Ocean margins and to the basins of the Sahara and Bénoué.

One of the general characteristics of the African shield structure is the persistence, throughout more or less all of the orogenies, of the directions of the folds and fractures which were initiated during the successive phases of the Pre-Cambrian. The same trend lines have often been reactivated since the fragmentation of the ancient continent of Gondwana until recent times. At the time of the formation of the Hercynican chains of the Appalachians, the Mauritanides and the Cape, the African-South American block was compressed and aligned orthogonally to the folds; fracturing took place in frequently encountered directions. The subsequent decompression involved distension at the origin of the fragmentation of the Gondwana continent. It is believed that the faults of the Eastern Rift (King 1970) were determined by other older ones, often Pre-Cambrian: they were situated in the north-east quadrant, just like the down-faulted trough of the Bénoué, which is interpreted (Grant 1971) as a deep fracture, temporarily under distension, then compressed, rather than as an inactive rift. Equally at Walvis Bay (the zone of Kaako), the alignment of the Cretaceous basalts (125 Ma according to Siedner and Miller 1968) appears to indicate a temporary distension fracture orientated transversely to the coast. The prolongation in the Walvis submarine ridge is considered by some (Emery *et al*. 1975, Le Pichon 1968) as a fracture continuing that of the shield zone and by others (Burke *et al*. 1972) as the wake of the African plate above a hot spot.

Amongst the transverse fractures of the Atlantic seaboard one must also take into account the hypothetical terminations of the inter-shield transformation faults. For example, in the Ivory Coast the Saint Paul fault controls the limits of the coastal basement rocks, and in Ghana the prolongation under the Nile delta would be at the origin of the transverse massif of Adamoua (Fail *et al*. 1970).

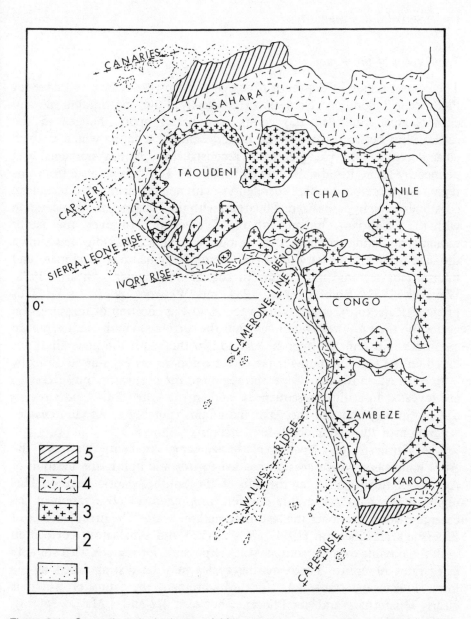

Figure 8.1 General geological map of Africa and the eastern Atlantic. Key: 1, ocean margins, 0–2000 m; 2, major continental basins; 3, uplifted shield zones; 4, sedimentation zones peripheral to the shield areas; 5, fold zones of the Alpine orogeny

2.0 PLEISTOCENE SHORELINES

2.1   *North of the Equator*

The coastal region of Southern Morocco contains the richest evidence for Pleistocene shoreline changes. Historically, the stratigraphical and chronological study of the coasts was based upon changes in the relationship between the Lusitanian and Senegalese fauna which enabled palaeo-oceanic and palaeoclimatic reconstruction within horizons well defined by their altitudinal limits (Biberson 1971). The evidence from this region has therefore enabled correlations with neighbouring Mediterranean coastlines to be hypothesized: Fouartian with the Plaisancian, Messaoudian with the Calabrian, Ouljian with the Tyrrhenian. However, the use of radiometric dating techniques in various regional scale studies has shown the significance of eustatic changes, regional fluctuations in climate and intermittent tectonic movements in coastal development (Stearns 1978, Weisrock 1981, Brebion *et al.* 1984 and Weisrock *et al.* 1985). This progress leads to the rejection of a too rigid classification of transgression cycles and their uplifted shorelines; thus the correlation with Mediterranean coastlines still remains hypothetical and to the south the generalisations based on the Guinean fauna make direct comparisons even more difficult.

In contrast, in the Safi–Cape Sim region to the north, the transgressions are revealed in sediment sequences, and in the Cape Sim–Agadir region the continuing uplift of the Atlas mountains (notably at Agadir) enables separation of the major ocean level maxima (figure 8.2).

The southern coast epeirogenic movements are centred around the Atlas mountains where erosion has led to isostatic uplift; the location of Agadir is, furthermore, at the site of the South Atlantic flexure. This region is the most favourable one for comprehensive observation of the emergent shorelines over the last three million years. The main features of Biberson's classification (1971) are observed and satisfactory correlation with the oceanic oxygen isotope cycles is possible for regions with suitably large rates of uplift. Three marine cycles may be distinguished in the lower Pleistocene (table 8.1). The Moghrebian, the fauna of which is clearly Quaternary and not Pliocene, between 4.2 and 3 Ma (at 360 m), the Fouartian between 2.8 and 2.4 Ma (at 180 m), then the Messaoudien between 1.8 and 1.1 Ma (between 83 and 117 m).

Subsequently, nine transgressive cycles over the last million years may be identified, representing a fluctuation rate twice as fast as in the Moghrebian. The oldest shorelines of this succession are found at

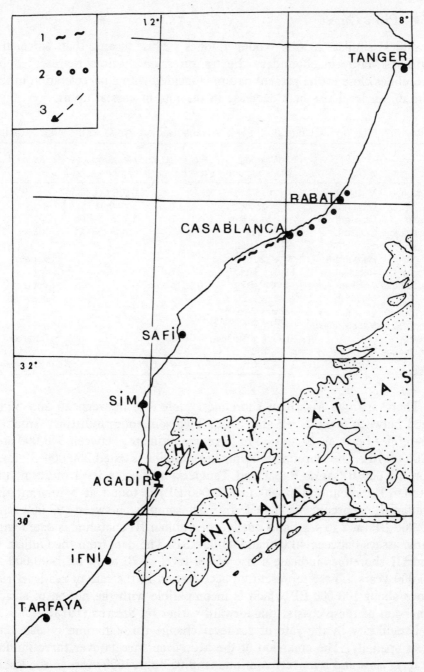

Figure 8.2 A map of the coast of Morocco showing the location of sites. Key: 1, coastline with an uplift rate of 0.065 mm/1000yr; 2, coastline with an uplift rate of 0.053 mm/1000yr; 3, the Harounian terrace at + 20 m, south of Agadir

altitudes similar to the younger ones. This means that since the Brunhes/Matuyama boundary the transgression maxima represented by shorelines close to the present datum coincided with an acceleration in the rate of sea level rise or a decrease in the rate of coastal uplift.

Table 8.1   The age, altitude and fauna of transgression cycles in the Atlas region

		Altitudes (Atlas region)	Estimated age (million years)	Measured Age (milion years)	Fauna
Holocene	Mellahian	+ 1 to 2 m		0.006 to 0.003	
	Ouljian III	+ 0.5 m		0.04	
Upper	Ouljian II	+ 2 to + 4 m		0.095 to 0.06	
Pleistocene	Ouljian I	+ 6 m (+ 8 m Agadir)		0.148 to 0.11	Warm
	Harounian-	+ 20 m		0,26	Temperate
Middle	Rabatian	(+ 5 m Agadir)			
Pleistocene	Anfatian	2 shorelines	0.52 to 0.34		Temperate
	Maarifian	+ 20 to + 50 m	1 to 0.6		Temperate
		5 shorelines			
	Messaoudian	+ 83 to + 117 m			
Lower		(+30,40 m at Tarfaya)	1.8 to 1.1		Tropical
Pleistocene	Fouartian	+ 180 m	2.8 to 2.4		
	Moghrebian	+ 360 m	4.2 to 3.0		Warm Quaternary

There are five Maarifian shorelines (table 8.1) between 20 and 50 m aged between 600 000 BP and 1 Ma. Two sometimes indistinct Anfatian shorelines between 20 and 30 m have age estimates between 340 000 and 520 000 BP. The Harounian–Rabatian shoreline is dated 260 000 BP (and not 148 000 BP as at Rabat and Tangiers) and has a level of 20 m, the Ouljian I shoreline (148 000 to 110 000 BP) is found at 5 to 6 m, the Ouljian II shoreline is dated by six samples between 97 000 and 60 000 BP (at 2 to 4 m) and finally, the Ouljian III shoreline is dated with three assays between 40 000 and 43 000 BP. The data from the Ouljian II and III shorelines indicate a rise of sea level of 20 to 50 m in 40 000 to 70 000 years. These represent an acceleration in the rate of sea-level rise since about 100 000 BP which is incompatible with the notion of steady emersion of these coasts, put forward earlier by Stearns (1978).

Irregularity in the rate of sea-level change through time is also very clear spatially. The emersion of the Moroccan Meseta over three million years is slow and relatively continuous: 0.053 mm/1000 years in the Rabat region and 0.065 m/1000 years in the Casablanca region (figure 8.2). In the southern sector, the Moghrebian shoreline has an altitudinal difference of 150 m over approximately 30 to 40 km and the Messaoudian maximum level covers a 50 m interval in the Haut Atlas (figure 8.2). The altitude of the Maarifian varies between 20 and 50 m while the Harounian only reaches its highest point of 20 m to the south of Agadir. Finally, the Ouljian, which can be followed continuously between Cape Sim and Agadir, shows altitudes ranging from 0 to 10.12 m.

At the latitude of Morocco, the sea-level maxima correspond to the inter-Pluvial periods and the minima to the Pluvials. However, the periods of warming which correspond to the main phases of transgression are of unequal intensity. The Moghrebian and Ouljian waters were particularly warm whereas those of the Maarifian, the Anfatien and the Harounien were relatively more temperate (cf. table 8.1).

At Tarfaya, at the boundary of Morocco with Western Sahara, a contracted sequence of marine terraces may be observed (table 8.2). The Moghrebian is now only at 50 m and the Messaoudian at 30 to 40 m is the sole feature of Sidi bou Maleh and was formerly attributed to the Maarifian by Lecointre (in Weisrock 1981). Below 5 m, the Ouljian shorelines (or Harounian–Rabatian) are still hypothetical and, further south, the dominant Guinea fauna leads to difficult direct comparisons (Brebion and Ortlieb 1976).

In Western Sahara, a *lumachell* slab observed at 30 m can be followed until about 23°N; the Aioujian which is equivalent to Ouljian I and Ouljian II, can be followed along more than 100 km of coast to the north of Cap Blanc (figure 8.3). The Inchirian has been radiocarbon dated several times and despite the uncertainty of the measurements, corresponds to Ouljian III (Hoang *et al.* 1978).

In Mauritania and Senegal, Pleistocene sea levels are marked by slightly uplifted terraces and sediments in infilled embayments (Elouard 1976). Unfortunately to this day, these levels have not been the subject of extensive radiometric analysis except for radiocarbon analyses. A comparison with those of the Atlantic coast of the Sahara (Weisrock 1980) suggest a correlation between Ouljian I and the Tafaritian, the Ouljian II and the Aioujian, and the Ouljian III and the Inchirian. In Senegal, deposits of younger than 150 000 BP, are generally buried at depths indicating weak post-sedimentary epeirogenic movements, for example, the sandstone beaches of the Inchirian are commonly at −20 m in the basement of the Senegal delta (Monteillet 1979).

2.2 South of the Equator

Using data from very detailed fieldwork (Mascarenhas Neto 1960, Feio 1960, Soares de Carvalho 1961), analyses of faunal assemblages (Kouyoumontzakis and Giresse 1975), and particularly isotopic datings (Giresse *et al.* 1984), it

Table 8.2 Correlation of transgression cycles in Morocco, Tarfaya, Western Sahara, Mauritania and Senegal

Atlas (Morocco)	Tarfaya	Western Sahara	Mauritania	Senegal
Mellahian (+1 to +2 m)		Holocene (−1 to +2 m)	Taffolian (−3 m) Nouakchottian (+3 m)	Dakarian (+1 m) Taffolian (−2 m) Nouakchottian (+2 m) Tchadian (−20 m)
Oujian III (+0.5 m) Oujian II (+2 to +4 m) Oujian I (+6 m)	Oujian I (+4 m)	Inchirian Oujian or Aïoujian (+2 to +5 m)	Inchirian Aïoujian Tafaritian	Inchirian
Harounian-Rabatian (+20 m) Anfatian		0 ? ? ?		
Maarifian (+20 to +50 m) Messaoudian (+83 to +117 m) Fouartian (+180 m)	Messaoudian (+30 à +40 m)			
Moghrebian (+300 m)	Moghrebian (+50 m)	Moghrebian (+30 m)		

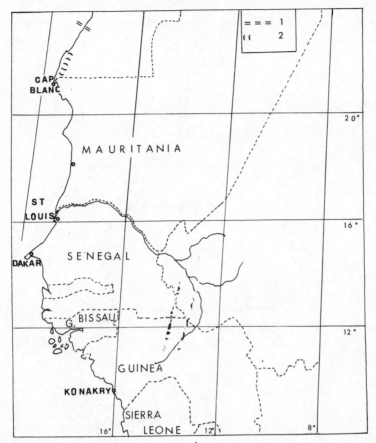

Figure 8.3 A map of the west coast of Africa showing the location of sites. Key: 1, southern limit of the *lumachell* slab at 30 m; 2, coast with the Aioujian terrace

is possible to reconstruct the history of the late Pleistocene for the coast south of Angola (Lobito and Mossamedes regions), and to evaluate a number of hypotheses regarding the structural evolution of this margin (figure 8.4).

Two ^{230}Th/^{234}U and ^{231}Pa/^{235}U dates of 36 000 BP corroborate several ^{14}C assays and refer to a level of 8–10 m for the Lobito–Benguela basin within the lower part of the terrace found at 8–20 m along this coastline. Marine deposits of the same age are observed on the coast of Namibia (Rust and Wieneke 1976, Rust 1979). With due reservations regarding radiocarbon measurements in this time period, Rust and Wieneke propose a sea level of +2 m between 27 100 and 25 250 BP on the coast of the central Namibian desert. This shoreline extends to the north, along the Squelette coast near Toscanini and Torrabaai.

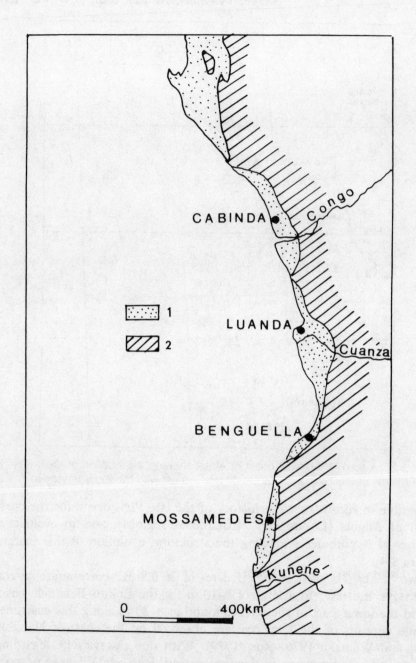

Figure 8.4 A map of the coast of Angola showing the location of sites. Key: 1, coastal sedimentary basins; 2, Pre cambrian shield areas

The upper part of the terrace between Lobito and Benguela is composed of older deposits at 12, 15, 20 and sometimes 25 m, which correspond to different sea-level maxima during the Eemian interglacial. By contrast, on the Mossamedes coast the marine deposits at the same altitude are much older. A comparison of these high sea levels with those in the schemes proposed by Bloom *et al.* (1974), Shackleton and Opdyke (1973) and Butzer (1975) leads to a tentative outline of the Eemian levels in this region. Only the 125 000 BP level (Eem I), which is widely observed between 6 and 10 m on several 'stable' coastal zones in the world, could represent a eustatic level greater than the present. Consequently, the observation in the Lobito–Benguela sector of four dated deposits corresponding to Eemian II and III and their absence in the Mossamedes zone, suggest coastal uplift in the former area. This epeirogenic movement affected the Eem II and Eem III shorelines which were initially formed at a level of approximately −10 m according to Davies (1981). Other dates obtained from the Mossamedes sector correspond to higher sea-levels. An age range of 133 000–174 000 BP was obtained for the 8–20 m terrace, which was subsequently covered by marine deposits of later age. A second date of >170 000–300 000 BP was obtained from the lower part, at 40 m, of a more slowly uplifted terrace, although the age is less certain. The apparent absence of any Riss–Mindel deposit in the 8–20 m Lobito terrace confirms the observation of more intense epeirogenic activity in this area than in the Mossamedes area.

These observations have led to a reconsideration of the correlation of the 'Ouljian' and 'Tyrrhenian' described by Soares de Carvalho (1961) at 20 and 90 m respectively. The 'Ouljian' terrace is covered with marine deposits from different oceanic sources. The 20 m cliff, which is sometimes difficult to follow over a large distance could result from processes during several phases of eustatic stability. The same conclusion could be envisaged for the high terrace and 50 m cliff. As a result of differential erosion, sediments of the same age can be preserved, for example, in one case at 5 m and in another at 15 m, without implying any local tectonic differences. On these coasts there does not exist a precise correlation between morphology (terrace and cliffs) and the littoral deposits which cover them; the latter are often present as isolated accumulations, sometimes juxtaposed, sometimes superimposed the one on the other, or sometimes widely separated.

In spite of the small number of radiometric datings available, an attempt at calculating the rate of epeirogenesis has been made. The rate seems to increase from the Riss (96 mm/1000 year) until the middle of the Würm (1125 mm/1000 year) and the Holocene (1420 mm/1000 year). This intensification can be considered as the expression of a phase of greater seismic activity in the region over several tens of thousands of years. As for the older deposits, they can be placed in the succession of calm and active periods. This regional epeirogenesis could be linked to a series of seismic epicentres aligned towards the west-south-west, that is to say parallel to the Walvis ridge; this direction is suggested by the presence of several centres of Mesozoic volcanic effusions (figure 8.5).

In the two zones studied, the Mesozoic and Cenozoic, strata are traversed by frequent distension faults and crossed by volcanic dykes from the Neogene and, no doubt, more recent. The intensity of this positive epeirogenesis clearly diminishes towards the equator: it disappears completely as the Congo estuary is reached. Towards the south, this epeirogenesis weakens in the Mossamedes basin and the northern part of Namibia and is no longer visible at the latitude of the central Namibian desert.

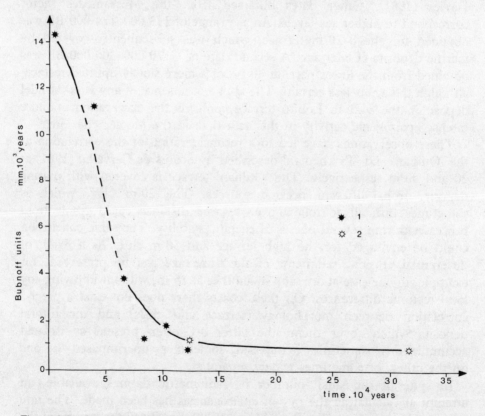

Figure 8.5   A graph comparing the rates of uplift of shorelines around Lobito (1.) and Mossamedes (2.), Angola

3.0 HOLOCENE SHORELINES AND LATE QUATERNARY SEA-LEVEL CHANGES

The evidence for Holocene sea-level changes has been observed on the majority of the African margins, but it is particularly well recognised on the Atlantic coast. The rise of sea level represents an oscillation of a general nature on a temporal scale of 10^3 to 10^4 years, but incorportes phases of local climatic and hydrological changes over 10^2 years and the storms or drought cycles of 10 to 10^2 years. The interplay of these with different regional factors leads to the various degrees of stability of the present coastline, which are currently the subject of international research programmes and monitoring under the patronage of Unesco.

The succession of coastal environments over the last ten thousand years is understood with increasing precision, notably in Senegal, the Ivory Coast, Benin, Nigeria, Gabon and Congo. In these regions, interdisciplinary studies (paolynology, sedimentology, palaeoclimatology, radiochronology) have been developed and have permitted the establishment of tables which sometimes integrate the analysis of a mass of buried and submarine evidence of sea-level change.

In general terms, in tropical and equatorial latitudes, the pre-Holocene fall in sea level corresponded with climatic conditions which were more arid than at present, whereas during the Holocene rise of sea level, humid environments developed at varying rates and degrees of intensity. Conversely, in tropical latitudes which begin in the south of the continent and the latitude of Swakopmund in Namibia and in the north at the latitude of the Hoggar, the transgression corresponded to a fluvial period and the environment during the Holocene rise of sea level (like that of the Mellahian in Morocco) coincided with hotter and drier conditions.

3.1 General and local chronologies of eustatic variations on the submarine platform

The variations in sea level, and in particular the rate of change during the Holocene, have had an obvious impact on the sequences of marine sediments. On the West African margin, the number of submarine shorelines which have been dated is much fewer than that of the emerged coastlines. Rather than trace a general curve for this margin based on information that is of necessity composite, the individual curves which have been proposed for the offshore zones of Mauritania, Senegal, the Ivory Coast and Gabon–Congo, are presented even though the rather provisional nature of these graphs must be recognised. In fact, the demonstration of the regional variability during the last 6000 or 7000 years shown by the curves (e.g. Faure and Hébard 1977), indicates that at least an equal variation should be envisaged for curves showing older sea-level movements.

The four curves illustrated (figure 8.6) show important differences. Even if some radiometric measurements are too close to the credible methodological limits to be entirely reliable, the majority of the data are acceptable. There is diachroneity in the onset of the major rise of sea level, which is slightly later on the Ivory Coast as compared with Mauritania and Senegal, and is much later off Congo. The cause of these variations could be linked to regional oscillations of the palaeo-geoid (the amplitude of which can reach 20 m: Pirazzoli 1984) and/or, epeirogenic movements the effects of which have been observed at the scale of the high sea levels of the Pleistocene.

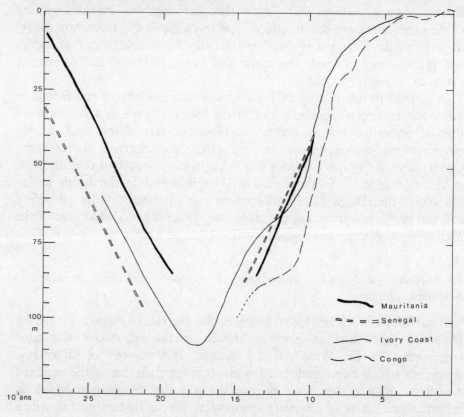

Figure 8.6 A graph of pre-Holocene and Holocene sea-level curves from Mauritania, Senegal, Ivory Coast and the Congo (the sources are cited in the text)

Three eustatic phases are common to these curves: a period of low level (at about 110 m) centred around 18 000 BP with a probable duration of 3000 years; a period of active eustatic rise 15 000 to 7000 years BP; a period from 7000 BP to the present with relatively stable sea levels.

Furthermore, the curves for the Ivory Coast and the Congo both show a period of marked slowing down of the rate of rise around 12 000 BP. This episode, which coincides with the Gothenburg geomagnetic movement and with a hypothermal pulsation on a planetary scale (Fairbridge 1977) is also reported off the coast of Senegal, as indicated by the development of a lagoon with *Cyprideis torosa* (Peypouquet 1977) which is located in the inter-dune depressions.

3.2 The succession of littoral environments in the Senegal and Mauritania region

At the maximum of aridity, major longitudinal dune sand seas developed, aligned north-east–south-west (presently fixed dunes). These are the 'red dunes' which correspond to the Ogolian in Mauritania and which extended onto the platform during phases of low sea-level (Hébrard 1973). The records of deep sea sedimentation (Sarthein and Koopman 1980) reveal that there was a major expansion of the Sahelian zone of influence between 12 000 and 8000 BP. This zone contracted rather than undergoing a true latitudinal displacement and the climate became more humid (Michel 1980), with an interruption around 7000 to 6500 BP when a short, dry period intervened. Off the coast of Mauritania (Arguin Bank), the climate remained relatively arid during the Holocene, but small variations in the composition of land-derived material (Diester-Haas 1981) indicate either a reduction in wind speeds or an increase in rainfall at about 10 000 years.

The first important coastal deposit of the Senegal platform is placed at around 10 000 BP when between −50 and −40 m sand beaches were established dominated by dunes of 10 to 15 m. At about 9000 BP a deceleration in the rate of sea-level rise led to a reworking of shell deposits which were distributed in steeply sloped bars. At about 8400 BP a further deceleration allowed the development of mangroves in a humid environment. Then, still under the same climatic conditions, the rate of rise increased and reached its maximum between 6800 and 4200 BP. This was the Nouakchottian (Rosso *et al.* 1977) which culminated between 1 and 2 m in Senegal and which reached 3 m in Mauritania. In Mauritania, the vestiges of this maximum include a mollusc fauna which is located at the limit of the Lusitanian and Senegalese provinces.

Then from 6500 BP to the present, a series of positive fluctuations from 1 m to 1.5 m or negative from −1 to −2 m are recorded, most often of very local significance. The principal marine maxima are dated at around 6700, 6200, 5600, 3400, 1850 and 1550 BP (Monteillet *et al.* 1981) in the interior basin of the Senegal river, where, independent of weak eustatic movements, the possible causes of these marine incursions could be linked to yearly, decennial or secular variations in the discharge of the Senegal river. During the Holocene, each of these incursions had important ecological and hydro-ecological consequences. The droughts supposedly responsible were of the order of those recorded three times (1913, 1941 and 1975) since the start of the century (Gac *et al.* 1983); these three drought maxima were also observed in the Sahel where they correspond each time to a minimum of sunspot activity (Faure and Gac 1981). The understanding of the periods of these variations has found an important application today in the context of the hydrological and agricultural management of the Senegal delta.

The most important negative oscillation occurred at around 4000 BP when a sea level at −2 m (Taffolian) controlled the closure of the gulf of the Senegal delta. Then the present landscape was defined as a function of the balance between eustatic factors and the oscillations of the water regime: for example, the extension in the Ferlo of salt water facies at about 3300 BP and between 1800 and 1500 BP corresponds to two periods when the flow of the Senegal river and the water table were higher than at present (Monteillet 1979).

One of the most original studies undertaken on the Quaternary geodynamics of this region involved the use of indirect measures of crustal flexing in the framework of the Rhéomarge project. In summary, for 7000 years, the oceanic margins of the continents have been subjected to variations in pressure imposed by the increase of the water mass. The models calculated by Clark and Bloom (1979) indicate a vertical elevation of the order of 5 to 10 m in several thousand years over several hundreds of kilometres measured perpendicularly to the coastline. The Senegal river basin, which forms an alluvial plain close to zero datum extending to nearly 150 km from the coast, *a priori* is a favourable site for the verification of Clark's models. Measurements which have been made there indicate a deformation of roughly 2 m over the last 7000 years and of one metre over 6000 years (Faure *et al.* 1980). As a consequence, the rigidity of the mantle or of the lithosphere under this part of the West African margin is more important than demonstrated in previous models based on Australia and Brazil (figure 8.7).

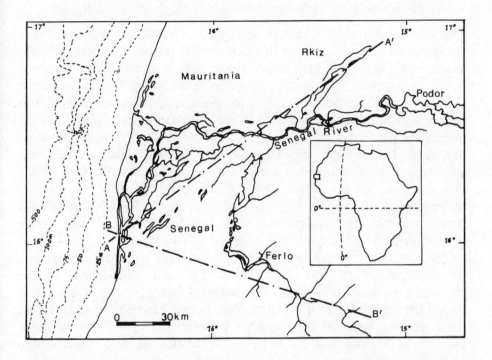

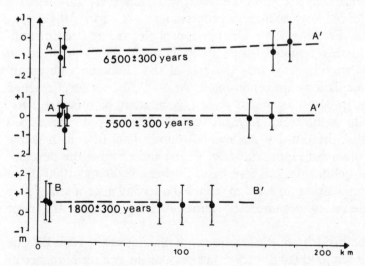

Figure 8.7 A map of the Senegal River delta showing the location of sections and a graph showing the reconstruction of possible geoid surfaces at 6500, 5500 and 1800 BP (after Faure *et al.* 1980)

3.3   *The succession of coastal environments in the Ivory Coast Region*

The climate during the eustatic minimum, 18 000 BP, was drier than today but no doubt included a distinctive rainy season: the increase in the amount of Gramineae and Cyperacaeae pollens confirm this (Frédoux 1980). Next, there took place a progressive transition to a more humid climate without the development of the present day vegetation cover; this climate enabled the development of deep valleys, especially in the interior part of the platform (Martin 1973). At about 12 000 BP, the development of a tropical climate intensified as shown by the association of fern spores and the pollen of ombrophile forest and mangrove taxa (Frédoux 1980). Off the coast of the Niger delta (Pastouret *et al*. 1978) the rate of sedimentation on the slope accelerated at about 11 500 BP indicating a strong renewal of precipitation and surface stream erosion before vegetation cover was established at about 10 000 BP.

The outer edge of the Ivory Coast shelf reveals a glauconite sediment accumulation which was concentrated by small movements of the shorelines around 18 000 BP. The sea-level curve reveals a stationary period between −100 and −110 m. Peat buried beneath the coast allows the increasing humidification and the development of ombrophile forest between 12 000 and 8000 BP to be traced. In the last 5000 years, swamp forest has been relatively stable on the coast, with, however, four negative interludes evidenced by sediments containing less than 10 per cent mangrove pollen (Frédoux 1980). Earlier morphological and sedimentological studies in this region (Tastet 1979, Pommel 1977) point to an evolution of the shoreline towards the end of the Holocene where only three negative oscillations are represented. At 6000 BP, sea level reached or exceeded the present level and a first generation of offshore bars, mainly of white sediments, formed, whilst lagoon peat developed upstream in the present-day valleys. Around 4000 BP, a negative oscillation was observed (approximately −1 m) and enabled the development of lagoons behind the offshore bars. Between 4000 and 1000 BP, a second positive oscillation (to *c*.2.5 m) enabled a second generation of bars of reddish material to accumulate; saline water penetrated the river valleys.

Isolation of the majority of the lagoons took place at about 1000 BP due to a slight fall of sea level (to *c*. −1.0 m) or once again as a consequence of the progradation of the offshore bars; the deltaic formations of the Bandama and the Comoe then emerged. A slight positive movement in sea level encouraged the partial erosion of the reddish offshore bars (evident at 0.5 m to 1 m dated 760 BP).

The return to present-day zero constitutes the final stage in this evolution of the outline of the Ivory Coast. This Holocene evolution of the Ivory Coast shoreline remains a provisional outline over which the writers cited earlier are not totally in agreement. It seems, however, that the detail and precision of the information supplied by pollen analysis form the best data base on the evolution of this coastal margin environment.

The subdued relief of Pleistocene colluvial deposits (terminal Continental) did not favour such a widespread development of bays and estuaries which could be infilled with sediment during the Holocene rise of sea level as compared to Senegal. Only deep valleys which incised the low plateaux were submerged, creating an important system of rias. The morphological study of Quaternary littoral formations indicates the role of the major break in relief of the Ivory Coast which separates a northern segment with basement rocks near the surface from a southern segment which has been subsiding since the Cretaceous; however Quaternary subsidence has not exceeded the average recorded in the basin since the Lower Cretaceous (approximately 5 cm per 1000 years).

The angle of the surgeline with the coast is lower to the east of the Canal di Vridi than to the west, which explains the large extension made up of sand bars to the east of Trou sans fond (Tastet 1979).

3.4   The succession of coastal environments of the Congo and southern Gabon regions

The accumulation which is most characteristic of the shorelines of 18 000 BP is made up of green sands from neighbouring depths of 120 m and from the top of the slope. Glauconite formation started after the deposition of calcareous muds around 22 000–24 000 BP (Giresse 1975). The cores are essentially made up of fecal pellets of limnic organisms whose increase in numbers is linked to the nutritional richness of the sediment. Despite the low sea level, the Congo's alluvial sediments, rich in organic and ferruginous suspensions, were deposited on this narrow platform: the concentration of these organic pellets diminishes with distance from the estuary. Oscillations in the shoreline and the modifications in the coastal morphology have controlled sediment accumulation varying between glauconite silts and almost pure glauconite sands; in the latter case, a major phenomenon resulting from the levigation occurred in the deep zone affected by the upwelling. This glauconite accumulation on the outer edge is the oldest of the platform; it is therefore the most advanced in the glaucono-genesis process (up to 6 per cent K_2O).

The accumulation on the outer edge of a fairly coarse calcareous bioclast sand seems to be the main sedimentary phenomenon associated with the last major eustatic sea-level rise. This 'Amphistegina fauna' (Lagaaij 1973), which is very rich in *Amphistegina gibbosa*, is also made up of molluscs and organisms of clear water littoral environments; other foraminifera, calcareous algae, Madréporaires and associated Bryozoa. It is found between −80 and −120 m off the coast of Gabon and Congo where it is extensive under the blanket of Holocene silts and further north, off Fernando Po, the Niger delta (Allen 1965) and the Ivory Coast, as indicated earlier. Several datings off the Congo give a range of between 10 200 and 12 620 BP. Although not very thick (0.5 to 2 m) this biogenic accumulation spreads out over a width of about 20 to 25 km and appears to correspond to a single sedimentary coastal prism markedly extended during storm events within the stillstand in sea-level rise observed between 13 000 and 11 000 BP on the sea-level curves from the Ivory Coast and Congo.

After this stage, the transgression quickly reached the inner parts of the platforms where it substantially re-shaped the alluvial layers or the pre-existing dune systems. Off the coast of Gabon and Congo, as soon as there was an incursion by the oceanic water body of the structurally defined depressions occupied by rivers or lagoons, infilling of the coast from 10 to 15 m developed at a rate of 2 to 3 m/1000 years. After 9000 BP the end of the infilling took place at a slower rate: 7 to 30 cm/1000 years in conditions which were already more or less littoral; finally, sedimentation was virtually non-existent at depths greater than 85 m (Giresse *et al.* 1984).

On the Congo platform, this sequence developed as the result of the deposition of massive quantities of suspended sediment from the Congo river onto the submerged platform.

Important mangrove peat remains were exposed at about −20 m by boring at Pointe-Noir. Dated on average at around 8000 BP they represent the maximum accumulation of organic sediments on this coast. The channels were incised in the middle of a shrubby mangrove landscape; they quickly silted up and thus pollen grains, roots, tree trunks and oysters could be preserved. The landscape very quickly became increasingly unstable, the channels diverged and at about 5000 BP, the marine shell sands reached present level. At this time, the mangrove was still lush and developed most rapidly at the edge of the rias where silting had not yet taken place: such as the case of the Kouilou palaeo-valley (Giresse and Moguedet 1980). The most frequently occurring species of the mangrove family were *Rhizophora mangle* and *R. harrisonii*, and

Acrostichum aureum and no other Gramineae pollens have been observed (Caratini and Giresse 1979)

At about 3000 to 4000 BP, sea level did not rise any further, or even dropped a little, as indicated by the coastal extension of the eolian features (Giresse and Le Ribault 1981). A final positive oscillation took place which managed to exceed slightly (0.5 m) present-day zero in an environment, which, although dominated by tropical forest and mangrove, saw the reappearance of Gramineae and Cyperaceae species. The last thousand years show, in the context of a humid climate, several signs of a tendency towards aridification.

As in the case of the Ivory Coast, the extent of fluvio-marine bays was limited, the estuaries were formed in deep rias incised in the colluvial material or below ancient eolian bars whose relief (from 10 to 30 m) has prevented a deeper marine invasion. It seems that the relative stability of sea level in the late Holocene did not favour the progradation of offshore bars as in the north of the Gulf of Guinea, in spite of the intensity of the transfer of material by longshore drift.

4.0 QUATERNARY SHORELINES AND HUMAN OCCUPATION IN WEST AFRICA

Generally, human occupation coincides with the occurrence of high level marine shorelines while the information relative to the low levels is sparse and is the result of good luck in the choice of dredging sites or underwater cores.

The most ancient known cultures on the coasts of West Africa are those of Angola. The stratigraphic study of tools associated with these cultures (Ramos 1981) is very useful in the analysis of shorelines, even if some of the deposits containing artificats are not always accumulations from marine terraces. The Australio–Anthropian populations reached the Angolan coast between the Lower and Middle Pleistocene, notably near Luanda, in the Lunda where a poorly developed Oldowayen industry has been described; this same industry is indicated in the 100 m terrace of south Lobito and the 35 m terrace of Ponta do Giraul–Mossamedes (Ramos 1982). In the Middle Pleistocene the Acheulian complex developed alongside the Archanthropian (Pithecanthropian) populations and deposits, notably from the Upper Acheulian, are described in several coastal sites, notably at Baia Farta, to the south of Benguela, at Benguela itself, at Ponta das Vacas, Ponta do Giraul and Porto Alexandre (Ramos 1982). In the Lower Palaeolithic there follows a complex of industries which are still related in their oldest stages to the Neanderthal peoples and in the most recent stages to the Neanthropian (*H. sapiens*). This complex development in the upper Pleistocene, where it forms the Middle Stone Age, is associated with shorelines which are traced all the way to the coasts of South Africa (Butzer 1975), where it is sometimes dated: the boundary between the Acheulian and the Middle Stone Age is certainly earlier than 125 000 BP (Davies 1981), the final Acheulian preceding the major regression established as being at about 140 000 BP.

In the Atlantic Sahara, it has been possible to define the positions of the Holocene shorelines according to climate and human settlement indicators (Petit-Maire *et al.* 1977, Delibrias *et al.* 1977). The Nouakchottian shoreline is dated several times as being between 6000 and 3000 BP, where it is observed below present day zero; if the climate between 4000 and 3000 BP was more humid than today, a relative aridification took place with a transitory lagoon phase in some areas. The process of aridification intensified from 2000 BP until today. The introduction of man only took place towards the end of the Nouakchottian and during the lagoon period when conditions were favourable for fishing and savannah fauna abounded. This example shows, however, a chronological discontinuity between the ecological optimum and the maximum of human occupation. The malacological study of culinary shell heaps on the fringe of the Nouakchottian palaeo-shore (Rosso and Petit-Maire 1978) revealed changes in the climate and the regime of the ocean current which have caused disruption of the littoral profile and the disappearance of numerous biotopes. The oscillations of the shoreline were able to determine the way of life of nearby inhabitants.

The culinary shell heaps constitute useful and frequent indicators of coastal occupation by man at the time of the approach of the Holocene sea: they are known in abundance in Mauritania, Senegal, the Ivory Coast, Benin, Gabon, Congo, Angola. On the other hand, they have sometimes been the source of confusion with true marine deposits, which are direct evidence of shorelines.

In the Congo, stone tools (Tshitolien) have been observed directly interstratified in the saline layers of about 3000 BP which outcrop at the mouth of the Songololo near Pointe Noire (Lanfranchi 1978). In the same region, cores at −35 m, off Djeno, have revealed this same industry at the base of the Holocene sequence to a rock bench parallel to the coast; such a favourable site for an encampment should have been above sea level between 7000 and 8000 BP (Manongo 1985).

The pollen spectra of Holocene coastal sediments also underline man's presence in Nigeria; the appearance of man at about 28 000 BP is indicated by the increase in the frequency of *Elaeis guineenis* pollen

(Sowunmi 1981), as in the Ivory Coast, and the recent degradation of the mangrove is attributable to anthropic activity (Frédoux 1980); this same historical recession of the magrove is also recorded on the Congo coast (Giresse and Lanfranchi 1984).

Typescript received 1986, February.

ACKNOWLEDGEMENTS

The author acknowledges with thanks the translation of this chapter by Veronique Thompson, Department of Geography, University of Durham.

REFERENCES

Allen, J. R. L. 1965: Late Quaternary Niger delta and adjacent areas: sedimentary environments and lithofacies. *Bull. Amer. Assoc. of Petrol. Geol.*, 49, 547–600.

Biberson, P. 1971: Index-cards on the Marine and Continental Cycles of the Moroccan Quaternary. *Quaternaria*, XIII, 1–76.

Bloom, A. L., Broecker, W. S., Chappell, J. M. A., Matthews, R. K. and Mesolella, K. J. 1974: Quaternary sea-level fluctuations on a tectonic coast. New ^{230}Th/^{234}U dates from the Huon Peninsula New Guinea. *Quat. Res.*, 4, 185–205.

Brebion, P. and Ortlieb, L. 1976: Nouvelles recherches géologiques et malacologiques sur le Quaternaire de la Province de Tarfaya (Maroc méridional). *Geobios*, 9, 529–50.

Brebion, P., Hoang, C. T. and Weisrock, A. 1984: Intérêts des coupes d'Agadir-Port pour l'étude du Pléistocène supérieur marin du Maroc. *Bull. Mus. natn. His. nat.*, Paris, 4, 6, 2, 129–51.

Burke, K., Dessauvagie, T. F. Y. and Whiteman, A. J. 1972: Geological history of the Benue Valley and adjacent areas. *African Geology*. Ibadan, 1970, 187–205.

Butzer, K. W. 1975: Geological and ecological perspectives on the Middle Pleistocene. In K. W. Butzer and G. L. Isaac (eds.), *After the Australopithecines*, The Hague, 857–74.

Caratini, Cl. and Giresse, P. 1979: Contribution palynologique à la croissance des environements continentaux et marins du Congo à la fin du Quaternaire. *C. R. Acad. Sc. Paris*, 288, 379–82.

Clark, J. A. and Bloom, A. L. 1979: Hydroisostasy and Holocene emergence of South America. *Proceedings of the 1978 International Symposium on Coastal Evolution in the Quaternary*, São Paulo, Brasil, 41–60.

Davies, O. 1981: A review of Wilson's theory that the Last Interglacial ended with an ice surge, and the South-African evidence therefor. *Ann. Natal. Mus.*, 24, 701–20.

Delibrias, G., Ortlieb, L. and Petit-Marie, N. 1977: Le littoral ouest saharien nouvelles dates ^{14}C. In *Recherches françaises sur le Quaternaire, INQUA, 1977, Suppl. Bull. AFEQ*, 50, 203–4.

Diester-Haas, L. 1981: Factors contributing to Late Glacial and Holocene sedimentation on the continental shelf and slope off NW Africa, Banc d'Arguin, 19°N. *Meteor Forsch-Ergebnisse, RC*, 35, 1–22.

Elouard, P. 1976: Application de la paléoécologie des Mollusques à un problème de stratigraphie: la différenciation de deux étages du Quaternaire marin de Mauritanie. *Notes africaines*, 151, 65–73.

Emery, K. O., Uchupi, E., Boivin, C. O., Phillips, J. and Simpson, E. S. 1975: Continental margin of Western Africa: Cape St Francis (South Africa) to Walvis Ridge (South West Africa). *Bull. AAPG*, 59, 3–59.

Fail, J. P., Montadert, L., Delteil, J. R., Valery, P., Patrait, Ph. and Schlich, R. 1970: Prolongation des zones de fracture de l'Océan Atlantique dans le Golfe de Guinée. *Earth and Planetary Sci. Letters*, 7, 413–19.

Fairbridge, R. W. 1977: Global climate change during the 13 500 BP Gothenburg geomagnetic excursion. *Nature*, 265, 430–1.

Faure, H., Fontes, J. C., Hebrard, L., Monteillet, J. and Pirazoli, P. A. 1980: Geoidal change and shore-level tilt along Holocene estuaries: Senegal River Area, West Africa. *Science*, 210, 421–3.

Faure, H. and Gac, J. Y. 1981: Solar cycle and drought in Sahel. 9th *International Congress of Biometeorology, Osnabruck and Stuttgart-Hohenheim*, (FRG), Abstract, 1, 92–93.

Faure, H. and Hebrard, L. 1977: Variations de lignes de rivage du Sénégal et en Mauritanie au cours de l'Holocène. *Studia Geologica polonica* L11, 243–57.

Feio, M. 1960: As praias levantadas da regiao do Lobito e da Baía Farta. *Rev. da Junta de Invest. do Ultramar Gaxia de Orto, Lisboa*, 8, 357–70.

Fredoux, A. 1980: Evolution de la mangrove près d'Abidjan (Côte d'Ivoire) au cours de quarante derniers millénaires. *Trav. et Doc. Geogr. tropicale, CEGET-CNRS, Talence*, 51–88.

Gac, J.-Y., Monteillet J. and Faure, H. 1983: Marine shorelines in estuaries as palaeoprecipitation indicators. In A. Street-Perrott, M. Beran and R. Ratcliffe (eds.), *Variations in the global water budget*, Dordrecht: D. Reidel Publishing Co.

Giresse, P. 1975: Essai de chronomètrie de la glauconitisation dans le Golfe de Guinée, exemple de vitesse diagénètique au Quaternaire supérieur. *C. R. somm. Soc. Géol-Fr.*, 163–164.

Giresse, P. and Lanfranchi, R. 1984: Les climats et les océans de la région congolaise. Bilans selon les échelles et les méthodes de l'observation. In J. A. Coteze and E. M. Van Zinderen Bakker Sr (eds.), *Palaeoecology of Africa*, Rotterdam, 16, 77–88.

Giresse, P., Malounguila-Nganga, D. and Delibrias, G. 1984: Rythmes de la transgression et de la sédimentation holocène sur les plates-formes sous-marines du Sud du Gabon et du Congo. *C. R. Acad. Sc. Paris*, 299, II, 327–30.

Giresse, P. and Moguedet, G. 1980: Chronoséquences fluvio-marines de l'Holocène de l'estuaire du Kouilou et des Colmatages côtiers voisins du Congo In, Les rivages tropicaux – Mangroves d'Afrique et d'asie – Talence. CEGET-CNRS. *Travaux et Documents de Géographie tropicale*, 39, 21–46.

Giresse, P. and Le Ribault, L. 1981: Contribution à l'étude exoscopique des quartz à la reconstitution paléogéographique des derniers épisodes du Quaternaire littoral du Congo. *Quat. Res.*, 15, 86–100.

Grant, N. K. 1971: South Atlantic Benoue Trough and Gulf of Guinea triple junction. *Geol. Soc. Am. Bull.*, 82, 2295–8.

Hebrard, L. 1973: Contribution à l'étude rhéologique du Quaternaire du littoral mauritanien entre Nouakchott et Nouadhibou-18-21° lat. N. Participation à l'étude des désertifications du Sahara. *Lab. Géol. Fac. Sci. Univ. Dakar*, 483p.

Hoang, C. T., Ortlieb, L. and Weisrock, A. 1978: Nouvelles datations $^{230}Th/^{234}U$ de terrasses marines 'ouljiennes' du Sud-Ouest du Maroc et leurs significations stratigraphique et tectonique. *C. R. Acad. Sc. Paris*, 286, D, 1759–62.

King, B. C. 1970: Vulcanicity and rift tectonics in East Africa. In T. N. Clifford and I. G. Grass (eds.), *African Magmatism and Tectonics*, Edinburgh: Oliver and Boyd, 263–83.

Kouyoumontzakis, G. and Giresse, P. 1975: L'évolution à la fin du Pléistocène et à l'Holocène du littoral angolais de Lobito, Benguela et Mossamedes. III° SASQUA Conference, Cape Town, *Ann. S. Afr. Mus.*, 71, 49–67.

Lanfranchi, R. 1978: Rapport des missions d'études et recherches préhistoriques pour l'année universitaire 1976–77. Roneo. Univ. Marien. Ngouabi, Brazzaville, R. P. Congo.

Le Pichon, X. 1968: Sea-floor spreading and continental drift. *J. Geophys. Res.*, 73, 3661–97.

Manongo, L. 1985: Le gisement sous-marin des phosphates de Djéno. Nouvelles observations. *D. E. A. Univ. Toulouse-Perpignan*.

Mascarenhas Neto, M. G. 2960: Géologie de la région Benguela-Cuio (bande sédimentaire). *Bol. Serv. géol. Min. Angola*, 3, 89–99.

Michel, P. 1980: The southwestern Sahara margin: sediments and climatic changes during the recent Quaternary. *Palaeoecology of Africa and the surroundings islands*, 12, 297–306.

Monteillet, J. 1979: Le Quaternaire du delta du Sénégal: synthèse des connaissances actuelles et nouvelles données sur l'Holocène. *Bull. IFAN Dakar*, 41, A, 1–20.

Monteillet, J., Faure, H., Pirazzoli, P. A. and Ravisé, A. 1981: L'invasion saline du Ferlo (Sénégal) à l'Holocène supérieur (1900 BP). *Palaeoecology of Africa and the surrounding islands*, 13, 205–16.

Pastouret, L., Chamley, H., Delibrias, G., Duplessy, J. C. and Theide, J. 1978: Late Quaternary changes in Western Tropical Africa deduced from deep-sea sedimentation off the Niger delta. *Oceanologica Acta*, 1, 217–31.

Petit-Maire, N., Delibrias, G. and Ortlieb, L. 1977: New radiometric data for the Atlantic Sahara (Holocene, 19° to 20°N), tentative interpretation. *X INQUA Congress, Birmingham*, Abstract.

Peypouquet, J. P. 1977: Les ostracodes, indicateurs paléoclimatiques et paléogéographiques du Quaternaire terminal (Holocène) sur le plateau continental Sénégalais. In 6th International Symposium *"Ecology and Zoogeography of Recent and Fossil Ostracoda"*, Saafeden (Salzburg), H. Loffer and D. W. W. Jung, publ., 369–94.

Pirazzoli, P. A. 1984: Secular trends of relative sea-level (RSL) changes indicated by tide-gauge records. *Intern. Symposium on Late Quaternary sea-level changes and coastal evolution*, Mar del Plata, Argentina, Abstracts, 82–5.

Pommel, R. 1977: Le niveau de la mer en Côte d'Ivoire depuis 5000 ans BP. *Comm. Congr. St Valéry s/Somme*, préprint.

Ramos, M. 1981: As exavações de Capangombe e o problema da M.S.A. no Sudoeste de Angola. *Leba*, 4, 29–35.

Ramos, M. 1982: Le Paléolithique du Sud-Ouest de l'Angola, vue d'ensemble. *Leba*, 5, 43–52.

Rosso, J. C., Elouard, P. and Monteillet, J. 1977: Mollusques du Nouakchottien (Mauritanie et Sénégal septentrional); inventaire systématique et esquisse paléoécologique. *Bull. IFAN*, 39, A, 465–86.

Rosso, J. C. and Petit-Maire, N. 1978: Amas coquillier du littoral atlantique saharien. *Bull. Mus. Anthrop. préhist. Monaco*, 22, 79–118.

Rust, U. 1979: Uber Konvergenzen im Wüstenrelief arm Beispiel der südwestafrikanischen Namib-wüste (Skellküste und Zentrale Namib). *Sonderdruck aus den Mitteilungen der Geographischen Gesellschaft in Munchen*, 64, 201–17.

Rust, U. and Wieneke, F. 1976: Geomorphologie der Kustennahen Zentralen Namib (Sudwest Afrika). *Münchener, geogr. Abdh*, 19.

Sarthein, M. and Koopmann, B. 1980: Late Quaternary deep-sea record on Northwest-african dust supply and wind circulation. *Palaeoecology of Africa and the surrounding islands*, 12, 239–53.

Shackleton, N. J. and Opdyke, N. D. 1973: Oxygen isotope and palaeomagnetic stratigraphy of Equatorial Pacific core V 28–238: oxygen isotope temperatures and ice volumes on a 10^5 year and 10^6 year scale. *Quat. Res.*, 3, 39–55.

Siedner, R. and Miller, J. 1968: K/Ar age determination on basaltic rocks from South-West Africa and their bearing on continental drift. *Earth and Plan. Sci. Let*, 4, 1451.

Soares de Carvalho, G. 1961: Alguna problemas dos terracos quaternarias de littoral de Angola. *Bol. Serv. geol. min. Angola*, 2, 5–15.

Sowunmi, M. A. 1981: Late Quaternary environmental changes in Nigeria. *Pollen et Spores*, XXIII, 125–48.

Stearns, C. E. 1978: Pliocene-Pleistocene emergence of the Moroccan Meseta. *Geol. Soc. Amer. Bull.*, 89, 1630–44.

Tastet, J. P. 1979: L'Holocène du littoral septentrional du Golfe de Guinée. *Proceedings of the 1978 International Symposium on coastal evolution in the Quaternary*, Sao-Paulo, Brasil, 588–606.

Weisrock, A. 1980: The littoral deposits of the Saharian Atlantic coast since 150 000 years. *Palaeoecology of Africa and the surrounding islands*, 12, 277–87.

Weisrock, A. 1981: Variations du niveau de l'océan et morphologie littorale du Haut-Atlas (Maroc) depuis cent mille ans. *Oceanis*, 7, 481–7.

Weisrock, A., Delibrias, G., Rognon, P. and Coude-Gaussen, G. 1985: Variations climatiques et morphogénèse au Maroc atlantique (30–33°N) à la limite Pleistocène-Holocène. *Bull. Soc. Géol. France*, 8, 565–9.

9

Sea-level changes on the East Coast of Africa during the Holocene and Late Pleistocene

Lars-Erik Åse

1.0 INTRODUCTION

To describe the present coast of eastern Africa is no easy task, and the problem becomes even more complicated if the development of the coast during the last c100 000 years is to be explained. The difficulties are due to many different factors. Modern studies of the shore and the shore displacement are very few. There are some older studies of a more general character like those of Valentin (1952) which include information on the present coasts of eastern Africa as part of a worldwide approach to describe the coasts partly in accordance with D. W. Johnson's (1919) classification of shorelines of submergence and shorelines of emergence. However, most of the information available is from rather limited coastal areas, written in many languages and by authors from countries like the USA, Japan and Sweden. Moreover, the terminology is rather confusing. For a long time, the now abandoned theory of contemporaneity between glacial ages in Europe and pluvial ages in Africa made a great impact on the studies of coastal changes in eastern Africa. Another disadvantage is the very few absolute age determinations that have been carried out in the area. Thus, a reliable chronology for the coast of eastern Africa is still missing and the indications presented in this article are essentially tentative.

2.0 GENERAL DESCRIPTION OF THE PRESENT EASTERN COAST OF AFRICA

From the physical point of view, the eastern coast of Africa is generally one of moderate to low wave energy. Except for the area of northern Madagascar and adjacent parts of the African mainland that are reached

by cyclones, waves are seldom greater than 2.4–3.6 m (Davies 1977).
South of the equator the south-eastern trade is the dominating wind; from
northern Tanzania northwards the north-east monsoon normally blows
during the months from December to March and the south-east monsoon
during the rest of the year. The north-east monsoon normally is the
stronger of the two (figure 9.1). The tidal range reaches its maximum in
the equatorial part of eastern Africa, e.g. 4.1 m in Mombasa and 3.5 m in
Dar es Salaam (East African Harbours Corporation 1976) whereas in the
Red Sea and west of Durban in South Africa the tidal range is less than
2 m. Unlike the western coast of Africa, the eastern coast has a warm
water current and coral reefs occur all along the coast from the Red Sea as
far south as southern Madagascar and in Mozambique as far as the Tropic
of Capricorn. Mangrove swamps show a similar distribution.

The following description of the coasts of eastern Africa derives mainly
from Valentin (1952, and figure 9.2). Thus, the coast of the Red Sea is
characterized mainly by fluvial action and coral reefs. The strong tectonic
influence of the coast might also be noted and it is difficult to describe the
coast in terms of emergence or submergence. At the Horn of Africa, cliff
coasts dominate in the north. At the Gulf of Aden and in the Afar
depression of Ethiopia Pleistocene coral reefs have been found above
present sea level indicating that the whole coast is not actually one of
submergence (Faure *et al.* 1973). In southern Somalia and northern
Kenya dune ridges are the main characteristics of the coast. Sometimes at
least two generations of dune ridges can be found, the older probably
being of young Pleistocene age, the younger, closer to the sea, of
Holocene age (figure 9.3). Contrary to the general idea of African coasts
lacking a shelf, along the northern coast of Kenya the North Kenyan
Bank is 50–60 km wide off Ungama (Formosa) Bay (British Admiralty
1957).

Further southwards in southern Kenya and northern Tanzania the coast
becomes very complex. Cliffs formed by wave erosion in coral rocks with
raised shorelines might be the most prominent feature indicating a
shoreline of emergence. However, where fresh waters reach the coast,
deep creeks, such as the one at Mombasa, are found. The creeks should
normally indicate a shoreline of submergence, but the submergence could
have occurred earlier than the more recent emergence. Mangrove swamps
are very common, especially in muddy areas where fresh water enters the
coast. Between the cliffs small pocket beaches are found, which tend to
increase in size towards the north (towards the Malindi area) in Kenya
and towards the south (towards Dar es Salaam) in Tanzania. Often, the
present shore is fringed by a *c.*1 km wide dead coral reef, outside which

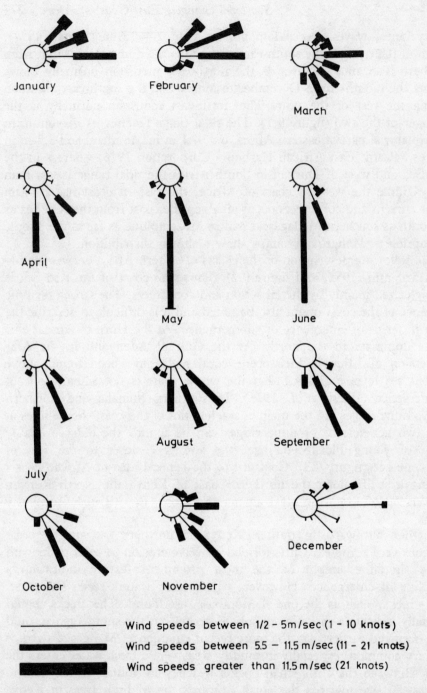

Wind speeds between 1/2 – 5 m/sec (1 – 10 knots)

Wind speeds between 5.5 – 11.5 m/sec (11 – 21 knots)

Wind speeds greater than 11.5 m/sec (21 knots)

Figure 9.1 Wind roses from Tanga, Tanzania 1931–1960 (Source: East African Meteorological Department).

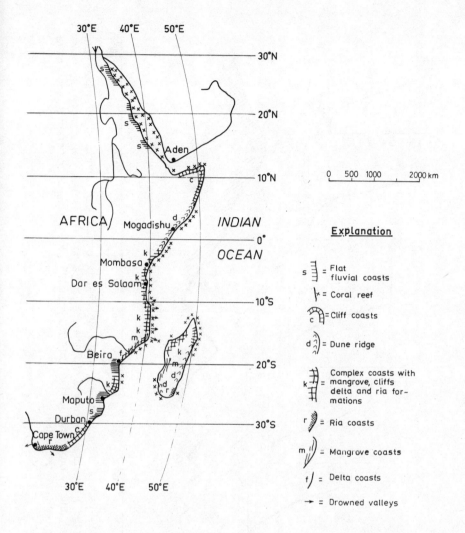

Figure 9.2 A map of eastern Africa showing the main coastal geomorphologial features (redrawn from Valentin 1952).

the present coral-building animals and plants flourish.

In southern Tanzania and Mozambique the coast gradually changes to one of submergence. Mangrove swamps are still very frequent, but Valentin has noted the occurrence of drowned valleys (shown on figure 9.2 as arrows). More recent data on the Holocene transgression in the delta area of Zambezi are given by Jaritz *et al.* (1977).

The coast of Madagascar is generally very complex. In the north-east, cliff coasts are found, but otherwise the steep eastern coast mainly shows

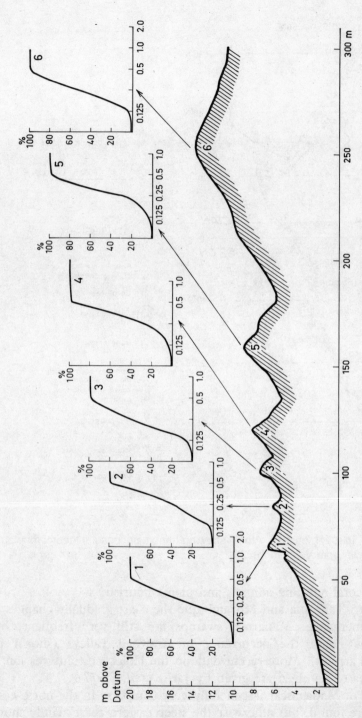

Figure 9.3 The profiles of dune ridges south of Watamu, Malindi, Kenya, showing the particle size distribution of samples from each ridge (1–6). According to Åse (1981), the ridges belong to two different generations: ridges 1–5 have a similar grain size distribution, orientation and sand colour, and are probably younger than 1000 years BP; ridge 6 has a smoother profile and a more reddish coloured sand and belongs to an older generation

the characteristics of tectonic movements although a thin coastal plain with dune ridges and features formed by marine deposition fringes the coast. The western coast of Madagascar is more like the coast of East Africa. The rocks are often sedimentary. Mangrove swamps and coral reefs occur even in the southernmost part of the west coast.

In South Africa the coast of Natal shows a coastal plain with late Tertiary sands masking the Cretaceous beds in most parts of the area (King 1951). Lagoons are typical of the coastal zone. These lagoons, according to King, are not features of a coastline of emergence, that is lagoons locked-in behind offshore bars on a rising coast but fundamentally drowned and filled by river deposits. Further southwards both King (1951) and Valentin (1952) recognize the drowning of river mouths, that is a ria coast. However, as will be noted later, raised shorelines also occur along the coast of South Africa and it seems highly questionable whether the altitude of these shorelines only reflects eustatic sea-level changes. While the whole idea of distinguishing between shorelines of emergence and shorelines of submergence might be of limited value (Shepard 1976) it still seems to be the most relevant classification in this area.

A more useful approach than the general description given above might be a careful examination of late Quaternary shorelines from limited areas. For that purpose, firstly the coasts of southern Kenya and northern Tanzania and secondly the coast of southeastern Africa i.e. southern Tanzania, Mozambique, Madagascar and northeastern South Africa, have been selected.

3.0 THE SHORELINES OF SOUTHERN KENYA AND NORTHERN TANZANIA

Several authors have studied the shorelines and terraces along the East African coast using various methods, and their evidence is summarized in Table 9.1. Although the list is far from complete (cf. Temple 1970), it indicates two different approaches. Some authors present a generalized pattern of the number of terraces recorded either during a field-based geological mapping survey or from aerial photographs whereas others (Cooke 1974, Åse 1978) used field levelling for the determination of the altitude of each marine terrace, relative to either mean sea level (Cooke) or lowest tide level, which equals Kenyan Datum (Åse). Thus, *c.*2 m should be added to the figures of Cooke to make them correspond to those of Åse (see tables 9.1 and 9.2).

The Sakura terrace of Alexander (1968) is in doubt for Temple (1971) wrote that the feature in the Dar es Salaam area is called a terrace 'for

Table 9.1 Correlation of marine terraces on the coast of Kenya and northern Tanzania according to various authors

Author / Area	Caswell (1953) (Mombasa–Kwale)	Thompson (1956) (Malindi)	Battistini (1966) (Dar es Salaam)	Alexander (1968) (NE Tanzania)	Hori (1971) (Mombasa)	Cooke (1974) (Tanga)	Åse (1978) (Mombasa–Malindi)
Upper Terrace	Not studied	Not studied	Reef I	Sakura	Changamwe	41 m (Nguvumali?)	Not studied
Middle Terraces	120 feet c.36 m	120 feet	Reef II	Tanga	Upper Mombasa	24–27 m (Tanga)	
	30 feet c.9 m	25 feet c.8 m			Lower Mombasa		Levels IV–VII (?)
Lower Terrace	15 feet c5 m		Flandrian	Mtoni	Shelley Beach	4.5–6 m beach 2–3 m beach	Levels I–III (?)

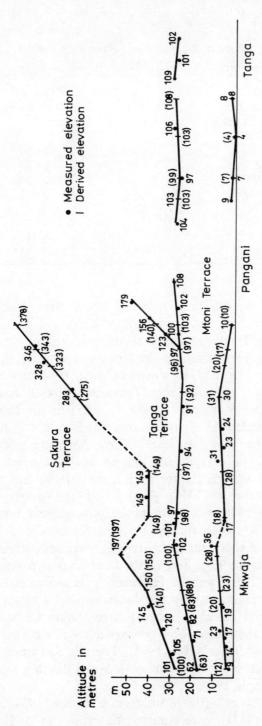

Figure 9.4 A graph to show the altitude of terraces along the coast of northern Tanzania between Mkwaja and Tanga (Redrawn from Alexander 1968).

Table 9.2   Stratification by altitude of shore elements between the Kenyan–Tanzanian border and Malindi below 21 m above Datum (see figure 9.5)

(1) Stratum (level)	(2) Altitude at 0 km (m above Datum)	(3) Number of elements	(4) Inclination S–N	
I	4.79	19	−0.0042	±0.0021
II	5.93	55	+0.626	±0.0028
III	8.88	12	+0.0016	±0.004
IV	10.04	21	+0.009	±0.004
V	12.74	21	±0.00	±0.004
VI	14.44	5	+0.35	±0.019
VII	17.01	5	+0.02	±0.012
VIII	20.07	6	+0.013	±0.004

convenience'. Temple is also very sceptical about the tilting of the Sakuran and Tangan terraces south of Pangani suggested by Alexander (figure 9.4). The single Tanga terrace of north-east Tanzania (Alexander 1968) seems to be a double feature on the Kenyan coast, the Upper and Lower Mombasa terrace (Hori 1971), whereas Cooke (1974) also considers it a single phenomenon although the Nguvumali terrace might well correspond to the Upper Mombasa terrace of Hori. In the Bagamoyo–Mkwaja section, Alexander (1968) recognizes beach ridges indicating a 'changing position of the Tanga sea level'. Thus, Alexander seems to be able to agree at least upon a regionally limited double character of the Tanga terrace, but the altitude figures do not correspond with those of Caswell (1953) and Thompson (1956). According to the investigations of the present author (Åse 1978, 1981), where the zone between 0 and 21 m above Kenyan Datum has been studied between Kanamai and Malindi, there is a great variety of shoremarks (figure 9.5) that can be grouped and 8 levels (I to VIII on figure 9.6). Five of the levels may correspond with (the lower part of) the Tanga terrace. However, as is shown in table 9.2, the levels VI–VIII are found at very few locations and it might well be that only level V around 12–13 m above Kenya Datum i.e. *c.*10–11 m above mean sea-level is significant. This corresponds well with the altitude of the 'Lower Mombasa terrace' (Hori 1971). There is also a raised beach level at 12 m above mean sea level as far south as the Baganoyo peninsula (cf. Chittick 1962, Temple 1970).

Below *c.*10 m above low tide (the Mtoni terrace) Cooke (1974) identifies two terraces. Chittick (1962) also recognizes two terraces in the Bagamoyo area north of Dar es Salaam at 2 and 8 m above mean sea level. It seems

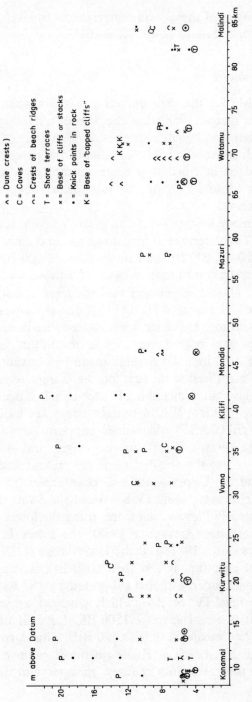

Figure 9.5 A graph to show the distribution of seven shore elements on the coast of Kenya between Kanamai and Malindi. The zero altitudinal datum is the lowest low tide (after Åse 1981).

reasonable that the lower of these levels corresponds to levels I and II (cf. table 9.2) and the upper one to levels III and IV.

3.1   The age of the shorelines

Few data are available for the determination of the absolute age of the shorelines. Alexander states (1968) that the Sakura terrace is 'probably a Pleistocene terrace that may be either the result of an early stillstand or an early interglacial high sea level'. In the opinion of the present author, the Sakura terrace could be ascribed to a more recent age, e.g. the 'great' interglacial between Mindel-Riss or the interglacial between Riss and Würm (i.e. the Eemian).

Alexander (1968) made a number of ^{14}C assays of coral rocks found in connection with the Tanga terrace. The datings group themselves into two categories, i.e. 24 000–30 000 BP and more than 32 000 BP. Alexander himself considers these figures minimum figures for the ages of the terraces, e.g. the coral capping should be younger than the terrace, but this seems a little doubtful, as the ^{14}C assays of Hori (1971) do *not* show an increasing age with increasing altitude. If the terraces, instead, are cut into the coral rock, the ^{14}C assays are instead very crude maximum figures. Even Temple, who (1971) criticizes the datings made by Alexander seems to agree at least on a late Pleistocene age for the Tanga terrace (Temple 1970). The datings give an indication of interstadial Würmian age (cf. Bird 1984, where two 'Middle Würm transgressions are indicated in the time-interval 25 000–50 000 BP). Alexander supports very strongly the view that the Tanga terrace is of eustatic origin and of interstadial Würmian age which is also the standpoint of the present author as far as the Tanga terrace and its 'Upper Mombasa' counterpart (in the sense of Hori) is concerned. However, Hove (1980) dated the 38 m terrace of the south Kenya coast to early Pleistocene. Concerning the lower terraces, for example the Mtoni terrace (Alexander 1968), the lower Mombasa and Shelley beach terraces (Hori 1971) and the lower levels (I–IV) studied by Åse a late Postglacial age, that is less than 6000 BP, is suggested. This idea is favoured by Alexander and also supported by ^{14}C assays of shells probably related to level IV of Åse which gave an apparent age of *c*.2000–2200 BP, that is a real age of *c*.1500 BP. Level II of Åse is in a similar way dated to late medieval time (*c*.500 BP). This corresponds well with the fact that the 2 m beach at Kaole (in the Bagamoyo area) forms the foundation for the 13th–16th century mosque and former town (Temple 1970).

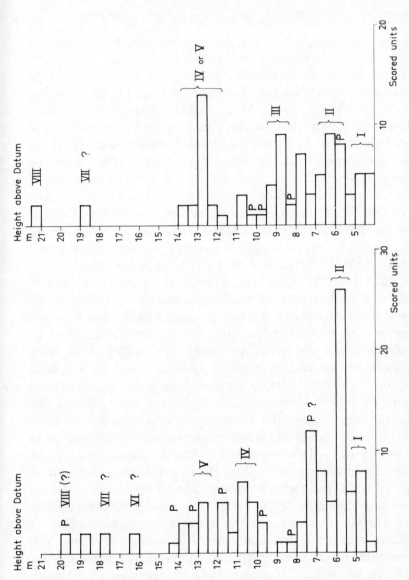

Figure 9.6 The vertical distribution of shore elements at 0.5 m intervals on the coast of southern Kenya. The various types of sea-level indications have been given numerical values and summed; the sum of the scored units is shown on the horizontal ax's (cf. Åse 1978, 1981). The graph on the left shows the distribution of elements between Shimola-Tewa, 15 km north of Mombasa and Kilifi; the graph on the right shows the distribution between Kilifi and Malindi. The levels I to VIII represent ages from the present (I) to late Würmian time (VIII)

3.2   *The shorelines as indications of land and sea-level movements*

In the foregoing discussion, it has been assumed that the shore terraces of the East African coast correspond to eustatic movements of sea level. However, if the datings are reasonably correct, the terraces would be found well below sea level if no rise of land had occurred during the time in question (cf. Fairbridge 1961, Mörner 1976, Bird 1984). Thus, a general rise of land during the time concerned must be considered. The magnitude and the nature of such a rise are not known in detail. If the dating of the Tanga terrace to *c*.30 000 BP and Bird's (1984) curve are correct, a rough estimate of *c*.60–80 m uplift, that is an average rate of 0.2–0.3 m per century, might be given. The figure fits remarkably well to the datings of level II and IV of the present author, cited above. Level II *c*.1 m above the present shoremarks (level I) has an age of *c*.500 BP indicating a rise of *c*.0.2 m per century. Level IV *c*.5–6 m above level I with an age of *c*.2000 BP indicates a rise of *c*.0.3 m per century.

As to the reasons for the uplift the picture is less clear. One possible reason could be a readjustment of the littoral zone in response to the loading by water during the Eemian transgression between the Riss and Würm glaciations (*cf.* Bloom 1967). Another explanation (suggested by Hori 1971) could be an isostatic readjustment to the loading of the more than 100 m thick littoral reef. A third explanation could be a general isostatic rise of the whole African continent in response to general denudation. Faure (1980) gives a figure of about 100 m uplift of the Precambrian basement under the Cenozoic volcanics of the Saharan massifs since the beginning of Miocene, which is far too small a figure to explain the movements on the coast of East Africa. To some extent the two latter explanations contradict each other. Hori's explanation seems to be the only one that can explain why the Sakuran and Tanga terraces show a general dip towards the north (figure 9.4) in Tanzania. If the coral loading was heavier in the north compared to the south, which seems probable if the reef-building organisms prefer equatorial conditions, the land rise would also be faster in the north compared to the south. However, this idea is also contradicted by a probable altitude increase towards the north of the lower Kenyan shorelines, indicated by Åse (1981, and table 9.2), as the Kenyan coral reefs according to Hori seem to be thicker in the south (e.g. the Mombasa area) than further northwards (e.g. the Malindi area). Finally, tectonic movements cannot be excluded. Tectonic movements might have caused the sharp increase in altitude towards the north of the Sakura and Tanga terraces south of Pangani (Alexander 1968) and can often be traced in the dipping of sedimentary strata on the coast in Kenya.

4.0 THE SHORELINES OF SOUTH-EASTERN AFRICA

In south-eastern Africa, that is, southern Tanzania, Mozambique, Madagascar and South Africa, research has mainly been carried out by French and South African scientists (e.g. A. and R. Battistini 1965, 1978, Weydert 1973, King 1951, Maud 1968, Davies 1969a,b). In Mozambique an important contribution has been made by Jarritz *et al.* (1977). The studies of A. and R. Battistini provide a link between the African mainland (i.e. Tanzania) and Madagascar. R. Battistini distinguishes two major coastal cycles, the Tatsimian and Karimbolian. In the Dar es Salaam area the Tatsimian level (also called Reef I) is found in places as high as 120 m above sea level (Battistini 1965). The high altitude, which corresponds to the highest altitudes of Alexander's Sakura level south of Pangani (Alexander 1968) is obviously due to faulting. In northern Madagascar (Battistini 1965) the Tatsimian reef reaches a maximum altitude of 25 m above sea level. Weydert (1973), from studies in south-west Madagascar (Tulear region), recognizes a 'Flandrian' transgression, younger than the Karimbolian. Cilek (1976) gives a figure of 30 m above present sea level from the Kunduchi–Wazo Hill area north of Dar es Salaam for the Tatsimian Terrace, which he considers identical with the Tanga terrace. On the east side Cilek (1976, p. 2) writes that 'this terrace borders the so-called Mtoni Terrace, corresponding to reef II, Karimbolian on Madagascar. The cliff of the Mtoni Terrace is about 8 to 12 m high and typically developed between Bagamoyo and Kaole where it forms the shoreline'. R. Battistini (1965) gives figures ranging between 6 and 15 m above sea level for the Karimbolian shoreline in northern Madagascar. In a later study A. Battistini (1978) presents age data obtained by the [130]Th/[234]U method for the Karimbolian reef that fall into three age-classes, i.e. 150 000, 120 000 and 100 000–80 000 BP. These figures correspond to an Eemian or early Würmian age of the Karimbolian reef, which makes the correlation between the Karimbolian and the Mtoni terrace very doubtful, unless an early Pleistocene age of the Tanga terrace, as assumed by Hove (1980), is accepted. It seems more probable that the Sakuran terrace of Alexander corresponds to the Tatsimian reef and the Tanga terrace to the Karimbolian, whereas the Mtoni terrace should be equivalent of Weydert's Flandrian level. Even this attempt is doubtful, however, as according to the previous discussion the age of the Tanga terrace in Tanzania and southern Kenya seems to be about half the age obtained for the Karimbolian reef at Madagascar.

4.1   *Mozambique*

In Mozambique, the studies of Jaritz *et al.* (1977) concentrate on the northern coast from the Zambezi delta northwards, whereas studies of Barradas (1945, 1965a,b) cover parts of southern Mozambique, especially the Beira and Maputo areas. ^{14}C-datings cited by both Barradas (1965a) and Jaritz *et al.* (1977) indicate a high water level, that is above present sea level, *c.*30 000–35 000 BP. This fits in well with the assumed Würm-interstadial age of the Tanga terrace in northern Tanzania and southern Kenya. Jaritz *et al.* (1977) mention the possibility that the carbonate samples used for the datings could be contaminated by younger ^{14}C and therefore older than the ^{14}C age indicates, but the fact that five out of six dated samples from various parts of Mozambique fall in the interval 30 000–35 000 BP contradict the contamination idea. (The sixth sample yielded a ^{14}C age of 28 540±490 BP.) After an assumed Würm interstadial (*Zwischenwarmzeit* according to Jaritz *et al.* 1977) *c.*33 000–35 000 years ago the sea level dropped and the rivers of Mozambique started to erode down to a low, late Pleistocene sea level. The 'down-cutting' of Rio des Elefantes reached at least 27 m and in the Limpopo area the erosion ('*Übertiefung*') reached 250 km inland from the coast. During the Holocene, sea level started to rise in response to the melting of Würmian ice sheets. In figure 9.7 the ^{14}C data obtained by Jaritz *et al.* (1977) are summarized. The dated samples fit reasonably well to the assumed general sea-level curve, but a closer analysis shows that 11 out of 21 samples are found below the curve and the remaining samples at least 'touch' the curve with their indicated time deviations. This could be due to a general lowering of the coast of Mozambique as the samples were normally taken from areas outside the Beira–Nova Sofala area where the East African Rift Valley reaches the coast. On the other hand, the Flandrian transgression in Mozambique, seems to have reached well above the present sea-level during its maximum *c.*6000 BP when extensive formation of beach ridge systems started in the Zambezi area (cf. Jaritz and Ruder 1977). Holocene terraces of the rivers of southern Mozambique are found as high as 4.5 m above present sea level (Jaritz *et al.* 1977) but in the late Holocene rivers have cut down *c.*2 m in the lower parts of the river valleys. Even archaeological evidence from Situndo (Königsson, written comm. Jan. 1984) where Iron Age sites possibly from the first century AD (one ^{14}C determination of charcoal) are found below the present coastal dunes favours the idea of a slight subsidence of land in the late Holocene.

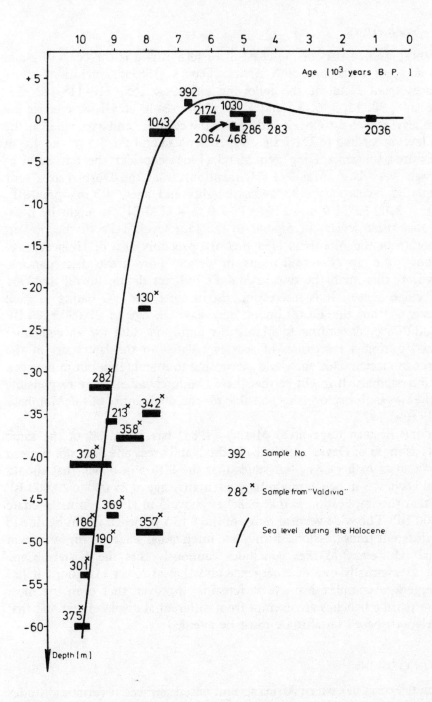

Figure 9.7 A sea-level curve from Mozambique (Jaritz *et al.* 1977)

4.2   South Africa

The best-studied part of the coast of eastern Africa is the coast of Natal and adjacent areas in South Africa. Davies (1969a,b) mentions shore terraces from Natal at the following altitudes: 155, 110–115, 82, 73, 60–61, 48, 30, 18, 9, 6, 3.5 and 1.5 m above sea level. Of these levels the 60 m level is well developed and carries the earliest hand axes whereas the 6 m level according to Davies is Post-Acheulean and the 3.5 m and 1.5 m levels are Holocene. King and Maud (1964) consider the 6 m level at Durban 'very late'. Maud (1968) mentions from the Durban area four postglacial levels at the following heights and ages: 4.5 m – 5500 BP; 2.4 m – 3800 BP; 1.5 m – 2200 BP; 1.0 m – 1220 BP. It might be possible that these levels correspond to the four levels I–IV of the present author from the Mombasa area that are probably also of Holocene age although the age determinations in detail show great discrepancies. However, this might be due to Maud's indirect dating (using the 1961 Fairbridge curve). It is interesting also to note that ^{14}C dating of shell fragments from the East London area gave an age of 29 090±400 BP (Maud 1968). According to Maud this dating is valid for an aeolianite formed during a regression of sea level dated to the later part of the Würmian glacial. This age could, according to Maud (1968) fit in between two interstadials. It might be that these two interstadials were responsible for the two high sea levels responsible for the dual nature of the Mombasa level (Hori 1971).

In the Eastern Cape area, Marker (1984) has found about the same levels as those of Davies (1969a,b) in the Natal area. She does not present any ^{14}C data of her own, but states that the 8 to 5 m bench that should equal Davies' 6 m bench might have a tentative age of 25 000 to 29 000 BP and that the implication is that benches above 5 m altitude must predate 30 000 BP. The wide vertical range of the 8 to 5 m bench might be due to two different transgressions during late interstadial stages of the Würmian glacial. However, Marker concludes cautiously that the Eastern Cape coast is essentially one of emergence and that at lower elevations it has undergone a complex history. It remains unproven that even the most recent marine benches are exempt from differential displacement and that correlations based on altitude must be avoided.

5.0   CONCLUSIONS

Along the coast of eastern Africa several raised terraces at various altitudes are found. Due to difficulties in dating it has not been possible to correlate the terraces from East Africa with those of South Africa. On the whole, there seems to be evidence, however, for a high water level during the late Pleistocene and it might also be that this high water level (responsible for the Tanga terrace in Tanzania and the 6 m level in the Natal area) is of a late interstadial age. For the lower terraces a Holocene age is suggested. It is tempting to correlate these terraces with the so-called Flandrian, Tapes and Litorina transgressions of Europe, and one of the lowest terraces on the coast of East Africa seems to be of late mediaeval age, which may correspond with a shoreline of similar age found in Stockholm (Åse 1984). It is interesting to note that just as the number of Holocene sea-level fluctuations tends to increase as research proceeds, so do the number of possible Holocene terraces along the coasts of eastern Africa. Needless to say as long as no certain correlation has been found between the terraces on the west coast of the Indian Ocean, no correlation should be attempted beteen eastern Africa and Europe. Most probably, no such correlation really exists.

Revised typescript received 1986, March.

REFERENCES

Alexander, C., 1968: The marine terraces of the Northeast coast of Tanzania. *Z. Geomorph., Suppl. Bd.* 7, 133–54.

Åse, L.-E., 1978: Preliminary report on studies of shore displacement at the southern coast of Kenya. *Geografiska Annal.* 60 A 209–21.

Åse, L.-E. 1981: Studies of shores and shore displacement on the southern coast of Kenya – especially in Kilifi District. *Geografiska Annal. 63 A*, 303–10.

Åse, L.-E., 1984: Den medeltida strandförskjutningen vid Stockholm och övriga Mälarstäder (Shore displacement at Stockholm and other Lake Mälar towns in Nordic medieval times.) Riksantikvarie-ämbetet och Statens historiska museer. Rapport 1984: 2.

Barradas, L., 1945: As formações quaternarias do Sul do Save e as suas relações com a Préhistória. *Bol. Soc. Est. Col. Moçambique* 47, 1–34.

Barradas, L., 1965a: Cronologia da Beira-mar do Sul de Moçambique. *Mem. Inst. Invest. Cient. Moç. Sér. B*, 7, 23–35.

Barradas, L., 1965b: Rochas do quaternario da Beira-mar (Sul de Moçambique). *Mem. Inst. Invest. Cient. Moç. Sér. B*, 7, 37–84.

Battistini, A., 1978: Observations sur les cordons littoraux pléistocènes et holocènes de la Côte Est de Madagascar. *Revue de Géogr. Madagascar*, 33, 9–37.

Battistini, R., 1965: Problèmes géormorphologiques de l'extrême nord de Madagascar. *Revue de Géogr. Madagascar*, 7, 1–60.

Battistini, R., 1966: Le quaternaire littoral des environs de Dar es Salaam

294 Lars-Erik Åse

(Tanzanie): essaie de correlations avec le quaternaire littoral malagache. *Bull. Ass. Fr. Etude Quaternaire*, 3, 191–201.

Bird, E. C. F., 1984: *Coasts. An introduction to Coastal Geomorphology*, 3rd edn. Oxford: Basil Blackwell.

Bloom, A. L., 1967: Pleistocene shorelines: a new test of isostasy. *Geol. Soc. Am. Bull.*, 78, 1477–94.

British Admiralty, 1957: Chart Malindi-Ras Chiambone.

Caswell, P. V., 1953: Geology of the Mombasa-Kwale area. *Rep. Geol. Survey Kenya*, 24.

Chittick, N., 1962: Recent discoveries in Tanganyika. *Proc. Pan-African Congr. Pre & Proto-history*, 3, 215–23.

Cilek, V. G., 1976: Review of Coastal Geology of United Republic of Tanzania. CINCWIO (Nairobi 25th–31st March, 1976), Roneo.

Cooke, H. J., 1974: The coastal geomorphology of Tanga, Tanzania. *Geogr. Rev.* 64, 517–35.

Davies, J. L., 1977: *Geographical Variation in Coastal Development*. Longman Geomorphology Text 4, 2nd edn. London: Longman.

Davies, O., 1969a: The Quaternary beaches of South Africa – with special reference to the 200-foot beach in Natal and the Eastern Province. *South African Archaeol. Bull.*, 24, 125–6.

Davies, O., 1969b: Quaternary Studies in South Africa. *Bull. Assoc. Sénégalaise pour l'Etude du Quaternaire Africain*, 22, 112–4.

East African Harbours Corporation, 1976: Tide Tables for East African Ports 1977.

Fairbridge, R. W., 1961: Eustatic changes in sea level. In L. H. Ahrens *et al.* (eds.), *Physics and Chemistry of the Earth 4*, London: Pergamon Press, 99–185.

Faure, H., 1980: Late Cenozoic vertical movements in Africa. In N.-A. Mörner (ed.), *Earth Rheology, Isostasy and Eustasy*, Chichester: John Wiley & Sons, 465–9.

Faure, H., Hoang, O. and Lalou, C., 1973: Structure et Géochronologie ($^{230}Th/^{234}U$) des Récifs Coralliens soulevés a l'Ouest du Golfe d'Aden (TFAI). *Rev. de Géographie Phys. et de Géol. Dyn.* 15, 393–403.

Hori, N., 1971: Raised coral reefs along the southeastern coast of Kenya, East Africa. Department Geography, Tokyo Univ. 1970 (5), 25–47.

Hove, A. R. T., 1980: The 38-metre sea level: a reconstruction of the early Pleistocene palaeogeography of the south Kenya coast. *Comm. Coll. Intern. Géol. Paris*, Sectr. 08, Symp. 23 661.

Jaritz, W. and Ruder, J., 1977: Fotogeologische Charakterisierung des Küstengebietes von Moçambique. *Geologisch. Jb.* (B), 26, 95–121.

Jaritz, W., Ruder, J. and Schlenker, B., 1977: Das Quartär im Küstengebiet von Moçambique und seine Schwermineralführung. *Geologisch. J.*(B), 26, 1–93.

Johnson, D. W., 1919: *Shore Processes and Shoreline Development*. New York: Wiley.

King, L. C., 1951: *South African Scenery*, 2nd edn. Edinburgh: Oliver and Boyd.

King, L. C. and Maud, R. M., 1964: The Geology of Durban and Environs. *Geol. Survey South Africa Bull.*, 42.

Marker, M. E., 1984: Marine benches of the eastern Cape, South Africa. *Trans. geol. Soc. S. Africa*, 87, 11–18.

Maud, R. M., 1968: Quaternary geomorphology and soil formation in coastal Natal. *Z. Geomorph. Suppl. Bd.*, 7, 155–99.

Mörner, N.-A., 1976: Eustatic changes during the last 8000 years in view of radiocarbon calibration and new information from the Kattegatt region and other northwestern European areas. *Paleogeogr., Paleoclimatol., Paleoecol.*, 19, 63–85.

Shepard, F. P., 1976: Coastal classification and changing coastlines. *Geoscience and Man*, 14, 53–64.

Temple, P. H., 1970: Geomorphology. In Dar es Salaam: City, Port and Region. *Tanzania Notes and Records*, 71 (1970), 20–54.

Temple, P. H., 1971: Discussion of C. S. Alexander's paper on marine terraces of the northeast coast of Tanganyika. *Z. Geomorph. N.F.*, 15 236–40.

Thompson, A. O., 1956: Geology of the Malindi area. *Rep. Geol. Survey Kenya* 36.

Valentin, H., 1952: *Die Küsten der Erde.* Petermanns Geogr. Mitteilungen. Ergänzungsheft 246.

Weydert, P., 1973: Les formations récifales de la région de Tulear (côte SW de Madagascar). *Ass. Sénégalaise pour l'Etude du Quaternaire Africain*, 37–38, 57–81.

10

Late Quaternary sea-level changes in the Australian region

John Chappell

1.0 INTRODUCTION

Two objectives of sea-level studies are to provide information about vertical crustal movements and to provide information which is essential for understanding coastal history. Sea-level changes can be investigated on time scales of tens of years to tens of millions of years. These objectives will be illustrated briefly by referring to sea-level studies covering the period since the last glacial maximum i.e. within the last 20 000 years.

Sea-level rise caused by melting of late Pleistocene icecaps constitutes a geophysical change of global extent. Analysis by a succession of authors in the 1970s emphasised the point that the globe has responded differentially to the melting and decantation into the oceans of the northern icecaps. Resulting vertical isostatic movements, and changing gravitational effects of the icecaps themselves, mean that sea-level changes differ between different parts of the world. The widely cited models of Clark *et al.* (1978) are used to demonstrate this. Hence, accurate studies of postglacial sea-level change provide primary data for analysing one set of the Earth's geophysical properties.

Regarding studies of coastal history, postglacial sea-level rise is one of the most important factors. This is true where either sedimentation or biohermal reef growth is dominant in the coastal and nearshore zone. Postglacial sea-level rise drowned the continental shelves in a mere 10 000 years, redistributing sediment, invading fluvial valleys, and preparing the way for late Holocene coastal development. In some parts of the world, processes such as coastal sedimentation and coral reef growth still are affected by consequences of the sea-level rise which terminated about 6000 BP.

To be useful for either geophysical or coastal geomorphologic research, sea-level studies must be accurate and conducted with the expectation that each region of interest may have its own sea-level history. Accurate studies require sites where the evidence for sea-level change is accessible, is as continuous through time as possible, and is dateable. These conditions usually are best met where Holocene coastal and nearshore deposits form continuous sediment bodies which are dateable by radiocarbon assays. This paper focuses on Holocene sea levels in Australia and nearby regions because Australia is regarded as a stable continent with very little evidence of tectonic deformation since the Mesozoic, and with Tertiary sedimentation confined to marginal shelf basins. Selected Pleistocene results from this region are also reviewed. Radiocarbon chronology is used here in the Holocene and late Pleistocene context, with

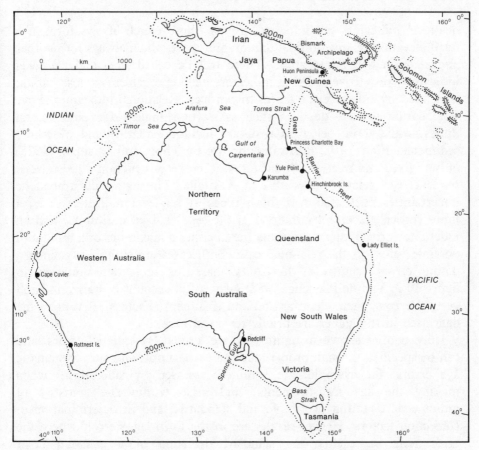

Figure 10.1 A map of Australia and adjacent areas showing places referred to in the text

ages based on the Libby half-life of 5568 years. To ensure age comparability, results used are those which follow the conventions, (1) of calculation with respect to Modern Standard = 0.95 NBS Oxalic Acid standard, (2) correction for isotopic fractionation, and (3) correction for the seawater reservoir effect where applicable, (see Stuiver and Polach 1977, and Gillespie and Polach, 1979, for explanation of these conventions.) Most of the studies which will be mentioned explicitly follow these conventions, and exceptions will be indicated. On figure 10.1, localities referred to in the text are shown.

2.0   SEA-LEVEL INDICATORS AND CURVE ENVELOPES

Sea-level indicators fall into two groups, those which always form at a fixed elevation relative to tidal datum, and those which always form either above, or below, tidal datum. These will be called *fixed* and *relational* indicators, respectively. Fixed indicators include organisms whose habitat is defined by tide levels, such as mangroves. Relational indicators above tidal datum include deposits such as storm shingle ridges and coastal dunes, while those below tidal datum include estuarine and nearshore sediments. Figure 10.2 illustrates the use by Thom and Chappell (1975) of both fixed and relational indicators in their reconstruction of postglacial sea-level rise relative to south-east Australia. The figure illustrates the uncertainties associated with both types of sea-level indicators, i.e., a finite vertical uncertainty interval in the case of fixed indicators, and an indefinite vertical interval terminating in either a maximum or a minimum possible value, in the relational case. Both cases are subject to standard dating errors, shown as horizontal bars for each determination in figure 10.2. Van de Plassche (1982) gives a full account of horizontal and vertical errors, their identification and treatment. Factors relevant to the data used in this paper are briefly reviewed here.

Uncertainties shown in figure 10.2 are termed 'systematic' errors, and can be specified through proper study of each sample and site. Systematic age errors, for example, are routinely assessed by laboratories when making the age measurements, and arise within the statistics of radiometric counting of sample and standards, and in determination of correction factors. Hence, results are in the form 'age±error' where the error term represents one standard deviation of a gaussian error distribution, unless otherwise stated (see Stuiver and Polach 1977, Pearson 1979). In comparison, systematic vertical errors in the sea-level estimate are often given as a maximum possible range. In the case of fixed

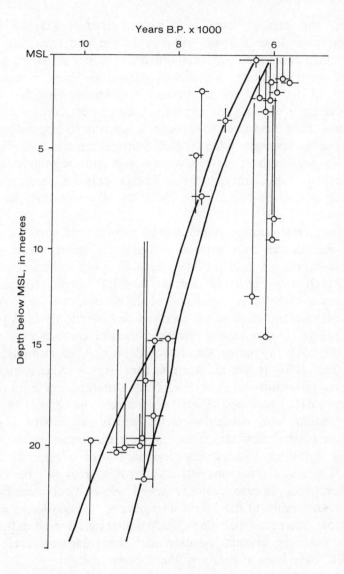

Figure 10.2 A sea-level envelope graph using error bars attached to fixed and relational sea-level indicators (after Thom and Chappell 1975). Fixed indicators have short vertical error bars of equal length; relational indicators have one long error bar extending below or above the indicator point. Horizontal error bars are shown for each indicator and represent one standard deviation of the mean age of each indicator

indicators, the method used by Chappell *et al.* (1983) of assessing maximum range is as follows. Suppose that a particular site contains deposits which contain an intertidal indicator, as well as having a modern equivalent in the vicinity. Let the maximum elevation of the modern indicator = A metres (above datum) and its minimum elevation = B. Let the maximum elevation in a given outcrop or core = a and the minimum = b. It is assumed that the indicator is in its original position in its stratigraphic context. When the ancient indicator is higher than the modern, the maximum sea-level change is a–B and the minimum is b–A. The systematic uncertainty is the difference between these. Analogous relations apply when the ancient indicator is lower than its modern equivalent.

Systematic errors can be minimised by careful field survey and dating analysis. Results can be expressed precisely and their effects reckoned with in constructing a local sea-level curve. It is not so with unsystematic errors, which may arise in dating through sample contamination, misassociation of dated material and sea-level indicator, or ignorance of carbon reservoir correction factors (see van de Plassche 1982). A particular risk in sea-level studies is that reworked shell or carbonaceous matter is used as the basis for dating shore-zone deposits. For example, Donner and Jungner (1981) report radiocarbon ages from a modern high energy barrier beach in south-east Australia. Three different taxa from the beach surface gave 8110, 4080 and 290 BP respectively. As regards vertical sea-level indication, one particular factor which can falsify a result is compaction of the substrate. This can be treacherous where Holocene sediments are thick and rapidly deposited with a high initial water content. These and other unsystematic error sources will be mentioned where appropriate, in case studies reviewed below. Where such factors are suspected, the results of fixed indicators have to be regarded as relational. For example, where compaction is likely the elevation of an indicator may be lower than the original position and the palaeo-sea-level must be assumed to have been at or above the surveyed height.

Once a set of reliable data from a given area has been assembled, it can be plotted as shown in figure 10.2, on a fixed or relational basis as appropriate to each point, with systematic error bars. Thom and Chappell (1975) drew an 'envelope curve' around their data, as shown in figure 10.2. The envelope constitutes an upper and a lower line with the data lying between these. The 'real' sea-level curve lies somewhere within the envelope, but its actual course is unknown. This conservative approach avoids the risk of inferring a fallacious curve which can arise by drawing a single line through the mid-points of separate determinations.

It should be borne in mind that the envelope itself can be misleading, in that it suggests continuity across gaps between data points.

3.0 THE PROBLEM OF HOLOCENE SEA-LEVEL FLUCTUATIONS

Graphical time/elevation plots suffice to show general trends and also indicate the density and uncertainty of data. They may conceal real fluctuations which lie within the bounds of the envelope, or which occurred between data points. Obviously, the smaller the systematic errors and the denser the data the better the definition of relative sea-level variation. It is possible for information about oscillatory fluctuations to be destroyed, however, due to processes of shoreline erosion and burial or non-deposition which might occur in a transgression/regression cycle.

On figure 10.3 two cases are illustrated, where a sea-level oscillation has no morpho-stratigraphic expression in one, but has some expression in the other. Both are actively prograding sites, but the case in figure 10.3(a) is a high energy coast, whereas a low energy case is represented in figure 10.3(b). The sea-level indicator in the high energy example is assumed to be a typical beach/foredune facies interface with strandline shell lenses, while that in the low energy example is a mangrove organic facies. Both cases commence with prior progradation under steady sea-level (shown at (i) in both 10.3(a) and 10.3(b)).

The depth to which intertidal to nearshore sediment exchange occurs is the active zone, shown as Z in figure 10.3. In south-east Australia this exceeds 15 m on high energy coasts (Wright *et al.* 1980). It is assumed, for the purposes of the argument, that the depth of the active zone exceeds the amplitude of sea-level oscillation in figure 10.3(a), but is less than the amplitude in 10.3(b). Given continued sediment supply, regressive intertidal deposits accumulate during minor sea-level fall in both cases (shown as (ii) in 10.3(a) and 10.3(b)). During subsequent sea-level rise, these regressive deposits may be reworked shorewards in the high energy case, leaving no stratigraphic trace of the oscillation (shown at (iii) on figure 10.3(a)). In the low energy case (10.3(b) iii) there is little reworking and there might be a gap of the indicator facies above the regressive/transgressive wedge. Figure 10.3(b) illustrates one type of ideal case for the discovery of relatively small sea-level fluctuations. However, because the evidence is stratigraphic, it must be found by careful drill coring or by trenching. Further, if the oscillation is small relative to the vertical interval occupied by the sea-level indicator, which may easily occur in macrotidal environments, then the evidence may be hard to read,

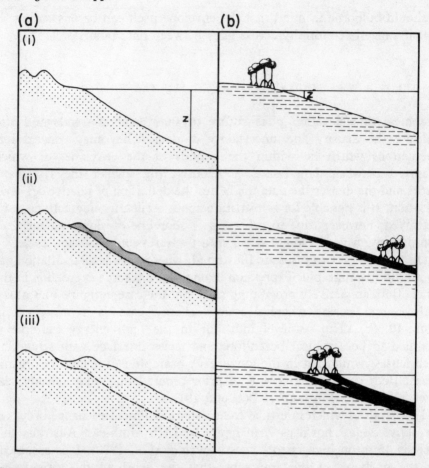

Figure 10.3 An illustration to show the possible effect of sea-level oscillation on prograding (a) high energy and (b) low energy coasts. Z represents the depth of the active zone of sediment agitation. The sequence shows: (i), high sea-level; (ii), low sea-level with regressive deposits; (iii), return to high sea-level

even on rapidly prograding coasts. It is not my intention to query the careful stratigraphic analyses of minor transgression/regression cycles, such as those by Tooley (1974, 1982) in northern England, but to illustrate the considerations involved when interpreting Australian results which are described below.

Because the evidence for temporary low sea levels is less accessible than for higher sea levels, or is prone to eradication, there has been a tendency to argue that groups or 'clumps' of Holocene radiocarbon dates, supported by lithostratigraphic information, represent minor fluctuations in sea level (Shennan *et al.* 1983). This indirect technique warrants a separate discussion as it has been applied to Australian data by overseas writers (Geyh 1980), and has certain pitfalls.

4.0 BOUNDARY CONDITIONS FOR FORMATION OF INDICATORS

Growth or deposition of sea-level indicators always have preconditions. For example, for the growth of intertidal coral forms such as micro-atolls it is necessary that the parent coral reef exists with an intertidal flat. Holocene reefs had to struggle to keep pace with postglacial sea-level rise, and frequently did not catch up with sea level until some time after the rise terminated. In such cases, the oldest intertidal corals do not represent termination of sea-level rise. Dating studies by McLean *et al.* (1978) in the Great Barrier Reef indicate that many coral reef flats did not begin to form until about 4000 BP, whereas other evidence from the region shows that sea level peaked some 2000 years earlier (Chappell *et al.* 1983). In this instance, sea-level stability for a few thousand years often is a precondition to formation of sea-level indicators.

In general, formation of all sea-level indicators requires appropriate boundary conditions, and, when boundary conditions change, there may be a significant lag before specific indicators again begin to form a deposit. Formation of most indicators depends on wave climate and sedimentation, and in some cases meteorological regime. This is additional to the phenomenon of lag following rapid change of sea level or of other boundary conditions. Observed gaps or variations in the temporal spacing of Holocene sea-level indicators must be examined with all such factors in mind. For example, Geyh (1980) infers that putative 'clumps' of upper Holocene dates from prograded coastal barriers in New South Wales (data from Thom *et al.* (1978)) are due to effects of sea-level fluctuations. A different explanation is advanced by Thom (1978), who argues that storm frequency may have varied, giving rise to episodes of transgressive dune formation and reduced progradation. In the case of chenier plains in the Gulf of Carpentaria in northern Australia, Rhodes (1980) and Rhodes *et al.* (1980) interpret apparent clumping of chenier ridge dates as being due to interaction of variable sediment supply and storm frequency. Alternative explanations clearly are possible, and it is not wise to infer sea-level oscillations simply from patterns of radiocarbon dates alone.

Ultimately, accurate determinations of relative sea-level change come down to stratigraphic and dating analysis. However, because of problems outlined here and in figure 10.3, it is valuable to have independent evidence about relevant boundary conditions. Detailing this can be as expensive of time and laboratory analysis as can sea-level studies themselves. Assessment of past fluctuations of wave climate is difficult, for example. Nonetheless, Chivas *et al.* (1986) provide an example relevant to the central coast of Queensland. These authors show that episodic storm accretion to coral shingle ridges at two widely separated sites in the Great Barrier Reef has been statistically constant over the last several thousand years. In figure 10.4 their data are reproduced and indicate that there has been no recognisable fluctuation in the rate of storm-ridge accretion, at least for more than the last 3000 years. This implies constancy of storm or cyclone frequency. Only when comparable data are assembled for all boundary conditions, such as sediment input, and other relevant climatic factors, can sea level be introduced as a possible explanation for fluctuations in a temporal histogram of sea-level indicator dates.

5.0   HOLOCENE SEA-LEVEL CHANGES IN AUSTRALIA

The best sea-level information is based on data from within a single region, using fixed sea-level indicators which are densely arrayed through time, with every effort being made to minimise errors. It may be that we do not yet have any ideal data sets in Australia, and the reader will have to reflect on the accuracy and interpretation of results reviewed below. My method will be first to outline what I consider to be the best data set, and then to examine others from areas which are geographically distant from the first set. Some effects of unsystematic errors will be identified in each case, and regional differences between relative sea-level curves then are discussed in terms of isostatic and other crustal movements. As the evidence for sea-level over the last 6000 years is better than for the preceding millennia, this is taken first.

5.1   North Queensland sea-levels: fringing reef data

Fringing coral reefs of the inner continental shelf and mainland coast, north Queensland, form broad intertidal flats sloping gently seawards. A particular coral growth form which occurs near low spring tide level (LSWL) is the micro-atoll, described by Scoffin and Stoddart (1978). Bird (1971) recognised that dead micro-atolls occur on some reef flats at higher elevations than living ones, and in a particular case study showed that these are up to several thousand years old.

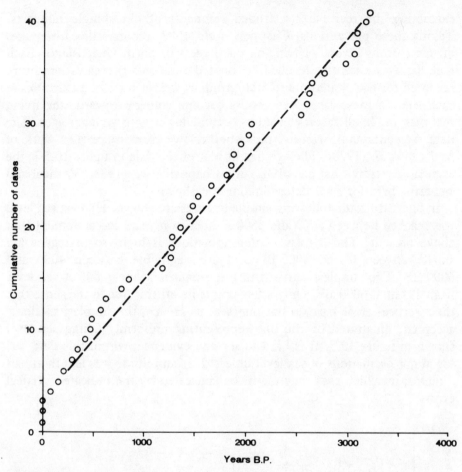

Figure 10.4 A cumulative age/time graph of coral shingle ridge dates from Lady Eliot Island, Queensland. The distribution is not significantly different from a statistically uniform rate of accumulation (after Chivas *et al*. 1986)

Coral micro-atolls have several advantages as fixed sea-level indicators. They are easily identified, they grow within a small vertical range, they are easily dated by radiocarbon, and the date exactly represents their time of growth. They grow on a coral reef substrate which is sufficiently solid to resist compaction, at least in Holocene time. They are susceptible to two potentially falsifying factors, however. They can be transported across a reef flat by cyclonic waves, and they can grow at levels higher than LSWL in situations such as shallow lagoons and in ponds impounded by shingle ridges. Transport can be detected by excavating the micro-atolls to find evidence for *in situ* growth. Potential ponding can be identified by examining the reef flat for eroded remnants of old shingle ramparts. Taking these precautions, Chappell *et al.* (1983) report radiocarbon ages of micro-atolls across 11 fringing coral reefs in north Queensland. Each reef flat was carefully levelled to tidal datum and the elevations were recorded for each dated micro-atoll group as well as for living examples at each site. In most cases, age results become younger towards the living reef margin. In all cases, elevations become lower with younger ages. The data set contains 45 results, plus another five from the earlier work of McLean *et al.* (1978). The age-height plot of the data in figure 10.5 is the same as given by Chappell (1982) and Chappell *et al.* (1983). Vertical and age-error bars for each determination are shown.

In figure 10.5 the following simple features are shown. Highest sea level was reached between 6000 and 5500 radiocarbon years ago at about 1.0 m above present. The density of determinations is high, so that gaps are small between 0 and 4000 BP and are negligible between 4000 and 6000 BP. The simplest curve fitting the data is a linear fall of sea level from 1.0 m at 6000 BP. Only a few points lie off this line in the sense that their vertical error bars do not intersect it. Hence, the simplest model is accepted, illustrated by the line representing uniformly falling sea level shown in figure 10.5. It is hard to see any evidence, within this data set, for minor oscillations of sea level unless their amplitude was less than half a metre, in which case they might be concealed by the indicated vertical errors.

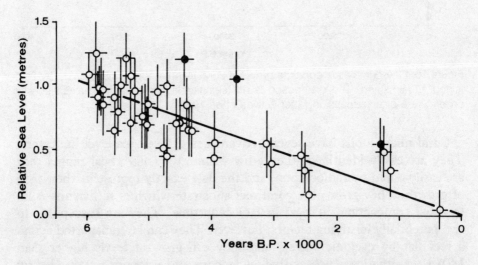

Figure 10.5 Age/height plot of coral micro-atolls from North Queensland. Key: open circles are samples from reefs on the inner shelf; solid circles are samples from Yule Point on the mainland coast (after Chappell *et al.* 1983)

Figure 10.5 is used in this paper as the best available upper Holocene sea-level data assay for north-eastern Australia, and will be used as a curve of reference against which other results are compared. The micro-atoll data are very consistent between different north Queensland sites, and systematic errors are small. One shortcoming of this type of evidence, however, is that short-lived regression/transgression events are apt to go unnoticed, because indicators of temporary low sea-levels would be buried by subsequent coral overgrowth. Such oscillations seem quite unlikely in the 6000–4000 BP interval, where the data in figure 10.5 are dense, but could slip between the gaps in the post-4000 BP period.

5.2   North Queensland sea levels: prograded coasts

There is a potential on rapidly prograding low-energy coasts to record in the stratigraphy a detailed sea-level history, including minor sea-level oscillations (figure 10.3(b)). Mangrove-fringed chenier plains in northern Australia are a good example. Contrasting with fringing coral reefs, these plains are easily cored or sectioned by trenching. The mangrove sedimentary facies is marked by roots and other organic material and is reliably keyed by mangrove pollen (Chappell and Grindrod 1984, Grindrod and Rhodes 1984). It appears to be an excellent sea-level marker. However, these plains have the disadvantage that the soft Holocene sediments may be affected by slow compaction.

A stratigraphic section across a typical low-energy coastal plain in north Queensland is shown in figure 10.6. The example occurs at Princess Charlotte Bay (14°15'S, 144°15'E) and is described by Chappell and Grindrod (1984). The plain has a series of chenier ridges separated by bare saline mudflats, and a zoned mangrove forest lies at its seaward edge. The stratigraphy was examined with a series of backhoe trenches plus some cores on two traverses. On figure 10.6 one traverse with positions marked of trenches and cores is shown, and the lateral equivalent positions of trenches on the other traverse are indicated. Each trench and core reveal an organic-rich horizon, which macrofossil and pollen evidence shows to have formed beneath mangrove forest. Although the trench and core sampling does not supply continuous exposure, the sampling density seems sufficiently high to infer that the mangrove facies is continuous at a nearly constant level beneath the plain. Radiocarbon dating indicates progradation, with a palaeosurface at successive time-points shown by the 'timelines' in figure 10.6. The nearly-uniform level of the prograded mangrove facies suggests that sea level was virtually constant relative to this site, since about 5500 BP. This disagrees with the

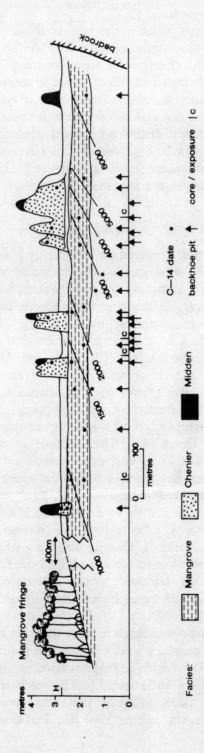

Figure 10.6 A stratigraphic cross-section from the chenier plain at Prince Charlotte Bay, north Queensland. Key: solid dots indicate the position of ^{14}C dated samples; sloping lines show inferred past shore profiles; arrows above the baseline show the locations of stratigraphic pits on a second profile (after Chappell and Grindrod 1984)

trend of sea level shown on figure 10.5, and the difference is unlikely to be due to vertical crustal movement because one of the main sets of fringing reef sites used in figure 10.5 lies within 10 km of the chenier plain site. The discrepancy is attributed to progressive compaction of the Holocene muds beneath the chenier plain, which is consistent with observed increase of their bulk density with age (Chappell and Grindrod 1984). About 1 m of compaction appears to have occurred in 6000 years, showing that the mangrove facies in this particular case is not a reliable fixed indicator of sea level. Setting this point aside, there is nothing in the observed section (figure 10.6) to suggest any transgression/regression cycles due to minor sea-level oscillations unless these were less than 0.5 m or so.

A second example of the same type is shown in figure 10.7. Described by Rhodes (1980), this prograded chenier plain occurs near Karumba in the Gulf of Carpentaria (17°28'S, 141°52'E). This is chosen because it shows a significant difference from figure 10.5 which cannot be attributed to compaction. The sea-level indicator in this case is the interface between the base of each chenier ridge and the underlying muds. In northern Australia, these ridges are observed to form near the top of the intertidal zone, within or behind the mangrove fringe, piled up by storms. The bases of modern ridges occur within a narrow vertical range. Figure 10.7(a) shows the extent of the chenier plain which has prograded over the last 6000 years. Figure 10.7(b) is an age–height plot of the chenier ridge-base data, with vertical and age errors shown as for figure 10.5. A smooth fall of over 2 m in the last 6000 years is indicated. This significantly exceeds the result from the fringing reefs and cannot be eliminated in terms of vertical errors. Any compaction, such as was shown in the Princess Charlotte Bay chenier plain, will have reduced the real change of relative sea level. Hence, the fall over the last 6000 years shown in figure 10.7(b) should be regarded as a minimum estimate. The difference between this and the fringing reefs results must imply differential crustal movements, which are discussed later.

5.3 South Australia coastal carbonate banks

Low-energy coastal and nearshore sediments in the Spencer Gulf of South Australia have been extensively studied using stratigraphic vibrocoring and dating techniques. Results are reported in a series of papers and that by Belperio *et al.* (1984) reports Holocene morphostratigraphy of nearshore and intertidal carbonate banks. Figure 10.8(a) shows the cross-section at Redcliff (32°42'E, 137°50'S). The diagnostic fixed sea-level

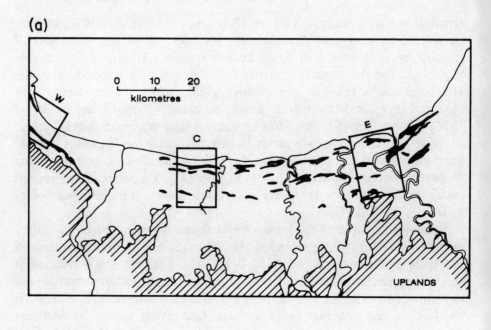

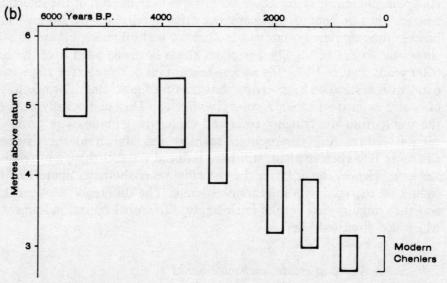

Figure 10.7 The coastal chenier plain near Karumba on the south-east shore of the Gulf of Carpentaria, showing the distribution and age/height relationships of the cheniers. (a), a map of the coastal chenier plain described by Rhodes (1980). Boxes W, C and E were surveyed in detail and dated; (b), a graph to show the age/height plot of dated and modern chenier ridge bases (Rhodes 1980)

indicator used by these authors is the interface between intertidal sandy facies and underlying *Posidonia australis* seagrass facies. The latter is a poorly sorted mixture of skeletal carbonate detritus, quartz sand, terrigenous and calcareous clay, and cellulose fibres and rhizomes of *Posidonia* seagrass. The upper growth limit of the *Posidonia* is spring low water level (LWD in figure 10.8). Radiocarbon dates from the top of the *Posidonia* facies, mostly based on seagrass fibres, are shown in figure 10.8(a). The dates become generally younger seawards, although there is a reversal in this pattern near the steeper-sloping central part of the section.

An independent study of the same Spencer Gulf region is reported by Byrne (1982). Byrne obtained most of his stratigraphic dates from the base of the intertidal facies rather than from the underlying *Posidonia* seagrass facies. The section with the greatest number of dates is shown in figure 10.8(b). Age results are based on intertidal *Spissula* shells, and figure 10.8(b) shows that these do not depict a regular age-distance distribution. Byrne also gives 16 dates from shell ridges which occur on the intertidal and supratidal flats in nothern Spencer Gulf. One of these occurs on the section in figure 10.8(b).

Byrne (1982) and Belperio *et al.* (1984) interpret their data differently. Byrne concludes that uniformly falling sea level at 0.5 m/1000 yr is 'consistent with most of the data' and invokes interaction between sedimentation and tides to explain some vagaries in the data. As the area shows some seismic activity, minor tectonism in the region is considered by both Byrne and Belperio *et al.* but in different ways. Byrne suggests that slow uplift might account for the apparent lowering of relative sea level from a high mid-Holocene position. Belperio *et al.* suggest minor sea-level fall between about 5700 and 2000 BP, followed by a rapid fall of nearly 2 m between about 2000 and 1500 BP. This rapid fall is attributed to tectonic uplift, and Belperio *et al.* suggest that tectonic movements may have varied along Spencer Gulf. These different interpretations of overlapping data warrant discussion.

Figure 10.8(c) is an age/height plot of data from figures 10.8(a) and 10.8(b). Heights of dated *Posidonia* facies from Belperio *et al.* (1984) are measured from their LWD level, which is the top of present *Posidonia* sediments. Vertical error bars represent sample thickness indicated by these authors, and graphic estimates in figure 10.8(c) are consistent with those given by Belperio *et al.* (1984, figure 5). Heights given for the basal intertidal indicators in figure 10.8(c) are the sea-level change estimates given by Byrne (1982, table 1, errors not stated). The sloping straight line in figure 10.8(c) represents Byrne's summary of sea-level change, while

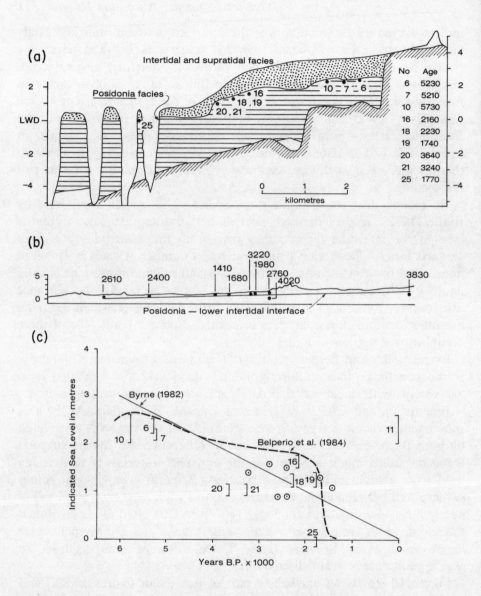

Figure 10.8 The stratigraphy and age/height relationships of samples from two nearby sites on Spencer Gulf, South Australia. (a), stratigraphic section at Redcliff, showing locations of dated samples from the top of the *Posidonia* facies and their ages (after Belperio *et al.* 1984); (b), a section at Fisherman Bay showing locations of dated samples from base of intertidal facies (after Byrne 1982). The shell ridge lies immediately to the right of date 2760. Age errors are given in Byrne, 1982; (c), age/height plot of data from Redcliff and Fisherman's Bay with sea-level curves according to Byrne (1982) and Belperio *et al.* (1984)

the dashed curve is copied from Belperio *et al.* (1984). Adding more of the data from less specific sea-level indicators, which are given by both authors, does not resolve the question of which of these two curves, if either, is 'correct' for northern Spencer Gulf. It is noted that systematic vertical errors are not stated by either author. However, it seems likely that some of the discrepancies are due to unsystematic errors. Firstly, substantial wave transport and mixing of detritus across the upper subtidal and intertidal zone in this area occurs intermittently, on meteorological (Radok and Raupach 1977) and sedimentary grounds (Hails and Gostin 1978). The irregular spatial distribution of *Spissula* shell dates and the placement of the dated shell ridge in figure 10.8(b) appear to reflect this. Secondly, mixing processes may affect the upper subtidal seagrass facies. The occurrence of a 5730 BP and a modern date apparently in the same sample (result 10, figures 10.8(a) and (c) and 11, not shown) suggests mixing and is not discussed by Belperio *et al.* (1984). Thirdly, the apparent age of a sample from the top of the *Posidonia* seagrass facies does not necessarily reflect the maximum height to which this facies accumulated, as it may have been truncated by later planation. The level *Posidonia* surface seemingly backed by a low scarp on the left of the section in figure 10.8(a) suggests planation and back-cutting. If this were so, the age/height result for sample 25 (figures 10.8(a) and (c)), on which Belperio *et al.* place much reliance, is nullified.

In the light of these factors, this author regards the relative sea-level curve of Belperio *et al.* (1984), shown in figure 10.8(c), as unproven, and considers the linear falling curve of Byrne (1982) as the simplest approximation to the data. This conclusion may readily be interpreted as reflecting bias, but, it is consistent with the pattern inferred from the north Queensland fringing reef data and with the results from the Gulf of Carpentaria, in both of which I have personally been involved. It is regrettable that this personal element has played a large part in disputations – usually sterile – about sea-level results from different places. It was my hope in writing the first sections of this paper that data can be placed on a common footing by duly estimating error sources. Only when this is done consistently can the real differences between different sites be perceived and measured. Such differences, amongst sites already mentioned plus others, are examined later.

5.4 *The question of upper Holocene oscillations in Australia*

The sea-level synthesis of Fairbridge (1961) has been influential in Australia, particularly as many of the inferred upper Holocene oscillations are named from Western Australian sites described quite thoroughly by Fairbridge in his earlier publications. Higher relative sea levels in the last 6000 years, bearing the names 'Older Peron', 'Younger Peron', 'Abrolhos', and 'Rottnest', were interpreted as having been separated by oscillations with amplitudes of up to several metres (Fairbridge 1961). Others, particularly Gill working in Victoria for over 40 years or so, have supported Fairbridge's general synthesis although details have been modified (cf. Gill 1983). Such oscillations, if real, can be invoked to explain height differences between shoreline features from different localities. Although it is the author's view that the evidence summarised in figures 10.4 and 10.5 does not admit of oscillations of several metres, at least in north Queensland, the matter should not be so easily laid to rest.

The Western Australian sites which are central to Fairbridge's (1961) synthesis have been re-examined by several authors and other data from the Perth region have been described (reviewed by Brown 1983). Conflicting interpretations still exist in the critical Perth area. Kendrick (1977) documents shell beds associated with the lowest river terrace in the Swan River estuary at Perth. These form a dated series ranging over 6600 to 4500 BP, and Kendrick concludes that water level has not been higher than 0.5 m above present in Holocene times in the estuary. Playford and Leech (1977) re-examined the critical sites at Rottnest Island, seaward of the Swan estuary, and concluded that sea level rose to a single maximum of +3 m at 5500 to 6000 BP after which it fell to its present position by about 5000 BP. Shepherd (1981), supported by Woods and Searle (1983), details evidence from a bench-ridge plain about 30 km south of the Swan which also indicates sea level about 2.5 m above present at 5500 to 6000 BP. The differences between these and Kendrick's (1977) results from geographically close sites are hard to reconcile unless local tectonic movements have occurred, which Playford and Leech (1977) suggest. Both sets of authors discount the sea-level oscillations proposed earlier by Fairbridge (1961), but final analysis of these sites lies in the future.

Field evidence in Victoria cited by Gill (1983) to support upper Holocene oscillations appears to require further data for confirmation. The problem is the familiar one, that until a sufficiently dense time series of well-dated and unequivocal fixed indicators is thoroughly described, oscillations cannot be inferred. It will be apparent to the reader that the writer is prejudiced in favour of the simple falling sea-level model illustrated in figures 10.5 to 10.8, and it must be left to later workers to demonstrate unequivocal oscillations relative to Australia.

5.5   Post-glacial sea-level rise

The sea-level rise which terminated about 6000 radiocarbon years ago is widely attributed to melting of the late Pleistocene icecaps, and is referred to here as the postglacial sea-level rise. Australian evidence for this rise was introduced in figure 10.2, to illustrate the treatment of uncertainties in sea-level indicators. Since publication of figure 10.2 by Thom and Chappell (1975), many new data have been described and some of those used by Thom and Chappell have been recalibrated for radiocarbon age corrections. Thom and Roy (1983, 1985) have published a new age/depth plot for all data from New South Wales, including new and revised results. This is shown in figure 10.9(a). The graph differs from figure 10.2 in that error bars are not shown. Instead, data points are divided into two relational indicator groups, i.e. those which formed at or below mean sea level (MSL), and those formed above MSL, which simplifies the plot, which otherwise would be crowded with error bars. The shaded band depicts the sea-level envelope according to Thom and Roy (1985). Justification for placing this to the left of all 'at or below MSL' indicators is that palaeo-sea-level must be higher than each point, and that unsystematic contamination error making apparent ages too young is all too frequently likely. Solid lines in figure 10.9(a) show the sea level envelope estimated earlier by Thom and Chappell (1975) and shown on figure 10.2. The effect of the new and revised ages is to move the envelope somewhat to the left around 8000 BP, implying that relative sea level was rather closer to present at that time than was formerly thought. As for the culmination of this transgresion, Thom and Roy (1983, 1985) estimate that it reached a peak between 0 and +1 m, 6000 to 6500 BP, relative to the New South Wales coast.

New data from elsewhere in Australia can be compared with figure 10.9(a). Most come from north Queensland, where drilling studies of an extensive mangrove swamp by Grindrod and Rhodes (1984) provide a series of fixed indicator data, and drilling studies of coral reefs by Hopley (1983) and Davies and Hopley (1983) provide relational data. Grindrod and Rhodes describe 19 drillholes through the mangrove in Missionary Bay, Hinchinbrook Island. Each drillhole reached the land surface which was flooded during postglacial sea-level rise, and a basal organic sediment was shown by pollen analysis to represent transgressive mangrove swamp in each hole. Vertical control is excellent, but the possibility of age error due to mixing during the transgression cannot be excluded. Age/depth data are plotted on figure 10.9(b), superimposed on the sea-level envelope of Thom and Roy (1983). Most of the results fall

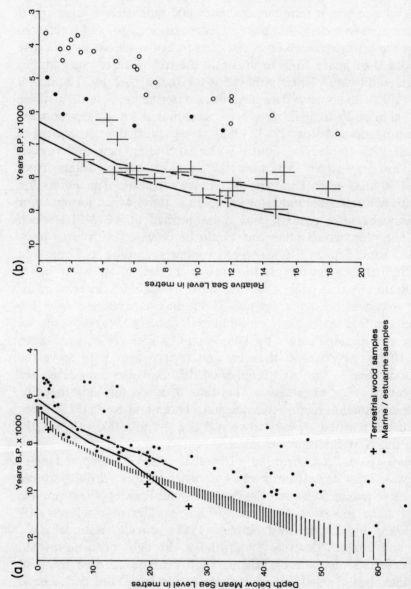

Figure 10.9 Late Pleistocene and Lower Holocene sea-level rise (a), from south-east Australia, and (b), from Hinchinbrook Island, Queensland. Key: (a), sea-level envelope curve from Thom and Roy (1983); (b), crosses are dated transgressive mangrove facies (Grinrod and Rhodes 1984); solid circles are dated sub-tidal corals from drill holes in the inner Great Barrier Reef (Grinrod and Rhodes 1984; Hopley 1983; 1984); open circles are dated sub-tidal corals from drill holes in the outer Great Barrier Reef; the sea-level envelope is the same as the one shown in figure 10.9(a). Further details are in the text

within or very close to the envelope, and others suggest some in-mixing of younger carbon during the transgression.

Contrasting are relational data from numerous coral reef drillholes from the Great Barrier Reef. Vertical control is good in the drillholes, but corals for the most part are relational indicators which form in a range of water depths. Data given by Hopley (1983) from two inner-shelf fringing reefs (Orpheus, Rattlesnake) and from two outer-shelf reefs (Grub, Wheeler) are also plotted in figure 10.9(b). Age errors are not shown for these coral data but are similar to those for the transgressive mangrove dates. It appears that all the corals sampled by drill were growing sub-tidally at their time of formation, and the reefs generally took a few thousand years to achieve sea level, after it stabilised about 6000 BP. Davies and Hopley (1983) and Hopley (1984) give a full account of this. The coral reef results are included here to illustrate the open-ended uncertainty which arises when only sub-tidal relational indicators are available. Other recent data from sub-tidal indicators have been presented from elsewhere in Australia, e.g. by Belperio *et al.* (1984) from Spencer Gulf, and likewise cannot be used to identify the exact course of postglacial sea-level rise.

To summarise, the postglacial sea-level rise is so far defined from sites in eastern Australia. It culminated 6000 BP, or slightly earlier, at a level ranging from 0 to 1 m in New South Wales (Thom and Roy 1983, 1985) up to +2 or even +3 m at other coastal sites around the continent, from the Gulf of Carpentaria, Spencer Gulf, and south-western Australia. A well defined maximum of $+1\pm0.5$ m is established in north-east Queensland. These differences should not be attributed to minor sea-level oscillations having different effects on different coasts, as the Queensland data (figures 10.5 to 10.7) indicate.

6.0 DIFFERENTIAL VERTICAL MOVEMENTS DURING THE HOLOCENE IN AUSTRALIA

The data from north Queensland fringing reefs, the Gulf of Carpentaria chenier plains, and Spencer Gulf appear to be the most complete sets of upper Holocene sea-level results from Australia. Setting aside the interpretational differences between Byrne (1982) and Belperio *et al.* (1984) in the Spencer Gulf case, these data show generally falling sea level from a high point which was reached about 6000 BP. Results from Western Australia also show a relative fall since 5000–6000 BP, although the course may be different. There are interesting differences in the magnitude of this fall, for example a 1 m fall relative to the inner shelf islands of the Great Barrier Reef, about 2.2 m for the southern Gulf of Carpentaria, and about 3 m in northern Spencer Gulf. These differences exceed the errors, and indicate differential vertical movements. In addition, Hopley (1983) interprets the extensive set of surface and drillhole results from outer Great Barrier coral reefs as showing that sea level has not been higher than present in Holocene times, relative to the outer margin of the north Queensland shelf. Hopley's interpretation is based on many more results than those illustrated in figure 10.9(b). Hence, there appears to have been differential vertical movement across the Great Barrier Reef shelf. Figure 10.10 shows contours of post-5500 BP relative sea-level change around north-east Australia, estimated by Chappell et al. (1982). These contours, representing the 5500 BP sea-level 'isobase', were computed by using a model of hydro-isostatic deflection. Details of calculation and of lithosphere/asthenosphere parameters are given by the authors. Empirical values of post-5500 BP sea level change shown in figure 10.10 are based on the studies described above, other comparable studies outlined by Chappell et al. (1982), and results given by Hopley (1982). Hopley's estimates of sea level near the outer shelf margin in the Townsville region are lower than the model 5500 BP isobase, and Hopley (1983) suggests that this may reflect slow tectonic subsidence. Otherwise, agreement between data and the hydro-isostatic model appears to be quite good. However, more exact geophysical analyses of the isostatic problem, at both global (Nakiboglu et al. 1983) and more local (Nakada 1986) levels, are likely to revise the predictions of Chappell et al. (1982) shown in figure 10.10. It is expected that such calculations will eventualy explain much of the variation of mid-Holocene sea level around 'stable' Australia.

Separation of tectonic and isostatic factors should be based on data which are different from the Holocene results reviewed thus far. While tectonic uplift can readily be identified from Holocene shorelines in fast-rising islands such as New Guinea, tectonics and isostasy may be indistinguishable in some upper Holocene areas in mainland Australia. Separation of these should utilise their primary difference, which is that tectonic movement usually continues in the same direction for millions of years, while hydro-isostatic movement reverses direction according to whether sea level is falling or rising. Shorelines of oxygen isotope stage 5e correspond to the ice minimum (interglacial) of 120 000 BP. Therefore, there should be negligible isostatic displacement between 120 000 BP and upper Holocene shorelines, but 120 000 years is long enough for tectonic displacement to accumulate even at low rates of movement. In contrast,

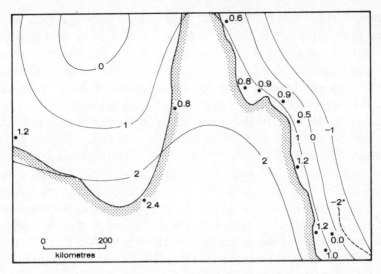

Figure 10.10 Contours of difference between the 5500 BP sea-level isobase and present sea level in north-east Australia according to hydro-isostatic calculation, compared with observational results from coral reef and chenier plain sites. Heights are in metres. Sources: dashed line −2* is from Hopley (1983); all other results are from Chappell *et al.* 1982

shorelines formed during the last glacial low sea level, 18 000 BP, will have accumulated relatively little tectonic displacement but should show maximum hydro-isostatic displacements relative to present sea level. Variations from one place to another of the height difference between present and 120 000 BP shorelines is essentially due to tectonics. Variation from one place to another of the vertical difference between present and 18 000 BP shorelines should largely be due to hydro-isostasy unless local tectonic rates are high.

7.0 THE 18 000 BP LOW SEA LEVEL IN AUSTRALIA

Exact definition of relative sea levels lower than present is more difficult than for higher than present levels. Even when sea-level evidence is accessible by land-based drilling the error problems are significant, as figure 10.8 illustrates. When the lowest sea levels are sought from submarine evidence on the outer shelf, problems are considerable. Evidence lies at depths greater than scuba divers can reach, and is generally sampled by dredges or corers lowered from a ship. Results often show considerable age/depth scatter and sample mixing, such as those from the East China Sea reported by Emery *et al.* (1971). Direct sampling by manned submersibles of shoreline features which have been identified by echogram survey can be more satisfactory. There are some data on the 18 000 BP low sea level around Australia, collected by ship-based and submersible sampling. Three studies can be singled out.

The slope at the edge of the southern Great Barrier Reef was traversed by submersible and sampled above and below a terrace feature at 165 m water depth (Veeh and Veevers 1970). A beachrock sample from 150 m dated at 13 860±220 BP and a *Galaxea* coral from 175 m dated at 13 600±220 BP. The ^{14}C age of the coral was checked by uranium-series dating, which gave 17 000±1000 BP. Veeh and Veevers inferred a low sea level of −175 m from the coral, but this should be treated as a relational indicator as *Galaxea* grows down to over 15 m below sea level (Veron and Pichon 1979). The data can be compared with results from the outer north-western shelf of Australia. Using short core samples, van Andel and Veevers (1967) report a change from lagoonal to marine sedimentation at 132 m water depth, between 18 900±1500 and 17 400±1000 BP. Jongsma (1970) reports beach rock at 150 m in the same region, and gives a date of 18 700±350 BP, although this result does not come from the *in situ* beach rock which was seen by submersible, but was recovered by dredge in about the same depth. Significance of the differences amongst these results is unclear, as variations between the reported ages make it uncertain whether the same low sea level has been sampled at each site. Site descriptions lack desirable details, which is understandable given their positions. The results place sea level somewhere between 130 and 165 m below present around 18 000 BP, relative to outer margins of north Australian shelves. On the basis of the *in situ* beachrocks observed in the Queensland and north-west shelf submersible dives, a working figure of about 150 m was adopted by Chappell (1982). Further work is needed before this figure is more precisely specified, and before any differences around Australia can be declared. It is noted that Chappell (1974) and Chappell and Shackleton (1986) adopt a figure of 130 m relative to north-east New Guinea, where there is no shelf and isostatic differentials will be negligible.

It is important to establish the value of the 18 000 BP low sea level, as figures much less than 130 to 150 m are reported elsewhere in the world, and are used not only in global isostatic calculations (Clark *et al.* 1978), but also in comparisons of sea level and isotope records (Johnson and Andrews 1986, Chappell and Shackleton 1986).

8.0 THE 120 000 BP SEA LEVEL IN AUSTRALIA

The time of the last interglacial peak is identified with oxygen isotope stage 5e about 120 000 BP (Shackleton and Opdyke 1973). A high sea level at this time is confirmed by uranium-series dating of Pleistocene coral reefs in many places which are remote from plate boundaries (Veeh 1966, Broecker and Thurber 1965, Ku *et al.* 1974, Marshall and Thom 1976, Kaufman 1986). The age estimates of these reefs centre on 125 000 BP and their elevations mostly fall in the range 2 to 10 m above present sea level. Hence, the '125 000 BP high sea level' has come to be a reference point or palaeo-datum used in studies of tectonically rising coasts bearing raised dated reefs and shorelines. Studies of raised reefs dating to this high sea-level episode suggest that it may have persisted for about 10 000 years, although Kaufman (1986) concludes that the interval was shorter, and it was possibly interrupted by a minor regression/transgression cycle, with the first peak perhaps being the higher by a few metres (Ku *et al.* 1974, Chappell and Veeh 1978).

Shorelines and coral reefs identified with stage 5e occur at many localities around Australia. Identification of sea-level indicators and measurement of their elevations is good in most cases, as the features commonly occur above present tidal levels and frequently are clearly exposed in low erosion cliffs. Sites a few metres above present sea level dated around 120 000 BP by uranium series, occur in Western Australia (Veeh 1966), South Australia (Schwebel 1984), and in northern New South Wales (Marshall and Thom 1976). Sites, which have been correlated with these, on morphologic or morphostratigraphic grounds, occur in Western Australia (Denham and van de Graaf 1976), Tasmania (Bowden and Colhoun 1984), Spencer Gulf in South Australia (Hails *et al.* 1984), and have been noted in Victoria (Gill 1977) and far north Queensland (Rhodes 1980). Pickett *et al.* (1985) report coral reefs near Brisbane at about present sea level, apparently dated to 105 000 BP. However, Pickett (pers. comm.) reports that these have been redetermined and are 120 000 to 130 000 BP.

Most of the dated results show sea level in the range 2 to 8 m above present. These are from widely separated parts of the continent, and the range is similar to that which encompasses '120 000' (or 125 000) BP results reported from sites remote from plate boundaries elsewhere in the world. Uncertainty about the exact course of sea level in the 130 000 to 120 000 BP interval (Chappell and Veeh 1978), coupled with the fact that some of these observations may not reflect the full original extent of the

'120 000 BP shoreline' at each site, makes it unrealistic to try to refine the palaeo-sea-level data between 2 and 8 m. Differential movements should not be inferred amongst Australian sites in this range, at present, but future work will no doubt improve the situation.

Vertical movement, presumably tectonic, appears to have raised the 120 000 BP shoreline significantly in some parts of Australia. Most conspicuous is northern Tasmania, particularly the north-east corner, where beach-ridge plains rise to about 25 m. Morphological parallels with 120 000 BP barriers in New South Wales described and dated by Marshall and Thom (1976) compel correlation with stage 5e (Bowden and Colhoun 1984). Uplift also is indicated in south-east South Australia (Schwebel 1984), and may have occurred locally at Cape Cuvier in north-west Western Australia (Denham and van de Graaf 1976). The absence of 120 000 BP sea-level indicators from long reaches of coast, particularly southern New South Wales and the Great Barrier Reef coast of north Queensland – both of which have been well studied (Thom *et al.* 1981, Hopley 1982) – may show that these areas have subsided somewhat, although this remains to be proven.

The broad result is that the 120 000 BP sea-level marker is a useful guide to longer-term vertical movements, when the vertical uncertainty factor is taken into account. Future work should reduce the value of 6 m uncertainty which attaches to this marker in the Australian context.

9.0 SEA-LEVEL DATA FROM RAPIDLY RISING COASTS

Tectonically active islands of the south-west Pacific lie to the north and east of Australia, notably Papua New Guinea, the Bismark, Solomon, and Vanuatu (New Hebrides) systems and New Zealand. By virtue of their rapid uplift, these have the potential to raise glacial-stage shorelines above present sea level. The most complete such record so far reported is that from Huon Peninsula, north-east Papua New Guinea (figure 10.1) where a flight of raised coral reefs of unusual extent and morphostratigraphic clarity has been described (Chappell 1974), and has been the subject of two uranium-series dating studies (Veeh and Chappell 1970, Bloom *et al.* 1974). The uplift rate varies along the terrace flight, from 3.3 m/1000 yr in the south-east to 0.7 m/1000 yr in the north-west. Each terrace includes an intertidal reef facies at its crest, as well as shallow-water reef facies within its growth structure. The flight of offlapping reefs records a sequence of transgressions and regressions, interpreted as being caused by glacio-eustatic oscillations superimposed on the rising land.

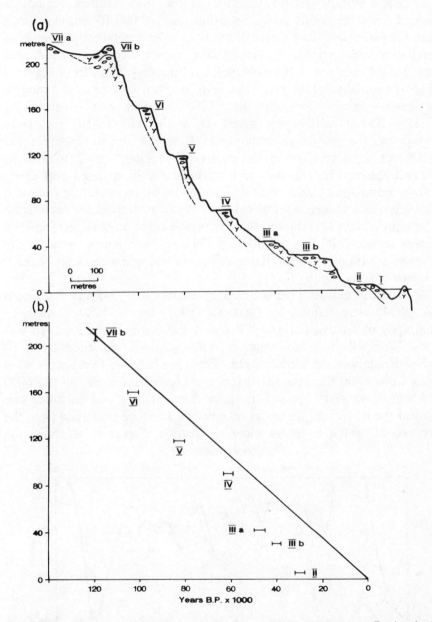

Figure 10.11 (a), A typical cross-section of raised reefs on the Huon Peninsula, New Guinea (Sialum-Kwambu section). Roman numerals are the reefname code used by Chappell (1974); (b), a graph to illustrate the uniform uplift assumption used as a first step in sea-level reconstruction.

The glacio-eustatic record, relative to the New Guinea region, is separated from the uplift factor by using the 120 000 BP sea level as a means for estimating uplift rate. This is done independently at each of several surveyed sections. Figure 10.11(a) shows a typical section, and figure 10.11(b) illustrates the exercise of subtracting uplift from sea-level change. Essentially, uplift rate relative to a given section is assumed to have been constant over the last 120 000 years and is given by $u = (H - B)/120$ (m/1000 yr), where H is the 120 000 BP reef crest elevation on the particular section and B is the actual height of the 120 000 sea level relative to the Australian region, i.e. 2 to 8 m as explained above. The relative sea level indicated by a dated reef crest, elevation h and age t (1000 years) is $S_t = h - ut$. By repeating this across a set of different sections, a set of sea-level values is derived for each dated reef. Bloom *et al.* (1974) showed that the results agree quite closely between different sections. The amplitudes of sea-level oscillations between the reef crests are estimated from the thickness of transgressive facies beneath the separate reefs (figure 10.11).

The Huon Peninsula results given by Chappell (1974) and by Bloom *et al.* (1974) were refined by Chappell (1983) on the basis of detailed stratigraphy of a particularly well exposed and fast-rising section. In that report, Chappell included small step-like changes recorded by cliff-notches throughout the terrace flight. These are believed to reflect sudden seismic uplifts, on the grounds that several are manifest in the last 6000 years when sea level appears to have been stable, and includes one historical event. Hence, these step-like jumps are to be smoothed from the Huon record insofar as it has wider application. Figure 10.12 shows the

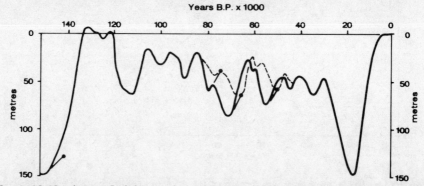

Figure 10.12 An age/height graph to show sea-level changes over the last 150 000 years in the Australian region interpreted from the New Guinea shoreline record with modifications according to comparisons with the deep ocean isotopic cores (Chappell 1982; Chappell and Shackleton 1986). Small bars, solid circles and the dashed line show modifications by Chappell and Shackleton (1986)

smoothed record back to the major transgression which led to the 120 000–130 000 BP high sea level. The extension to 320 000 BP given by Chappell (1983) is not reproduced here, as it is subject to greater uncertainties about dating and uplift rates and currently is being re-examined (Chappell and Shackleton 1986). The difficulty with sea-level reconstruction from flights of dated reefs is that the higher the uplift rate, the more the results are subject to dating uncertainties. Timing of high and low sea-level turning points differs between uranium-series dated Huon Peninsula reefs and deep-sea isotopic cores, especially before 120 000 BP. Differences within the last 120 000 years are significant at some of the low sea-level points. Figure 10.12 indicates these and details are given by Chappell and Shackleton (1986), who tabulate 'best estimates' of sea level relative to north-east New Guinea for each turning-point in figure 10.12.

Studies of raised coral reef terraces, dated by the uranium-series method, have been published from other rising islands in the south-west Pacific region, including the Vanuatu (New Hebrides) Group (Neef and Veeh 1977, Taylor *et al.* 1980), the Loyalty Islands (Dubois *et al.* 1977), and Timor (Chappell and Veeh 1978). In each case, the 120 000 BP marker is used as the basis for estimating uplift wherever possible. Estimation of uplift rates is a main objective in such studies, and they are not reviewed here as discussion of tectonic patterns lies outside the scope of this paper. Similarly, differential tectonic movements in New Zealand are studied from flights of raised shoreline features, in some cases using dated tephras to provide chronology and the Huon Peninsula curve as an independent reference (Pillans 1983, Bull and Cooper 1986), and in others using geomorphologic clues to identify the 120 000 BP surface as the primary basis for chronology and uplift (Ghani 1978, Wellman 1979, Yoshikawa *et al.* 1980).

10.0 CONCLUDING DISCUSSION

Tectonic and isostatic movements conveniently explain differences in the heights of sea-level indicators between one place and another. In rapidly rising island groups, differential tectonic movements are well demonstrated by tilted or disrupted terraces over distances of a few tens of kilometres. Some of the best examples are from the south and eastern coasts of North Island, New Zealand. An extreme case of disruptive tectonic uplift is documented by Selkirk and Selkirk (1983) in Macquarie Island on the plate junction in the Southern Ocean, where 100 m of Holocene uplift appears to have occurred at the northern tip of the island. In 'stable' continental Australia, differential isostatic movements appear to have occurred in Holocene times (figure 10.10) and the 120 000 BP marker indicates local tectonic uplift in some areas, particularly northern Tasmania. Detailed examination of regional variations of this marker, from plate margins (New Zealand through west Melanesia to Indonesia) to the margins of plate-centred Australia, are important for studying tectonic connections through a single plate. Australia may be the best case for such study.

This paper has emphasised that attention should be given to errors in palaeo-sea-level estimation. Only when this is fully addressed can palaeo-sea-level data be used properly, for geophysical and coastal geomorphologic studies. It is unfortunate when results from nearby sites, based on different and incompletely assessed forms of evidence disagree, that those results are brushed aside under the heading of 'local differential movements'. Discrepant results from neighbouring sites can occur, due to local factors such as compaction, as illustrated in the northern Barrier Reef *versus* Princess Charlotte Bay data (figures 10.5 and 10.6). Results from elsewhere must be examined in this light, particularly where data are widely cited as realistic and final. An example comes from the widely-used sea-level curve from the Caroline Islands produced by Bloom (1970) on the basis of dated paludal sediments of infilling lagoons. Bloom's curve shows sea level rising steadily towards present through upper Holocene times. Contrasting are results from Schofield (1977) based on dated coral/shingle ridges in the comparatively close Gilbert Islands, which indicate sea level at or above present in the upper Holocene period. The factor of progressive compaction appears not to be reckoned with by Bloom, while storm-building of ridges over a prior substrate as a complicating factor may not be fully considered by Schofield. The real meaning, in sea-level terms, of the conflict between these results cannot be assessed.

The data presented here have been selected, and are biased. They are the 'safest' results available in the Australian region. Further work will test the data and conclusions. In certain cases, such as the fringing reefs of north-east Australia, results in the upper Holocene appear to be sufficiently dense in time and sufficiently well-defined to prove a local set of sea-level curves. The conclusions are not reiterated; they are embodied in the diagrams which have been presented here. However, it is clear that future study should be aimed at detailing the Holocene and 120 000 BP sea-level records around the Australian continent, particularly where data are sparse but where suitable deposits are known, such as in the north and the west. Revised typescript received 1986, May.

REFERENCES

Andel, T. J. van and Veevers, J. J. 1967: Morphology and sediments of the Timor Sea. *Bureau of Mineral Resources, Geology and Geophysics, Australia. Bulletin* 3.

Belperio, A. P., Hails, J. R., Gostin, V. A. and Polach, H. A. 1984: The stratigraphy of coastal carbonate banks and Holocene sea levels of northern Spencer Gulf, South Australia. *Marine Geol.*, 61, 297–313.

Bird, E. C. F. 1971: The fringing reef near Yule Point, North Queensland. *Austral. Geogr. Studies*, 9, 107–15.

Bloom, A. L. 1970: Paludal stratigraphy of Truk, Ponape, and Kusaie, Eastern Caroline islands. *Geol. Soc. Am. Bull.*, 81, 1895–904.

Bloom, A. L., Broecker, W. S., Chappell, J., Matthews, R. K. and Mesolella, K. J. 1974: Quaternary sea-level fluctuations on a tectonic coast: New ^{230}Th/^{234}U dates from New Guinea. *Quat. Res.*, 4, 185–205.

Bowden, A. R. and Colhoun, E. A. 1984: Quaternary emergent shorelines in Tasmania. In B. G. Thom (ed.), *Coastal Geomorphology in Australia*, Sydney: Academic Press, 313–42.

Broecker, W. S. and Thurber, D. L. 1965: Uranium series dating of corals and oolites from Bahaman and Florida key limestones. *Science*, 149, 55–7.

Brown, R. G. 1983: Sea-level history over the past 15 000 years along the Western Australian coastline. In D. Hopley (ed.), *Australian Sea Levels in the Last 15 000 years: A Review*, Dept. of Geography, James Cook University of North Queensland, Townsville *Occasional Paper* 3, 29–36.

Bull, W. B. and Cooper, A. F. 1986: Uplifted marine terraces along the Alpine Fault, New Zealand. *Science*, 234, 1225–8.

Byrne, R. V. 1982: Relative fall of Holocene sea-level and coastal progradation, northeastern Spencer Gulf, South Australia. *BMR J. Austral. Geol. & Geophys.*, 7, 35–45.

Chappell, J. 1974: Geology of coral terraces, Huon Peninsula, New Guinea: a study of Quaternary tectonic movements and sea-level changes. *Geol. Soc. Amer. Bull.*, 85, 553–70.

Chappell, J. 1982: Evidence for smoothly falling sea-level relative to north Queensland, Australia, during the past 6000 years. *Nature*, 302, 406–8.

Chappell, J. 1983: A revised sea-level record for the last 300 000 years from Papua New Guinea. *Search*, 14, 99–101.

Chappell, J. and Grindrod, J. 1984: Chenier Plain formation in northern Australia. In B. G. Thom (ed.), *Coastal Geomorphology in Australia*, Sydney: Academic Press, 197–232.

Chappell, J., Chivas, A., Wallensky, E., Polach, H. A. and Aharon, P. 1983: Holocene palaeo-environmental changes, central to north Great Barrier Reef inner zone. *BMR J. Austral. Geol. & Geophys.*, 8, 223–315.

Chappell, J., Rhodes, E. G., Thom, B. G. and Wallensky, E. P. 1982: Hydro-isostasy and the sea-level isobase of 5500 BP in north Queensland, Australia. *Marine Geol.*, 49, 81–90.

Chappell, J. and Shackleton, N. J. 1986: Oxygen isotopes and sea-level. *Nature*, 324, 137–40.

Chappell, J. and Veeh, H. H. 1978: Late Quaternary tectonic movements and sea-level changes at Timor and Atauro Island. *Geol. Soc. Am. Bull.*, 89, 356–68.

Chivas, A., Chappell, J., Polach, H. A., Pillans, B. and Flood, P. 1986: Radiocarbon evidence for the timing and rate of island development, beach-rock formation, and phosphatisation of Lady Eliot Island, Queensland. *Marine Geol.*, 69, 273–87.

Clark, J. A., Farrell, W. E. and Peltier, W. R. 1978: Global change in post-glacial sea level: a numerical calculation. *Quat. Res.*, 9, 265–87.

Davies, P. J. and Hopley, D. 1983: Growth facies and growth rates of Holocene reefs in the Great Barrier Reef. *BMR J. Austral. Geol. & Geophys.*, 8, 237–52.

Denham, P. D. and van de Graaf, W. J. E. 1976: Emergent Quaternary marine deposits in the Lake MacLeod area, W. A.. *Geological Survey of Western Australia Annual Report 1976*, 32–7.

Donner, J. and Jungner, H. 1981: Radiocarbon dating of marine shells from southeastern Australia as a means of dating relative sea-level changes. *Annal. Acad. Scient. Fennicae III*, 131, 5–14.

Dubois, J. J., Dupont, A., Lapouille, A. and Recy, J. 1977: Lithospheric bulge and thickening of the lithosphere with age: examples in the southwest Pacific. In *International Symposium on Geodynamics in the Southwest Pacific*, Paris: Technip, 371–80.

Emery, K. O., Niino, H. and Sullivan, B. 1971: Post-Pleistocene levels of the East China Sea. In K. Turekian (ed.), *Late Cenozoic Glacial Ages*, New Haven: Yale Univ. Press, 381–90.

Fairbridge, R. W. 1961: Eustatic changes in sea level. In L. H. Ahrens *et al* (eds.), *Physics and Chemistry of the Earth*, 4, London: Pergamon Press, 99–185.

Geyh, M. A. 1980: Holocene sea-level history: case study of the statistical evaluation of ^{14}C dates. *Radiocarbon*, 22, 695–704.

Ghani, M. A. 1978: Late Cenozoic vertical crustal movement in the southern North Island, New Zealand. *N.Z. J. Geol. & Geophys.*, 21, 117–25.

Gill, E. D. 1977: Evolution of the Otway coast, Australia, from the last interglacial to the present. *Proceedings, Royal Society of Victoria*, 89, 7–18.

Gill, E. D. 1983: Australian sea levels in the last 15 000 years – Victoria, South-east Australia. In D. Hopley (ed.), *Australian Sea Levels in the Last 15 000 Years: A review*, Dept. of Geography, James Cook University of North Queensland, Townsville *Occasional Paper* 3, 59–63.

Gillespie, R. and Polach, H. A. 1979: The suitability of marine shells for radiocarbon dating of Australian prehistory. In R. Berger and H. Suess (eds.), *Proc. Ninth International Conference Radiocarbon Dating*, Univ. California Press, 404–21.

Grindrod, J. and Rhodes, E. G. 1984: Holocene sea-level history of a tropical estuary, Missionary Bay, north Queensland. In B. G. Thom (ed.), *Coastal Geomorphology in Australia*, Sydney: Academic Press, 151–78.

Hails, J. R., Belperio, A. P. and Gostin, V. A. 1984: Quaternary sea levels, northern Spencer Gulf, Australia. *Marine Geol.*, 61, 373–89.

Hails, J. R. and Gostin, V. A. 1978: Stranded shingle beach ridges, upper Spencer Gulf, South Australia: evidence for high wave energy dissipation during the late Pleistocene. *Trans. R. Soc. South Austral.*, 102, 169–73.

Hopley, D. 1982: *The Geomorphology of The Great Barrier Reef*. New York: Wiley Interscience.

Hopley, D. 1983: Evidence of 15 000 years of sea level change in tropical Queensland. In D. Hopley (ed.), *Australian Sea Levels in the Last 15 000 years: A review*, Dept. of Geography, James Cook University of North Queensland, Townsville, *Occasional Paper* 3, 93–104.

Hopley, D. 1984: The Holocene 'high energy window' on the Central Great Barrier Reef. In B. G. Thom (ed.), *Coastal Geomorphology in Australia* Sydney: Academic Press, 135–50.

Johnson, R. G. and Andrews, J. T. 1986: Glacial terminations in the oxygen isotope record of deep-sea cores: hypothesis of massive Antarctic ice-shelf destruction. *Palaeogeogr. Palaeoclimatol., Palaeoecol.*, 55, 107–38.

Jongsma, D. 1970: Eustatic sea-level changes in the Arafura Sea. *Nature*, 228, 150–1.

Kaufman, A. 1986: The distribution of ^{230}Th/^{234}U ages in corals and the number of last interglacial high-sea stands. *Quat. Res.*, 25, 55–62.

Kendrick, G. W. 1977: Middle Holocene marine molluscs from near Guildford, Western Australia, and evidence for climatic change. *J. R. Soc. Western Australia*, 59, 97–104.

Ku, T.-L., Kimmel, M. A., Easton, W. H. and O'Neill, T. J. 1974: Eustatic sea level 120 000 years ago on Oahu, Hawaii. *Science*, 183, 959–62.

Marshall, J. F. and Thom, B. G. 1976: The sea level in the last interglacial. *Nature*, 263, 120–1.

McLean, R. F., Stoddart, D. R., Hopley, D. and Polach, H. A. 1978: Sea-level changes in the Holocene on the northern Great Barrier Reef. *Phil. Trans. R. Soc. London, Series A*, 291, 167–86.

Nakada, M. 1986: Holocene sea levels in oceanic islands: implications for the archaeological structure of the earth's mantle. *Tectonophysics*, 121, 263–76.

Nakiboglu, S. M., Lambeck, K. and Aharon, P. 1983: Postglacial sea levels in the Pacific: implications with respect to deglaciation regime and local tectonics. *Tectonophysics*, 91, 335–58.

Neef, G. and Veeh, H. H. 1977: Uranium series ages and Late Quaternary uplift in the New Hebrides. *Nature*, 269, 682–3.

Pearson, G. W. 1979: Precise ^{14}C measurement by liquid scintillation counting. *Radiocarbon*, 21, 1–21.

Pickett, J. W., Thompson, C. H., Kelley, R. A. and Roman, D. 1985: Evidence of high sea level during isotope stage 5c in Queensland, Australia. *Quat. Res.*, 24, 103–14.

Pillans, B. 1983: Upper Quaternary marine terrace chronology and deformation, South Taranaki, New Zealand. *Geology*, 11, 292–7.

Plassche, O. van de 1982: Sea-level change and water-level movements in the Netherlands during the Holocene. *Mededelingen rijks Geologische Dienst* 36–1.

Playford, P. E. and Leech, R. E. J. 1977: Geology and hydrology of Rottnest Island. *Geological Survey of Western Australia, Report 6.*

Radok, R. and Raupach, M. 1977: Sea level and transport phenomena in St. Vincent Gulf. *Institute of Engineers 3rd Australian Conference on Coastal and Ocean Enginering*, 103–9.

Rhodes, E. G. 1980: Modes of Holocene coastal progradation, Gulf of Carpentaria. Unpublished PhD Thesis, Australian National University, Canberra.

Rhodes, E. G., Polach, H. A., Thom, B. G. and Wilson, S. R. 1980: Age structure of Holocene coastal sediments, Gulf of Carpentaria, Australia. *Radiocarbon*, 22, 718–27.

Schofield, J. C. 1977: Late Holocene sea level, Gilbert and Ellice Islands, west central Pacific Ocean. *N.Z. J. Geol. & Geophys.*, 20, 503–29.

Schwebel, D. A. 1984: Quaternary stratigraphy and sea-level variation in the southeast of South Australia. In B. G. Thom (ed.), *Coastal Geomorphology in Australia*, Sydney: Academic Press, 291–312.

Scoffin, T. P. and Stoddart, D. R. 1978: Nature and significance of microatolls. *Phil. Trans. R. Soc. London, Series B*, 291, 99–122.

Selkirk, D. R. and Selkirk, P. M. 1983: Preliminary report on some peats from Macquarie Island 7±2KA. In *Proceedings of the first CLIMANZ*, Dept. Biogeography & Geomorphology, Australian National University, Canberra, 115–17.

Shackleton, N. J. and Opdyke, N. D. 1973: Oxygen-isotope and paleomagnetic stratigraphy of equatorial Pacific core V28–238: oxygen isotopic temperatures and ice volumes on a 10^5 year and 10^6 year scale. *Quat. Res.*, 3, 39–55.

Shennan, I., Tooley, M. J., Davis, M. J. and Haggart, B. A. 1983: Analysis and interpretation of Holocene sea-level data. *Nature*, 302, 404–6.

Shepherd, M. J. 1981: The Rockingham coastal barrier system of Western Australia. *Western Geographer* 5, 67–81.

Stuiver, M. and Polach, H. A. 1977: Discussion: reporting of ^{14}C data. *Radiocarbon*, 19, 355–63.

Taylor, F. W., Isacks, B. L., Jouannic, C., Bloom, A. L. and Dubois, J. J. 1980: Coseismic and Quaternary vertical movements, Santo and Malekula Islands, New Hebrides Island arc. *J. Geophys. Res.*, 85, 5367–81.

Thom, B. G. 1978: Coastal sand deposition in southeast Australia during the Holocene. In J. L. Davies and M. A. J. Williams (eds), *Landform Evolution in Australasia*, Canberra: Australian National University Press, 197–214.

Thom, B. G., Bowman, G. M., Gillespie, R., Temple R. and Barbetti, M. 1981:

Radiocarbon dating of Holocene beach ridge sequences in southeast Australia. Dept. of Geography, University of New South Wales, Duntroon, *Monograph 11*.

Thom, B. G. and Chappell, J. 1975: Holocene sea levels relative to Australia. *Search* 6, 90–93.

Thom, B. G., Polach, H. A. and Bowman, G. M. 1978: Holocene age structure of coastal sand barriers in New South Wales, Australia. Dept. of Geography, University of New South Wales, Duntroon, *Special Publ. 1 (1978)*, 1–85.

Thom, B. G. and Roy, P. S. 1983: Sea level change in New South Wales over the past 15 000 years. In D. Hopley (ed.), *Australian Sea Levels in the Last 15 000 Years: A Review*, Dept. of Geography, James Cook University of North Queensland, Townsville *Occasional Paper* 3, 64–84.

Thom, B. G. and Roy, P. S. 1985: Relative sea levels and coastal sedimentation in southeast Australia in the Holocene. *J. Sediment. Petrol.*, 55, 257–64.

Tooley, M. J. 1974: Sea-level changes during the last 9000 years in north-west England. *Geogr. J.*, 140, 18–42.

Tooley, M. J., 1982: Sea-level changes in northern England. *Proc. Geol. Ass.*, 93, 43–51.

Veeh, H. H. 1966: Th^{230}/U^{234} and U^{234}/U^{238} ages of Pleistocene high sea-level stand. *J. Geophys. Res.*, 71, 3379–86.

Veeh, H. H. and Chappell, J. 1970: Astronomical theory of climatic change: support from New Guinea. *Science*, 167, 862–5.

Veeh, H. H. and Veevers, J. J. 1970: Sea level at −175 m off the Great Barrier Reef 13 600 to 17 000 years ago. *Nature*, 226, 536–7.

Veron, J. E. N. and Pichon, M. 1979: *Scleractinia of Eastern Australia, Part III*. Australian Institute of Marine Science, Monograph Series, V.4, Australian National University Press, Canberra, 201–11.

Welman, H. W. 1979: An uplift map for the South Island of New Zealand, and a model for uplift of the Southern Alps. In R. I. Walcott and M. M. Cresswell (eds), *The Origin of the Southern Alps*, Wellington: Royal Society of N.Z., 13–20.

Woods, P. J. and Searle, D. J. 1983: Radiocarbon dating and Holocene history of the Beacher/Rockingham beach ridge plain, west coast, Western Australia. *Search*, 14, 44–6.

Wright, L. D., Coffey, F. C. and Cowell, P. J. 1980: Nearshore oceanography and morphodynamics of The Broken Bay–Palm Beach region, N.S.W.: Implications for offshore dredging. Coastal Studies Unit, Sydney University, Sydney, *Tech. Report 80/1*.

Yoshikawa, T., Ota, Y., Yonekura, N., Okada, A. and Iso, N. 1980: Marine terraces and their tectonic deformation on the northeast coast of the North Island, New Zealand. *Geogr. Rev. Japan*, 53, 238–62.

11

Models of global sea-level changes

Nils-Axel Mörner

Mankind has always had to face the effects of sea-level changes; in the long term over many generations, as well as in the short term with more catastrophic effects. Hence it is not strange that sea-level changes are recorded in many myths and in early historical records. This paper, however, will be confined to the explanations and models offered in recent times. In order to shorten the text and avoid repetition, I have frequently made references to other papers where the problem in question is further discussed.

1.0 BACKGROUND

Stratigraphic sequences frequently give clear evidence of alternations between marine and continental beds. In order to explain this, one must identify, at least, one variable. During the eighteenth century there was an animated debate whether this variable was the sea (as claimed by the so-called 'neptunists') or it was the crust (as claimed by the so-called 'plutonists').

The Fennoscandian uplift was, for example, explained (see Mörner, 1979a) either in terms of a 'water diminuition' after the deluge (e.g. Celsius 1743, Linné 1745) or in terms of a land elevation (e.g. Runeberg 1765, von Buch 1810, Berzelius 1822, 1843, Lyell 1835).

Frizi (1785) gave a third explanation. He noted that the recorded sea-level rise in the Mediterranean area and the sea-level fall in Fennoscandia were consistent with an increase in the Earth's rate of rotation. This theory implies a deformation of the rotation ellipsoid. His proposal gained little or no credence, however.

The sea-level problem was, in fact, double; one was the origin (ocean or land, or rotation), the other was the number of 'floodings' giving evidence of many and not of only one single big flood – the deluge.

Playfair (1802) and von Buch (1810) gave strong arguments in favour of crustal changes, and formulated the so-called 'elevation theory'. When Lyell (1835) later subscribed to this theory, it gained a general acceptance.

So it was established that the crustal level was variable and hence capable of giving rise to relative sea-level changes.

On figure 11.1 the three main eighteenth and nineteenth century models (ocean, crustal and rotational) explaining the relative sea-level changes recorded in stratigraphic sequences are illustrated.

In the middle of the nineteenth century it became evident that the ocean level is also likely to have changed with time for reasons other than 'the deluge'. These reasons were: (1) the deflection of the plumb line, i.e. the geoid (von Bruckhausen 1846; Fischer 1868, Listing 1873, Penck 1882, von Drygalski 1887, Woodward 1888); (2) the ice ages (Maclaren

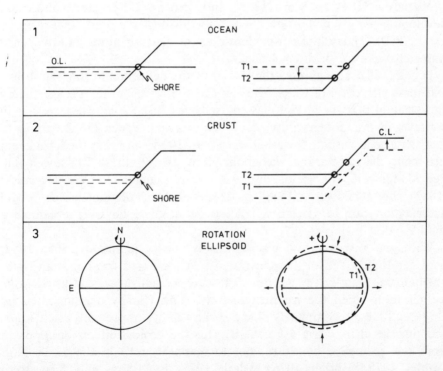

Figure 11.1 The three eighteenth and nineteenth century models to explain recorded relative sea-level changes. Left hand figures show the situation before an event (T1) and right hand figures show the situation after an event (T2) that leads to a change in sea-level. 1, changes in the ocean level (O.L.), ie, in water volume; 2, changes in crustal level (C.L.); 3, changes in the rate of rotation

1841, Tylor 1868, Penck 1882); and (3) the ocean basin subsidence (Chambers 1848, Suess 1888). This is illustrated in figure 11.2.

The deflection of the plumb line was established by the French expeditions under Bouguer to the Andes in Peru and to Lapland in northern Fennoscandia as early as 1735–45. Von Bruckhausen (1846) was the first to realize that this ought to imply that the ocean level (due to mass attraction of water) was likely to rise along the continents. Fischer (1868) calculated that this 'continental wave' might amount to several hundred metres (8 m per second deviation). Listing (1873) introduced the term, 'the geoid'.

With the realization of the existence of previous ice ages (e.g. Charpentier, 1835) it was a simple matter of logic to realize partly its effects on the volume of water in the oceans (i.e. glacial eustasy) and partly its effects via mass attraction of water on the geoid surface (i.e. geoidal eustasy).

Maclaren (1841), Tylor (1868) and Penck (1882) are pioneers in developing the glacial eustatic theory, formulated in a more final form by Daly (1910). Today it is self-evident that the glacial volume and the ocean water changes are in direct balance.

Penck (1882) also applied the theory of the deflection of the plumb line and mass attraction of water (the 'continental wave') to the ice age theory and claimed that the glacial mass must have caused a considerable rise in sea level in the close vicinity of the ice margins. Penck (1882) proposed that the glacial eustatic lowering was about 100 m and that the local geoid rise along the ice margins was about 90 m. Hergesell (1887) showed that Penck's figure of the geoidal rise was greatly exaggerated. Von Drygalski (1887) and Woodward (1888) made detailed calculations of the geoid deformation due to glaciations. All these studies, however, assumed a rigid Earth.

With the discovery of glacial isostasy (e.g. Jamieson 1865, 1882, De Geer 1888/90) it was demonstrated that the Earth was not at all rigid, but deformed under the additional load of ice and later readjusted to its former level when the ice melted away. This (finally demonstrated by De Geer 1888/90) completely changed the validity of previous calculations and theories using a rigid Earth. By this the geoidal effects disappeared from the geological literature, not to reappear until in the 1970s (e.g. Cathles 1975, Mörner 1976a, Clark 1976, Fjeldskaar and Kaneström 1980).

The formation of coral reefs according to Darwin (1842) implied a gradual sinking of the ocean floor, which was substantiated by later studies in the Pacific (Dana 1849). Chambers (1848) realized that this

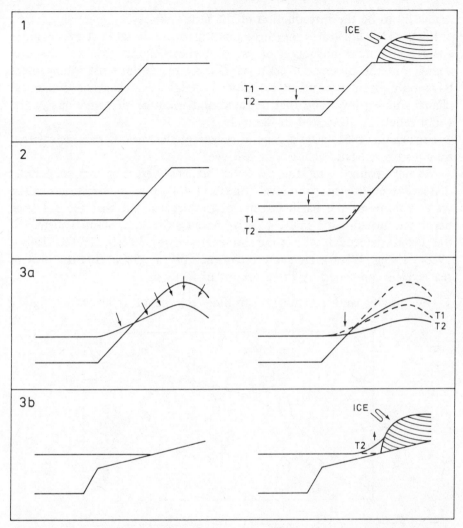

Figure 11.2 The three nineteenth-century models to explain absolute, eustatic changes in sea level. 1, glacial eustasy (ie, the water volume); 2, tectono-eustasy (ie, the basin volume); 3, gravitational mass attraction of water (ie, the water distribution) due to the continental mass (3a) and the ice mass (3b)

sinking would cause an expansion of the total ocean basin volume which, therefore, would lead to a fall in sea level. This is what we today call tectono-eustasy. Suess (1888) introduced the word 'eustasy'. The origin of the eustatic changes, however, he found in the formation of ocean basins (i.e. tectono-eustasy) and in the in-fill of sediments (i.e. sedimento-eustasy). He denied all forms of vertical crustal movements except for mountain and ocean basin building. The merit of Suess's paper seems primarily to be the introduction of the term 'eustasy'.

Figure 11.2 illustrates the three main models (glacial eustasy, tectono-eustasy and mass attraction of water) for explaining absolute sea-level changes in the nineteenth century. During the twentieth century there have only been two major additional models, viz. that of dynamical changes in sea level and that of rapid and irregular deformations of the geoid relief, as illustrated in figure 11.3.

Fairbridge (1961) gave a general review of the various parameters that may lead to eustatic changes in sea level.

Mörner realized that the sea-level changes were not simple parallel displacements of the shorelevel (figure 11.4(a)) due to variations in the water volume or the basin volume of the oceans, but that the sea level deformed horizontally (figure 11.4(b)) because the equipotential surface of the geoid deformed with time (Mörner 1971a, 1971b, 1976a, 1980a, 1983a, 1986a, 1986b). He showed (Mörner 1981a, 1983a) that the present sea level is controlled by three groups of factors:

1   by gravity and rotation controlling the geoid relief which has a

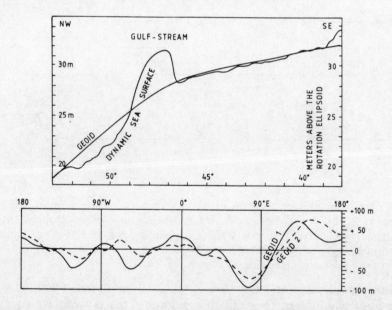

Figure 11.3   The additional twentieth-century models to explain ocean-level changes. The upper graph shows a profile across the Gulf Stream (redrawn from Mörner 1983a) and indicates how dynamic factors force the "dynamic sea level" to deviate from the geodetic sea level, ie, the geoid. In the lower graph, two geoid profiles are compared along latitude 10°N (geoid 1) and 10°S (geoid 2), and representing an hypothetical T2-time (redrawn from Mörner 1980a)

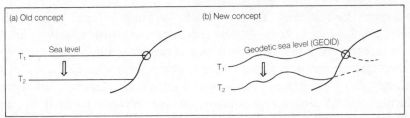

Figure 11.4 An illustration to show the old (a) and new (b) concepts of eustasy (redrawn from Mörner 1983a). The old concept assumed total parallelism and hence global synchronism. The new concept realises that two sea levels are never fully parallel and that gravitational changes must be compensated over the globe, making any global synchronism illusive

    maximum present difference of 180 m (i.e. somewhat less than 200 m);

2 by the attraction of the sun and the moon (and the planets) causing the tidal variations having a maximum amplitude of somewhat less than 20 m; and

3 by meteorological, hydrological and oceanographic factors controlling the dynamic sea level which has a deviation from the geoid surface of up to 2 m for the lower harmonics (Mather *et al.* 1979) and up to some 4–5 m over short distances over major currents like the Gulf Stream (Mörner 1983a, 1986a).

He also showed (Mörner 1976a, 1980a, 1981a, 1983a, 1986a,c) that the sea level was deformed with time due to four main variables: (1) glacial eustasy, (2) tectono-eustasy, (3) geoidal eustasy, and (4) dynamic sea level changes (cf. figure 11.5).

2.0 EUSTASY: DEFINITION AND ORIGIN

The use of the word 'eustasy' (Suess 1888) became generally accepted to denote any kind of absolute ocean-level changes except those caused by various dynamic factors and effective only in generating local or regional sea-level changes. Behind this line of reasoning lay the assumption that two eustatic levels were always parallel (figure 11.4(a)), i.e. the displacement was only vertical. Therefore, eustasy was defined as 'worldwide simultaneous changes in sea level' (the only exception being those sea-level changes that were caused by variations in the Earth's rate of rotation and in the tilt of its rotational axis, as discussed by Fairbridge 1961).

    With the discovery of deformations of the geoid relief and redistributions of the water-masses over the Earth (Mörner 1971a, 1976a, 1980a), the old concept of 'eustasy' was no longer tenable. Sea-level changes could no longer be claimed to be either 'worldwide' or 'simultaneous'. Therefore, Mörner (1976a, 1980a) redefined the word 'eustasy' simply to imply 'ocean-level changes', regardless of causation but with the exception of dynamic sea-level changes. These 'ocean-level changes' are, in fact, nothing other than geoidal changes in a broad sense, as they all represent deformations of the geoid surface, in the vertical as well as in the horizontal dimension. In order to keep the well known word 'eustasy', it was made a synonym of these geoid changes (in a broad sense) and its causal mechanisms were separated into (1) glacial eustasy (ocean water volume change), (2) tectono-eustasy (ocean basin volume changes), and (3) geoidal eustasy (ocean water distribution changes or geoid relief deformations). The dynamic sea-level changes were held outside the family of eustatic changes. This was in line with tradition and not for logical reasons. Previously, it was important to distinguish between the global changes (eustasy) and the local changes (dynamic). When it is now realized that no sea level changes can be strictly global (Mörner, e.g. 1983a) and that each region needs to define its own eustatic curve, it is no longer necessary to separate the geoidal and dynamic changes in absolute sea level. An inclusion of the dynamic variables within the general group of 'eustatic' changes would give even more reasons to keep the old term 'eustasy'.

Therefore, I propose a widening of the term 'eustasy' and that we define 'eustasy' as 'ocean-level changes' (Mörner, 1980a) or any 'absolute sea-level changes' regardless of causation and including both the main 'family' of vertical and horizontal geoid changes (see table 5.1) of Mörner, 1983a) and the dynamic changes (Mörner, 1986a,c).

Figure 11.5 gives a general summary of the 'eustatic' variables according to this definition (cf. Mörner 1983a, table 5.1).

The ocean basins change their volume due to a variety of crustal dynamic processes that may be included under the main heading of 'tectono-eustasy'. Ocean basin volume changes are nothing but deformations of the hypsographic distribution of continental heights and oceanic depths. The tectono-eustatic factors are usually very slow processes. The isostatic processes are somewhat faster, however (Mörner 1983a, figure 5.4; 1986a, 1986b).

The water volume of the ocean changes more or less in a total balance with the Earth's glacial volume and is known as 'glacial eustasy'. Water in sediments, lakes and clouds, evaporation and juvenile water may contribute to minor changes in the water volume. The glacial eustatic changes may reach fairly high rates (some 10 mm/yr) but are confined to periods of glaciation variations. Palaeoglacial volume changes can,

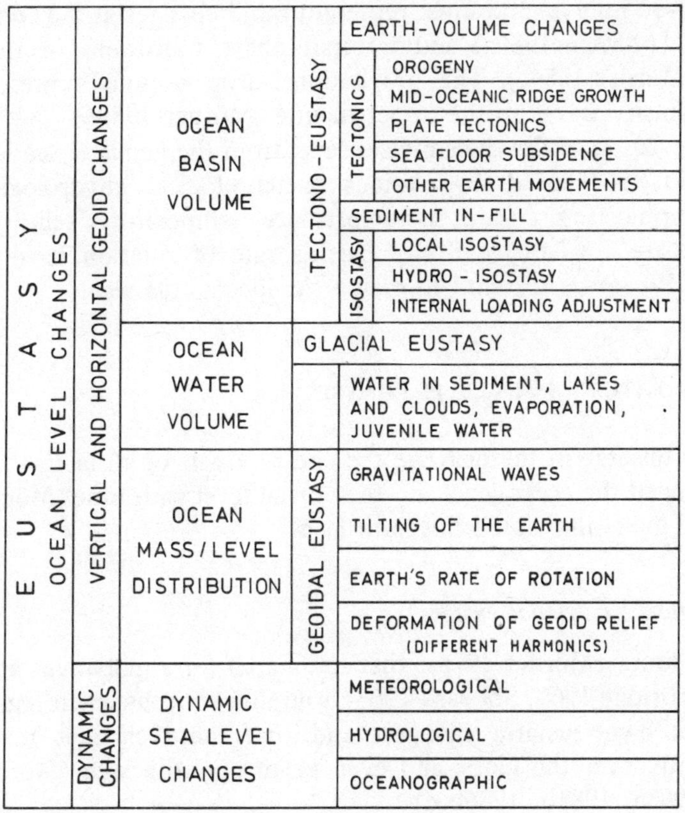

EUSTASY	VERTICAL AND HORIZONTAL GEOID CHANGES				
OCEAN LEVEL CHANGES		OCEAN BASIN VOLUME	TECTONO-EUSTASY	EARTH-VOLUME CHANGES	
				TECTONICS	OROGENY
					MID-OCEANIC RIDGE GROWTH
					PLATE TECTONICS
					SEA FLOOR SUBSIDENCE
					OTHER EARTH MOVEMENTS
				ISOSTASY	SEDIMENT IN-FILL
					LOCAL ISOSTASY
					HYDRO - ISOSTASY
					INTERNAL LOADING ADJUSTMENT
		OCEAN WATER VOLUME		GLACIAL EUSTASY	
				WATER IN SEDIMENT, LAKES AND CLOUDS, EVAPORATION, · JUVENILE WATER	
		OCEAN MASS/LEVEL DISTRIBUTION	GEOIDAL EUSTASY	GRAVITATIONAL WAVES	
				TILTING OF THE EARTH	
				EARTH'S RATE OF ROTATION	
				DEFORMATION OF GEOID RELIEF (DIFFERENT HARMONICS)	
DYNAMIC CHANGES		DYNAMIC SEA LEVEL CHANGES		METEOROLOGICAL	
				HYDROLOGICAL	
				OCEANOGRAPHIC	

Figure 11.5   An illustration to show the eustatic variables

however, neither be directly quantified from sea-level data nor from oxygen isotope records (Mörner 1981b, 1983b), because the sea-level records may be influenced, or may even be dominated, by geoidal changes, and because oxygen isotope records may be influenced (or dominated) by other variables, especially the interchange of water between the Arctic basin and the Atlantic.

The ocean-level (or water mass) distribution is the function of the gravitational and rotational potentials. The rotational ellipsoid may be deformed by changes in the tilt axis and the rate of rotation. More important is the new recognition of rapid and irregular deformations of the geoid surface (Mörner 1976a, 1980a, 1981a, 1983a, 1986b,d; Newman *et al.* 1980a, 1981) and large scale 'gravitational drop motions' (Mörner 1981c). All these changes of the geoidal surface configuration are termed 'geoidal eustasy'. The deformations of the geoid relief are often very rapid (some 10–30 mm/yr) and must represent rapid changes at the core/mantle interface (Mörner 1980a) and/or rapid phase transitions in the upper mantle (Mörner 1984a). The 'gravitational drop motions' represent some sort of density waves in the upper mantle (Mörner 1983c).

The deviation of the dynamic sea level from the geodetic sea level, i.e. the geoid, is caused by various meteorological, hydrological and oceanographic factors (such as air pressure, temperature, salinity, major currents, etc.). Changes in the Earth's rate of rotation have recently (Mörner 1986a) been found to play a significant role also.

3.0 REGISTRATION OF SEA-LEVEL CHANGES

What we observe in the field are the end products of all factors that may have changed the ocean level and the crustal level with time (Mörner, e.g. 1983d). This is illustrated in figure 11.6.

3.1 Regional v. global eustasy

We now know (Mörner 1976a) that the search for a global eustatic curve (e.g. Fairbridge 1961, Shepard 1963) is an illustion; that each region must define its own eustatic changes; and that these changes may differ significantly over the globe and even be of opposite sign (Mörner, e.g. 1981a, 1983a, 1984b, 1986b,d).

This means that sea-level data from different parts of the world must not be mixed together as previously done (e.g. Fairbridge 1961, Shepard

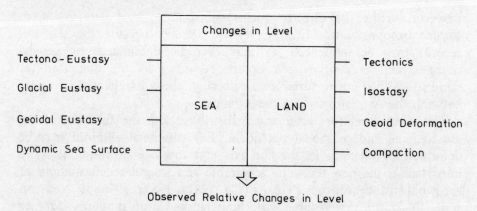

Figure 11.6 An illustration to show the main factors that control the level of the sea and the level of the land

1963, the IGCP-61 project goal, Bloom 1983).

Nowadays, each region must define its own relative sea level from which the crustal components are – if possible – later subtracted so that the regional eustatic changes are established. Until now, this has only been done for the north-west European region (Mörner, e.g. 1976b, 1979b, 1980b,c) and for the Brazilian coasts (Mörner 1981d, 1983a,d).

Comparisons of different regional eustatic curves and relative sea-level curves provide firm indications of geoidal deformations with time (e.g. Mörner 1981a,b,d, 1983a,d, 1986d).

3.2 Stability v. 'known' crustal movements

Crustal stability is very hard to determine with any accuracy. Already Newman and Munsart (1968) have suggested that 'coastal stability is a myth'. The present reference level is not a fixed datum but seems 'constantly to change' (Newman 1980, Mörner 1980d).

Mörner (1969, 1971c) therefore claimed that an area of 'known' crustal movements (linear or exponential) and of uplift with tilting is better for a study of absolute sea-level changes because the crustal component can be recognized and subtracted, and the fieldwork can be performed in greater detail and can be checked at different uplift rates. He applied this method to the south Scandinavian peripheral area of glacial isostasy and calculated a detailed eustatic curve for the last 13 000 years.

A similar approach has been applied to uplifted coral reef sequences. A 'eustatic' curve for the last 400 000 years has been established by this method from the New Guinea records (Chappell 1974, Bloom *et al.* 1974).

Hillaire-Marcel and Fairbridge (1978) applied a similar method to the 'staircase' of elevated beach ridges in northern Canada and calculated a detailed emergence rate curve.

3.3 Quantity and quality of data

The application of radiocarbon dating resulted in a revolution in sea-level studies. It meant the introduction of a firm dating control and opened the possibility of meaningful comparisons between different areas. Early curves were based on very few data points (e.g. Shepard 1963), and some recent curves still are. This only allows the reconstruction of main trends, a fact which, however, was very often forgotten.

What is needed is extensive radiocarbon dating (in combination with stratigraphic and morphologic control and independent corroboration by palynology or palaeomagnetism. Some examples of such studies are

Jelgersma's (1961) work and van de Plassche's work in the Netherlands, Scholl's work in Florida (1964), Mörner's work in southern Scandinavia (1969), Tooley's work in England (1974), the work of Suguio *et al.* (1980) in Brazil (See discussion, Chapter 1).

The quality of sea-level data differs very much. It is important that the data really are comparable, i.e. represent the same ecological, beach morphological or bathymetric levels. In order to determine this, one often has to go via painstaking sequences of analyses. An example of this is, for instance, the nice study of the coastal peats on Jamaica by Digerfeldt and Enell (1984).

3.4   Sea-level oscillations

In order to determine sea-level oscillations real stratigraphic evidence of rises and falls in sea level is needed. Temporary hurricane and storm deposits, local palaeotidal and estuarine river gradient changes and morphological changes of lagoonal inlets must be identified and excluded. At the same time, just because of such problems, real sea-level oscillations may be ignored. It is, for example, interesting to note that Scholl and Stuiver (1967) wrote 'the smooth nature of the submergence curve . . . should not be construed to indicate the lack of possible high-frequency low-amplitude oscillations in sea level during the last 4000 years.'

Sea-level oscillations were often constructed on the basis of diatom changes in single lagoonal basins (e.g. Iversen 1937). It is true (as often pointed out by 'smooth-curve believers') that such oscillations could easily be produced by changes at the lagoonal inlets. The reconstruction of similar changes in different basins and by different investigators, however, improves the picture.

Real evidence of eustatic sea-level oscillations can be obtained qualitatively or semi-quantitatively when the same level changes are recorded both in uplifted and subsided areas (Mörner 1969, 1979b, 1980c), and quantitatively when stratigraphic evidence can be combined with morphologically traceable shorelines (representing the transgression peaks) especially when these shorelines are tilted so that the differential rates of relative sea-level changes can be used to determine the exact amplitudes of the oscillations (Mörner 1969, 1971c, 1980e).

It seems significant that the more an area is investigated, the clearer it becomes that oscillations have occurred. In Europe, 16 Holocene low-amplitude oscillations are recorded whilst at the same time there are two high-amplitude oscillations recorded in Brazil (Mörner, 1981d, 1984c).

3.5 Pinnacle islands

Because of possible hydro-isostatic deformations of the ocean floors, Bloom (1967) suggested that the only place, where the 'true' eustatic water volume changes could be studied, might be on pinnacle islands which should behave like dipsticks.

Mörner (1984a) pointed out, however, that guyots and pinnacle islands show up on the present very short wave-lengths geoid maps. Guyots and pinnacle islands often create local geoid rises in the order of up to 4 m. He stressed that 'the largest geoid signal is likely to occur at the early phase of the formation of guyots and pinnacle islands, later to tend to be nivellated [levelled] by isostatic processes.'

This makes pinnacle islands unsuitable for eustatic analyses.

3.6 Hydro-isostasy

Rises and falls in sea level may cause a hydro-isostatic loading and unloading of shelves and ocean floors (Higgins 1965, Bloom 1965, 1967, Kaitera 1966, Flint 1969, Mörner 1971c, 1972, Cathles 1975, Clark 1980).

It was argued (Bloom 1967, Flint 1969, Mörner 1971c) that the glacial water volume changes caused corresponding hydro-isostatic adjustments of the ocean floors (i.e. a form of tectono-eustasy) so that the real eustatic ocean-level changes only amounted to some two-thirds of the water volume changes. Kaitera (1966) and Mörner (972) pointed out that the addition and removal of water load was not likely to generate opposed but comparable responses because the main tendency of the ocean floors is a general subsidence, which the addition of load may accelerate, but the removal of load could hardly reverse.

Another problem is the response to loading of the sub-lithospheric flow of partially melted mass in the asthenosphere. It may generate accelerations and decelerations of this flow and hence give rise to accelerations and decelerations of mid-oceanic ridge-growths and sea-floor spreading. This may drastically alter the expected effects of hydro-isostasy on the height of the water column. It will also generate deformations of the geoid configuration. Until these effects are better understood, the eustatic effects of hydro-isostasy on the ocean floors cannot be quantified in a meaningful and realistic way.

The postglacial transgression of shelves and coasts may be expected to lead to a hydro-isostatic deformation of the crust (Higgins 1965, Bloom 1965). Mörner (1971d, 1972) showed that the transgression of a coast may lead to: (1) no deformation at all; (2) a subsidence outside an axis of tilting; and (3) a subsidence with a compensational uplift inside an axis of tilting. Clark and Bloom (1979) applied various theoretical models to the coast of Brazil, none of which, however, concurs with the recorded uplift and inland tilting (Mörner 1981d, Martin *et al*. 1985, Suguio *et al*. 1980).

The problem is much more complicated. Rises and falls of the geoid mean changes of the isostatic equilibrium level (Mörner 1976a, 1984a). The following was stated by Mörner (1984a):

A eustatic rise (1) over a rising coast would accelerate the uplift because even less mass is now above the geoid, (2) over a 'stable' coast (a crust in equilibrium) would induce an uplift as less mass is now above the geoid, and (3) over a subsiding coast would decelerate (or reverse) this subsidence because less mass is now above the geoid. Similarly, a eustatic fall (1) over a rising coast would lead to a deceleration (or reversal) of the uplift due to increased mass above the geoid, (2) over a 'stable' coast (in equilibrium) would induce a subsidence, and (3) over a subsiding coast would accelerate this subsidence. Therefore, there does not exist a simple – predictable and calculable – relationship between sea-level (geoid) rise and coastal loading (hydro-isostasy) as often claimed.

This is summarized in table 11.1.

Table 11.1 The hydro-isostatic effect on an exposed (regression) or flooded (transgression) shelf or coast is primarily the result of the preceding crustal movements, *i.e.* isostatic equilibrium. All eustatic changes (except dynamic sea surface changes) imply vertical movements of the geoid level which means that more (fall) or less(rise) mass is above the geoid hence changing the preceding isostatic equilibrium conditions

Preceding crustal movements	Eustatic rise geoid rise	Eustatic fall geoid fall
Rising	Accelerated uplift	Decelerated uplift or even subsidence
Stable	Uplift	Subsidence
Subsiding	Decelerated subsidence or even uplift	Accelerated subsidence

3.7 Flexularity

The bending susceptibility (flexurality) of the crust and lithosphere to various geodynamic forces is of great importance for sea-level analysis. Various figures of this flexurality have been applied to calculate the expected relative sea-level changes of a hydro-isostatically deformed coast (e.g. Clark and Bloom 1979). As discussed above, however, the responses of a sea-level change are much more complicated than a simple hydro-isostatic loading response.

In all coastal areas where the flexural rigidity really has been tested or calculated, it has been found to be higher or much higher than generally assumed. This applies for Scandinavia (Mörner 1979a, 1980e, 1981e), West Africa (Faure *et al.* 1980), Brazil (cf. above) and Micronesia (Pirazzoli 1983). The relation between flexural rigidity and lithospheric thickness is 7.4×10^{24} Nm for a thickness of 100 km, 5.9×10^{25} Nm for 200 km and 1.1×10^{26} Nm for 250 km. More stable coasts and shelves of so-called passive continental margins are likely to have a lithospheric thickness in the order of 100–200 km.

There seem to be good reasons to conclude that in general, there is a higher flexural rigidity of the crust and the lithosphere (and a lower viscosity of the asthenosphere) than generally assumed.

3.8 Sub-lithospheric viscosity

The viscosity of the mantle determines the effects – in time and space – of a lithospheric loading. Ideas regarding the rheological properties of the mantle differ fundamentally and range from a non-linear profile with a low-viscosity asthenosphere (or channel flow) to a linear viscosity model lacking an asthenosphere. Different approaches have been applied to verify one or the other model. Furthermore, lateral differences are to be expected around the globe, not only between thin plates and thick craton areas but also in general.

For the region of Fennoscandian glacial-isostasy, it is possible to demonstrate by observational data that there must exist a low-viscosity asthenosphere (Mörner 1979a, 1980e, 1981e). Uplift rates, relaxation times, horizontal mass transfer, strain rates and general mode and geometry of the uplift all indicate the presence of a low-viscosity asthenosphere of $10^{19}–10^{20}$Pa.s.

4.0   GLOBAL UNIFYING MODELS

Changes of the water volume (glacial-eustasy), of the ocean basin volume (tectono-eustasy including hydro-isostasy) and of the deviation of the dynamic sea level from the geodetic sea level, and/or differential deformations of the crustal level are not sufficient to explain the differences between the recorded, observational, sea-level curves. A fundamental parameter must be missing (Mörner 1971a, 1971b, 1976a). The inconsistencies between existing sea-level records, that cannot be ascribed to different crustal regimes or errors, are of two types (Mörner 1976a): (1) partly cyclic alternations between periods of large differences and periods with little or no differences, and (2) partly quite irregular differences that include rapid high-amplitude changes (Mörner 1976a, 1980a). The origin of these changes must be large scale deformations of the geoid relief (Mörner 1976a, 1980a, 1981a, 1986d). Mörner (1978, 1980a) claimed that there was a correlation between palaeogeoidal, palaeomagnetic and palaeoclimatic changes. It is important that similar deformations seem to have occurred also in pre-glacial time (Mörner 1980f, 1981c, 1983a, 1986b).

If no low-viscosity asthenosphere existed, the loading from the ice caps would be transferred all over the globe via the mantle (like a hydraulic braking system). This would create differential isostatic adjustments all over the globe, creating inconsistencies in the relative sea-level records; for isostatic, not eustatic reasons (which is not often realized). This was proposed by Farrell and Clark (1976), Clark *et al.* (1978) and Clark (1980). Peltier (1982) was able to include the geoidal effects caused by the isostatic redistribution of mass by this loading. It is important to realize that this mechanism can only generate slow changes over long periods (thousands of years), and that the actual differences proposed for the regions outside the direct glacial isostasy (i.e. zones IV–VI of Clark 1980) only amount to some 5 m around 5000 BP and less than 20 m at the glaciation maximum (i.e. maximum about 1 m per millenium).

Mörner (1981b) pointed out that the above-mentioned theories were the only means of explaining the recorded sea-level inconsistencies, and called the first one 'the gravity model' and the second one 'the loading model'. These models are alternatives for the understanding of the dynamics of the interior of the Earth. They are, therefore, both key parts in unified theories of the complexity and interaction of the Earth's endogene and exogene processes. The gravity model implies a high-dynamic Earth, the loading model a low-dynamic Earth.

4.1 The loading model

This model (*e.g.* Clark *et al.* 1978) is really an isostatic model that could be called 'super-isostasy' or 'spherical isostasy', as the entire globe is involved. This model is based on an assumed absence of the astheno-sphere, and on a linear viscosity profile of about 20^{22} Pa.s. Peltier has done impressive work in improving the model and in testing the model by independent means (Peltier, 1982, Peltier and Wu 1983, Wu and Peltier 1983). By this, he has elevated it to a part of a unified theory of the Earth.

It must be emphasized, however, that the loading model is contradicted by several facts:

1 It does not concur with observational data indicating the presence of a low-viscosity asthenosphere (e.g. Mörner 1979a).
2 It can by no means explain the rapid Holocene oscillations recorded (e.g. Mörner 1981b).
3 The inconsistencies predicted (cf. above) are much smaller than those recorded (e.g. Mörner 1981a).
4 Even the trend of changes is often not compatible with the observational data (e.g. Blackwelder 1980, figure 1).

4.2 The gravity model

This model (Mörner 1976a, 1980a, 1984a,b,c) is a high-dynamic gravity model. According to this, any changes in the gravitational and rotational potentials must lead to deformations of the geoid surface and its topographic relief. It includes the presence of a low-viscosity asthenosphere and a glacial-isostasy that is more or less completely compensated by horizontal asthenospheric flow as indicated by the observational data from Fennoscandia (Mörner 1979a, 1980e). The sea-level changes explained by this model range from the long-term latitudinal 'vibrations' (Mörner 1981c) to the short-term Holocene changes of migrational type (Mörner 197a, 1980a, 1981a, 1981c; Newman *et al.* 1980a,b, 1981) and even deformations of the reference level (Mörner 1981a, 1984b). During periods of rapid Holocene eustatic sea-level changes, the deformation of the geoid reached up to 2–4 m in 100–200 years (Mörner 1981b, 1983d). The inconsistencies in global sea-level records during the last 20 000 years (Mörner 1981b, 1983a, figure 5.10) amount to many tens of metres. Rates of up to 10 mm/year are commonly recorded (Mörner 1981a, 1983a, figure 5.4).

This model is the only model that: (1) concurs with a low-viscosity asthenosphere, and can explain (2) the short-term eustatic oscillations undoubtedly recorded, (3) the amplitudes and pattern of observed sea-level inconsistencies, and (4) the pre-glacial sea level inconsistencies. Because of the complexity and number of presently unquantifiable variables, it cannot yet be expressed in a meaningful way by mathematical equations.

Because of the correlations between periods of major geoid deformation and periods of geomagnetic anomalies, a mutual core/mantle origin was originally proposed (Mörner 1976a, 1980a). With the establishment of rapid phase transitions within the upper mantle, there are no longer any problems either with the amplitudes or the rates or the correlations with other upper Earth geodynamic processes (Mörner 1984a, 1984c).

Mörner (1984c, 1986a,e) has shown that the same model could be used as the fundamental part in a new 'rotational–gravitational–oceanographic' model of explaining the short-term climatic changes and their relation to sea-level changes, geomagnetic signals and seismo-tectonic events. At the same time, however, this new climatic model reveals that the sea-level changes due to changes in the angular momentum of the hydrosphere play a more important role than previously understood. The gravity model is a typical unified theory of the Earth's geophysical–geodynamical behaviour (endogene as well as exogene) and its possible extra-terrestrial impulses (Mörner 1984c).

4.3   Possible combination

The loading and gravity models have been discussed as incompatible, alternative models. This does not preclude that they might both have operated simultaneously.

It is true that the Fennoscandian uplift data (Mörner 1979a) indicate that the loading was fully compensated on a regional basis within the asthenosphere, hence leaving insignificant or no room for internal loading (super or spherical-isostasy). We do not know, however, whether this is also the case with the glacial-isostasy of North America (data by Newman *et al.* 1980b, suggest so). *A priori*, the subcrustal parameters beneath North America may not be the same as under North-western Europe. Until this question is cleared up, we cannot rule out the possibility of internal loading (super/spherical-isostasy) effects from the North American ice caps.

Our Quaternary global sea-level records include inconsistencies (Mörner 1976a, 1981b, 1983a,d, 1986d) that cannot be explained in terms of local tectonic/isostatic differentiation but call for another mechanism. The loading model, generating fairly slow (up to 1 mm/yr) unidirectional or long-term sinusoidal changes, is only capable of explaining a minor part of these changes. The gravity model, on the other hand, is capable of explaining all the recorded inconsistencies. Still it is, of course, possible that both models have been in operation.

Because the loading model is often used for detailed calculations and even predictions, it is important to stress that it, under all circumstances, can only be responsible for a minor part of the recorded sea-level inconsistencies.

It is, therefore, concluded that the gravity model has played a dominant role for the differentiation of global, eustatic sea-level changes, and that the loading model might, or might not, have played a secondary role.

5.0 CONCLUSIONS

Quaternary sea-level data (Mörner 1976a, 1981b, 1983a,d, 1986d) include, in both the long-term and the short-term timescale, and even after adjustment for crustal movements, such large inconsistencies (vertical differentiation, compensational oscillations, cyclic trends) that they cannot be combined into something like a eustatic curve in the old sense of eustasy. Each region needs its own eustatic solution (Mörner 1976a).

The main trend of Quaternary sea-level changes is explained by glacial eustatic changes of the volume of water in the oceans.

The regional inconsistencies, cyclic pattern in differentiation and compensational oscillations are all explained by geoidal eustatic deformations of the geoid relief (i.e. of the equipotential surface). These changes have sometimes played a dominant role.

Some of the regional inconsistencies may be explained in terms of differentiation due to internal loading (super/spherical isostasy).

The local inconsistencies are generally caused by tectonic and isostatic processes. They often play a dominant role. The crustal component can often be quantified so that the eustatic component can be isolated (e.g. Mörner 1971c, Chappell 1974).

Minor, short-term inconsistencies in global sea level are undoubtedly caused by rapid deformations of the dynamic sea surface relief. More persistent changes are caused by general circulation changes (Mörner 1986a).

Some slow, long-term tectono-eustatic effects are also likely to be in operation. However, they are difficult to identify.

Revised typescript received 1986, April.

REFERENCES

Berzelius, J. 1822: Årsberättelse om vetenskapernas framsteg. *Chemie och Physik, Kungl. Vet. Acad.* Stockholm.

Berzelius, J. 1843: Några ord om den Skandinaviska vallens höjning öfver ytan af omkringlinggande haf och om afslipningen och refflingen af dess berg. *Förhandl. De skandinaviske naturforskarnes tredje möte i Stockholm 1842.*

Blackwelder, B. W. 1980: Late Wisconsin and Holocene tectonic stability of the United States' mid-Atlantic coastal region. *Geology*, 8, 534–7.

Bloom, A. 1965: Coastal isostatic downwarping by postglacial rise of sea level. *Geol. Soc. Am. Spec. Paper* 82, 14.

Bloom, A. 1967: Pleistocene shorelines: A new test of isostasy. *Geol. Soc. Am. Bull.*, 78, 1477–94.

Bloom, A. L. 1983: Sea-level movements during the last deglacial hemicycle. *Geological Correlation, Report of the International Geological Correlation Programme (IGCP)*, 11, 22.

Bloom, A. L., Broecker, W. S., Chappell, J. M. A., Matthews, R. K. and Mesolella, K. J. 1974: Quaternary sea-level fluctuations on a tectonic coast: new ^{230}Th/^{234}U dates from the Huon Peninsula, New Guinea. *Quat. Res.*, 4, 185–205.

von Bruckhausen, K. 1846: Manuscript sent to von Humbolt in 1846: see Penck (1882), 6.

von Buch, L. 1810: *Reise durch Norwegen und Lappland 2.* Berlin.

Cathles, L. M. 1975: *The Viscosity of the Earth's Mantle.* Princeton: Princeton Univ. Press.

Celsius, A. 1743: Anmärkningar om vatnets förminskande så i Östersjön som Vesterhafvet. *Kungl. Vet. Akad. Handl.* 1743.

Chambers, R. 1848: *Ancient Sea Margins, as Memorials of Changes of the Relative Level of Land and Sea.* Edinburgh: Chambers, Orr & Co.

Chappell, J. 1974: Geology of coral terraces, Huon Peninsula, New Guinea: a study of Quaternary tectonic movements and sea level changes. *Geol. Soc. Am. Bull.*, 85, 553–70.

Charpentier, J. de 1835: Notice sur la cause probable du transport des bloc erratiques de la Suisse. *Annales des mines*, 3me ser.

Clark, J. A. 1976: Greenland's rapid postglacial emergence: A result of ice-water gravitational attraction. *Geology*, 4, 310–12.

Clark, J. A. 1980: A numerical model of worldwide sea-level changes on a viscoelastic Earth. In N.-A. Mörner (ed.), *Earth Rheology, Isostasy and Eustasy*, Chichester: John Wiley and Sons, 525–34.

Clark, J. A., Farrell, W. E. and Peltier, W. R. 1978: Global changes in postglacial sea level: A numerical calculation. *Quat. Res.*, 9, 265–87.

Clark, J. A. and Bloom, A. L. 1979: Hydro-isostasy and Holocene emergence of South America. In K. Suguio, T. R. Fairchild, L. Martin and J.-M. Flexor (eds.) *Proceedings of the 1978 International Symposium on Coastal Evolution in the Quaternary.* São Paulo, Brasil, 41–60.

Daly, R. A. 1910: Pleistocene glaciation and the coral reef problem. *Am. J. Sci.,* 30, 297–308.

Dana, J. D. 1849: *US Exploring Expedition,* 10. New York.

Darwin, C. 1842: *The Structure and Distribution of Coral Reefs.* London: Smith, Elder & Co.

De Geer, G. 1888/90: Om Skandinaviens nivåförändringar under Quartärperioden. *Geol. Fören. Stockholm Förhandl.* 10, 366–79; 12, 61–110.

Digerfeldt, G. and Enell, M. 1984: Paleoecological studies of the past development of the Negril and Black River Morasses, Jamaica. Appendix to Environment feasibility study of peat mining in Jamaica (S. Björk), *Rep. Petroleum Corp. Jamaica,* 1–145.

Drygalski, E. von 1887: Die Geoiddeformation der Eiszeit. *Zeitschrift Gesell. Erdkunde Berlin,* 22, 169–208.

Fairbridge, R. W. 1961: Eustatic changes in sea level. In L. H. Ahrens, *et al.* (eds.), *Physics and Chemistry of the Earth.* 4, London: Pergamon Press, 99–185.

Farrell, W. E. and Clark, J. A. 1976: On postglacial sea level. *Geophys. J. Roy. Astr. Soc.,* 46, 647–67.

Faure, H., Fontes, J. C., Hebrard, L., Monteillet, J. and Pirazzoli, P. A. 1980: Geoidal change and shore-level tilt along Holocene estuaries: Sénégal River area, West Africa. *Science* 210, 421–3.

Fischer, P. 1868: *Untersuchungen über die Gestalt der Erde.* Darmstadt: Diehl.

Fjeldskaar, W. and Kaneström, R. 1980: Younger Dryas geoid-deformation caused by deglaciation in Fennoscandia. In N.-A. Mörner (ed.), *Earth Rheology, Isostasy and Eustasy,* Chichester: John Wiley and Sons, 569–74.

Flint, R. F. 1969: Position of sea level in a glacial age. Lecture, *INQUA VIII Congress, Paris 1969,* Roneo.

Frisi, P. 1785: *Opera 3.* Mediolani.

Hergesell, H. 1887: Über die Änderung der Gleichgewichtsflächen der Erde durch die Bildung polarer Eismassen dadurch verursachten Schwankungen des Meeresniveaus. *Beiträge Geophys.,* Abhandl. geogr. sem. Univ. Strasbourg I, 59–114.

Higgins, C. G. 1965: Isostatic effect of post-glacial rise of sea level. *Abstracts, INQUA VII Congress, Boulder, Colorado, USA, 1965,* 216–17.

Hillaire-Marcel, C. and Fairbridge, R. W. 1978: Isostasy and eustasy in Hudson Bay. *Geology,* 6, 117–22.

Iversen, J. 1937: Undersögelser over Litorina-transgressioner i Danmark. *Medd. Dansk Geol. Foren.,* 9, 223–32.

Jamieson, T. F. 1865: On the history of the last geological changes in Scotland. *Geol. Soc. London Quart. J.,* 21, 161–203.

Jamieson, T. F. 1882: On the cause of the depression and re-elevation of the land during the Glacial Period. *Geol. Mag. N. S.* 9, 400–7.

Jelgersma, S. 1961: Holocene sea-level changes in the Netherlands. *Meded. Geol. Sticht.* Ser. C, VI, No. 7, 1–101.

Kaitera, P. 1966: Sea pressure as a cause of crustal movements. *Ann. Acad. Sci. Fennicae*, A III, 90, 191–200.

Linné, C. von 1745: Öländska och Gothländska resa på Riksens häglofliga Ständers befallning förrättad 1741. Stockholm.

Listing, J. B. 1873: Über unsere jetzige Kenntnisse der Gestalt und Grösse der Erde. *Königl. Ges. Wiss. Göttingen, Nachrichten 1873*, 3, 33–100.

Lyell, C. 1835: On the proof of a gradual rising of the land in certain parts of Sweden. *Phil. Trans. Roy. Soc. London*, 10–38.

Maclaren, C. 1841: *The glacial theory of Professor Agassiz of Neuchatel.* Edinburgh: The Scotsman Office, 1841 (also: *Am. J. Sci.*, 42, 346–65, 1842).

Martin, L., Flexor, J.-M., Blitzkow, D. and Suguio, K. 1985: Geoid change indications along the Brazilian coast during the last 7000 years. *Proc. 5th Int. Coral reef Congr. Tahiti 1985*. vol. 3, 85–90.

Mather, R. S., Rizos, C. and Coleman, R. 1979: Remote sensing of surface ocean circulation with satellite altimetry. *Science*, 205, 11–17.

Mörner, N.-A. 1969: The Late Quaternary history of the Kattegatt Sea and the Swedish West Coast; deglaciation, shorelevel displacement, chronology, isostasy and eustasy *Sveriges Geologiska Undersökning* C-640, 1–487.

Mörner, N.-A. 1971a: The Holocene eustatic sea-level problem. *Geol. Mijnbouw* 50, 699–702.

Mörner, N.-A. 1971b: Relation between ocean, glacial and crustal changes. *Geol. Soc. Am. Bull.*, 82, 787–8.

Mörner, N.-A. 1971c: Eustatic changes during the last 20 000 years and a method of separating the isostatic and eustatic factors in an uplifted area. *Palaeogeogr. Palaeoclimatol. Palaeoecol.*, 9, 153–81.

Mörner, N.-A. 1971d: Late Quaternary isostatic, eustatic and climatic changes. *Quaternaria* 14, 65–83.

Mörner, N.-A. 1972: Isostasy, eustasy and crustal sensitivity. *Tellus*, 24, 586–92.

Mörner, N.-A. 1976a: Eustasy and geoid changes. *J. Geol.*, 84, 123–52.

Mörner, N.-A. 1976b: Eustatic changes during the last 8000 years in view of radiocarbon calibration and new information from the Kattegatt region and other northwestern European coastal areas *Palaeogeogr., Palaeoclimatol., Palaeoecol.*, 19, 63–85.

Mörner, N.-A. 1978: Palaeoclimatic, palaeomagnetic and palaeogeoidal change: interaction and complexity. *Évolution des Atmosphère Planétaires et Climatologie de la Terre*, International Colloquium, CNES Toulouse, 221–32.

Mörner, N.-A. 1979a: The Fennoscandian uplift and Late Cenozoic geodynamics: Geological evidence. *GeoJournal*, 3, 287–318.

Mörner, N.-A. 1979b: South Scandinavian sea-level records. A test of regional eustasy, regional palaeoenvironmental changes and global paleogeoidal changes. In K. Suguio, T. R. Fairchild, L. Martin and J.-M. Flexor (eds.) *Proceedings of the 1978 International Symposium on Coastal Evolution in the Quaternary*. São Paulo, Brasil, 77–103.

Mörner, N.-A. 1980a: Eustasy and geoid changes as a function of core/mantle changes in N.-A. Mörner, (ed.), *Earth Rheology, Isostasy and Eustasy*, Chichester: John Wiley & Sons, 535–53.

Mörner, N.-A. 1980b: Late Quaternary sea-level changes in north-western Europe: A synthesis *Geol. Fören. Stockh. Förh.*, 100, 381–400.

Mörner, N.-A. 1980c: The northwest European 'sea-level laboratory' and regional Holocene eustasy. *Palaeogeogr., Palaeoclimatol., Palaeoecol.*, 29, 281–300.

Mörner, N.-A. 1980d: Changes in the geodetic reference level – the geoid – (palaeogeodesy). *Bull. INQUA Neotectonics Comm.*, 3, 85.

Mörner, N.-A. 1980e: The Fennoscandian uplift: geological data and their geodynamic implication. In N.-A. Mörner (ed.), *Earth Rheology, Isostasy and Eustasy*. Chichester: John Wiley & Sons, 251–84.

Mörner, N.-A. 1980f: Relative sea level, tectono-eustasy, geoidal-eustasy and geodynamics during the Cretaceous. *Cretaceous Res.*, 1, 329–40.

Mörner, N.-A. 1981a: Space geodesy, palaeogeodesy and palaeogeophysics. *Annales Géophys.*, 37, 69–76.

Mörner, N.-A. 1981b: Eustasy, paleoglaciation and paleoclimatology. *Geol. Rundschau*, 70, 691–701.

Mörner, N.-A. 1981c: Revolution in Cretaceous sea level analysis. *Geology*, 9, 344–6.

Mörner, N.-A. 1981d: Eustasy, palaeogeodesy and glacial volume changes. In I. Allison (ed.), *Sea level, Ice and Climatic change*, International Association of Hydrological Sciences, 131, 277–80.

Mörner, N.-A. 1981e: Crustal movements and geodynamics in Fennoscandia. *Tectonophysics*, 71, 241–51.

Mörner, N.-A. 1983a: Sea Levels. In R. Gardner and H. Scoging (eds), *Mega-Geomorphology*, Oxford: Oxford University Press, 73–91.

Mörner, N.-A. 1983b: Illusions and problems in water budget synthesis. In A. Street-Perrot, M. Beran and R. Ratcliffe, (eds), *Variations in the global water budget*, Dordrecht: Reidel, 419–23.

Mörner, N.-A. 1983c: Earth's gravitational drop motions. *Abstracts, Lunar and Planetary Sci*, 14, Houston.

Mörner, N.-A. 1983d: Differential Holocene sea-level changes over the globe: evidence for global eustasy, geoidal eustasy and crustal movements. In *Abstracts: International Symposium on Coastal Evolution in the Holocene, Tokyo 1983*, 93–6.

Mörner, N.-A. 1984a: Geoidal topography: origin and time consistency. *Marine Geophys. Res.*, 7, 205–8.

Mörner, N.-A. 1984b: Palaeogeoid changes: rates, amplitudes and origin. *Bull. Neotectonics Comm.* 7, 54–62.

Mörner, N.-A. 1984c: Planetary, solar, atmosphere, hydrosphere and endogene processes as origin of climatic changes on the Earth. In N.-A. Mörner and W. Karlén (eds), *Climatic Changes on a Yearly to Millennial Basis*, Dordrecht: Reidel, 483–507.

Mörner, N.-A. 1986a: Dynamic sea surface changes in the past and redistribution of mass and energy. Submitted.

Mörner, N.-A. 1986b: Eustasy, unconformities and a revision of the Exxon 'Eustatic' curves. In: *Sea-level Changes – An integrated approach*, Society of Economic Palaeontologists and Mineralogists, in press.

Mörner, N.-A. 1986c: The concept of eustasy. A redefinition. *J. Coastal Res.*, Special Issue (1): 49–52.

Mörner, N.-A. 1986d: Quaternary sea level changes: Northern Hemisphere data. In R. J. N. Devoy (ed.) *Sea Surface Studies – A global view*, in press.

Mörner, N.-A. 1986e: Short-term palaeoclimatic changes. Observational data and a novel causation model. In *Proc. of a climatic symposium in honour of Prof. R. W. Fairbridge*, New York, May 1984, in press.

Newman, W. S. 1980: Sea-level changes and geoid deformation. *Bull. INQUA Neotectonics Comm.*, 3, 86.

Newman, W. S. and Munsart, C. A. 1968: Holocene geology of the Wachapreague Lagoon, eastern shore peninsula, Virginia. *Marine Geol.*, 6, 81–105.

Newman, W., Marcus, L., Pardi, R., Paccione, J. and Tomacek, S. 1980a: Eustasy and deformation of the geoid: 1000–6000 radiocarbon years BP. In N.-A. Mörner (ed.) *Earth Rheology, Isostasy and Eustasy*, Chichester: John Wiley & Sons, 555–67.

Newman, W. S., Cinquemani, L. J., Pardi, R. R. and Marcus, L. F. 1980b: Holocene delevelling of the United States' East Coast. In N.-A. Mörner (ed.) *Earth Rheology, Isostasy and Eustasy* Chichester: John Wiley & Sons, 449–63.

Newman, W. S., Marcus, L. F. and Pardi, R. R. 1981: Palaeogeodesy, Late Quaternary geoidal configurations as determined by ancient sea levels. In I. Allison (ed.) *Sea level, Ice and Climatic Change*, International Association of Hydrological sciences 131, 263–75.

Peltier, W. R. 1982: Dynamics of the ice age Earth. *Advances in Geophys.*, 24, 1–144.

Peltier, W. R. and Wu, P. 1983: Continental lithosphere thickness and deglaciation. Induced true polar wander. *Geophys. Res. Letters*, 10, 181–4.

Penck, A. 1882: Schwankungen des Meeresspiegel. *Geogr. Ges. München*, 7, 1–70.

Pirazzoli, P. A. 1983: An active flexuring of the lithosphere in the Society Islands (French Polynesia): Evidence from the Late Holocene shorelines. *Bull. INQUA Neotectonics Comm.* 6, 78.

Plassche, O. van de 1982: Sea-level change and water-level movements in The Netherlands during the Holocene. *Meded. Rijks Geol. Dienst*, 36–1, 1–93.

Playfair, I. 1802: *Illustrations to the Huttonian Theory of the Earth*. Edinburgh. Reprinted 1964, New York: Dover.

Runeberg, E. O. 1765: Om några förändringer på jordytan i allmänhet och under kalla climat i synnerhet. *Kungl. Sv. Vet. Akad. Handl. 1765*.

Scholl, D. W. 1964: Recent sedimentary record in mangrove swamps and rise in sea level over the southwestern Coast of Florida. Part I. *Marine Geol.* 1, 344–66.

Scholl, D. W. and Stuiver, M. 1967: Recent submergence of Southern Florida: a comparison with adjacent coasts and other eustatic data. *Geol. Soc. Am. Bull.*, 78, 437–54.

Shepard, F. P. 1963: Thirty-five thousand years of sea level. In T. Clements (ed.), *Essays in Marine Geology in Honor of K. O. Emery*, Los Angeles: University of S. California Press, 1–10.

Suess, E. 1888: Das Anlitz der Erde. II *Die Meere der Erde*. Wein.

Suguio, K., Martin, L. and Flexor, J.-L. 1980: Sea-level fluctuations during the past 6000 years along the coast of the state of Sao Paulo, Brazil. In N.-A. Mörner (ed.), *Earth Rheology, Isostasy and Eustasy*, Chichester: John Wiley & Sons, 471–86.

Tooley, M. 1974: Sea-level changes during the last 9000 years in northwest England. *Geogr. J.*, 140, 18–42.

Tylor, A. 1868: On the Amiens gravel. *Geol. Soc. Lond. Quart. J.*, 24, 103–25.

Woodward, R. S. 1888: On the form and position of the sea level. *U.S. Geol. Surv. Bull.*, 48, 1–88.

Wu, P. and Peltier, W. R. 1983: Glacial isostatic adjustment and the free air gravity anomaly as a constraint upon deep mantle viscosity. *Geophys. J. Roy. Astr. Soc.*, 74, 377–449.

12

Sea-level changes resulting from future retreat of ice sheets: an effect of CO_2 warming of the climate

James A. Clark and John A. Primus

1.0 INTRODUCTION AND PURPOSE

Production of energy by the burning of fossil fuels has released an enormous amount of CO_2 into the atmosphere during the twentieth century. This enrichment of the atmosphere's CO_2 content is expected to continue at an increased rate into the twenty-first century with doubling and perhaps tripling of the present amount by AD 2100 (Titus and Barth 1984). Because CO_2 is relatively transparent to energy emitted from the sun but absorbs energy that is radiated from the Earth, many scientists believe a doubling of CO_2 atmospheric content will increase the average temperature at the Earth's surface by 1.5 to 4.5°C (Charney 1979, Smagorinsky 1982). There are many possible responses and feedbacks of the Earth's physical and biological systems to this warming. Certainly the cryosphere will be affected, especially since most models of global warming predict that the polar regions of the world will experience substantially greater temperature increases than average (e.g. Manabe and Wetherald 1975, Schlesinger 1984, Hansen *et al* 1984). Any melting or retreat of ice sheets in polar regions will augment water volume with meltwater and cause the average level of the oceans to rise.

The goal of this study is to predict sea-level changes that would be observed anywhere resulting from retreat of the Antarctic ice sheet and/or melting of the Greenland ice sheet. The melting or retreat of ice sheets, however, does not result in a uniform rise in observed sea level everywhere. This is because observed sea-level change, that which would be detected, for example, by a tide gauge, is actually the difference between two dynamic surfaces – the geoid and the Earth's solid surface. A sea-level change will result if (1) if water volume of the ocean change (usually called the 'eustatic' change, but see discussion in Mörner, this volume), (2) the Earth's solid surface moves vertically, or (3) the geoid surface, a gravitational equipotential, is perturbed. Changes in ice volume, which result in accompanying changes in ocean volume, cause both the Earth's surface and its geoid to be affected everywhere because of the redistribution of mass on the Earth's surface and within the Earth. If the change in ice sheet thickness is known and if the Earth's rheology is known then the observed sea-level change can be determined. If ice sheet changes occurred long ago (i.e. 1000s of years) then the Earth rheology should most probably be modelled as some type of viscoelastic material. The viscous rheology of the Earth is not well-known and so errors in predicted sea-level change could result. However, for the present study, we are concerned with ice sheet changes caused by CO_2 atmospheric warming on a time scale of decades and so we make the good assumption that the Earth will behave solely as an elastic material. The Earth's elastic properties and density structure are well-known from seismological studies and so Earth rheology is not ambiguous.

2.0 THE SEA LEVEL MODEL

Farrell (1972) has determined the sea-level effect everywhere of a one kilogram point load placed on the Earth's surface where the Earth is modelled as a spherically symmetric, self-gravitating material with layered elastic and density structure given by a Gutenberg-Bullen Earth model. This Green function, $G(x)$, is found from:

$$G(x) = \frac{a}{M_e} \sum_{n=0}^{\infty} [1-h_n+k_n] \, P_n(\cos x) \qquad ....(12.1)$$

where x is the angular distance on the Earth's surface between the point
load and the observation point
a is the Earth's radius
M_e is the Earth's mass
P_n is the Legendre polynomial
h_n and k_n are load Love numbers described below.

Each term in the bracketed expression of equation (12.1) has a physical significance. The unity term gives the effect upon sea level of the geoid perturbation resulting from the mass of the load itself. The second term, h_n, accounts for sea-level change caused by vertical movement of the Earth's surface. The final term, k_n, accounts for geoid perturbation resulting from mass redistribution within the Earth caused by Earth deformation. The theoretical calculation of h_n and k_n for the Earth model used here is described by Farrell (1972).

If the actual load is represented as a collection of point loads then the sea-level change, s, at point x' is the convolution of the load, L, with the Green's function:

$$s(x') = \iint G(\,|\,x-x'\,|\,)L(x)dx \qquad \dots(12.2)$$

Earth's
surface

The load will be both an ice load, $\rho_r I$, with I the change in ice thickness and an associated meltwater load, $\rho_w s$, so:

$$s(x') = \iint G(\,|x-x'|\,)\rho_w s dx + \iint G(\,|x-x'|\,)\rho_I I dx + K \qquad \dots(12.3)$$

Oceans   Ice

The constant term, K, insures that mass is conserved so that the mass of ice melted equals the mass of water added to the oceans. The eustatic sea-level change is included in K.

This integral equation (12.3) is solved for realistic ice and ocean distributions by performing the integration numerically. The sea-level change, s, is found under an integral on the right side of equation (12.3) because the meltwater also loads the oceans and will itself affect Earth deformation and geoid perturbation. An iterative technique is used to solve this integral equation (see Farrell and Clark 1976).

For purposes of numerical integration the oceans are approximated by 452 grids shown in figure 12.1. Each rectangular grid is itself approximated by a cylindrical cap with area equal to that of the corresponding grid. Over each grid the ocean load is assumed constant but loads over different grids may vary independently. The ice loads are also approximated by grids and these will be considered in the next section. When an ice load thins by a known amount, I, equation (12.3) is solved for s at all ocean grid points. The sea-level change, s, can then be contoured giving a global depiction of sea-level change everywhere. Alternatively, once s, I, and K are known, these loads can be used to determine sea-level changes at discrete points anywhere (e.g. at any tide gauge location) by direct substitution into equation (12.3).

3.0   ICE SHEET THINNING

It is extremely difficult to determine the probable contributions to sea level that ice sheets will make. Not only are there uncertainties about the

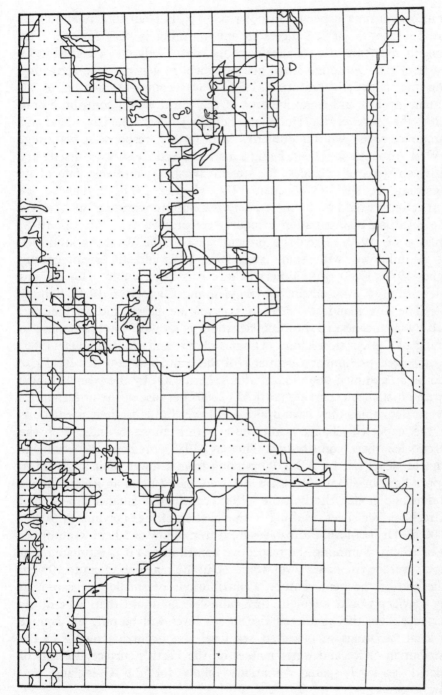

Figure 12.1 The ocean grid used in the numerical calculation. A total of 452 elements approximate the ocean

amount of warming expected in polar regions, but our understanding of the response of polar ice sheets to any warming is very limited. The Greenland and Antarctic ice sheets are the most likely major contributors to sea-level rise. Although small glaciers have, in general been retreating during the twentieth century (Meier 1984), complete melting of all mountain glaciers and small ice caps of the world would contribute only 34 cm to the sea-level rise (Hollin and Schilling 1982). The Greenland and Antarctic ice sheets will undoubtedly differ in their response to warming. The West Antarctic ice sheet, being a marine-based ice sheet, is itself very sensitive to sea-level changes, ice stream dynamics, and the state of its surrounding ice shelf (Weertman 1974, Hughes 1977). Enhanced ice stream activity would be its most likely response to warming but the rate of the resulting disintegration is poorly constrained (e.g. Mercer 1978, Thomas *et al.* 1979). Even the present state of the West Antarctic ice sheet is unknown with some suggesting it is already disintegrating (Hughes 1973, 1983) while others believe it is quasi-stable (Thomas and Bentley 1978) or even advancing (Sugden and Clapperton 1980, Bentley 1983). The Greenland ice sheet is not marine based and so melting, caused by an increase in snowline elevation, is its most likely response to warming of the Arctic regions. Thomas (1985) and Bindschadler (1985) have advanced preliminary estimates of the contribution to sea-level rise forced by an assumed doubling of atmospheric CO_2 by the year AD 2050 but with no change occurring until AD 2000. Because of the uncertainties in their calculations they gave upper and lower limits to their predictions with the expected change somewhere within those bounds. For the Antarctic ice sheet contribution Thomas (1985) predicts an oceanwide average sea-level rise by AD 2100 ranging from a lower limit of 20 cm to an upper limit of 80 cm. His estimates were based upon an ice stream/ice shelf dynamic model. Bindschadler (1985) considered enhanced melting of the Greenland ice sheet resulting from elevation of the snowline by 500 m to 1000 m. His sea-level estimates ranged from a low of 10 cm to an upper limit of 25 cm. Summing the respective contributions it is estimated that the total average rise in sea level would be in the range of 30 cm to 105 cm by the end of the next century. Contributions of smaller ice caps and valley glaciers would augment this value by no more than 34 cm. As indicated above, this predicted rise in sea level will be only an average with local variations in observed sea level rise occurring owing to the redistribution of ice and water masses on the Earth's surface. Results of predicted sea-level spatial variations follow for the Greenland and Antarctic cases.

4.0 RESULTS: MELTING OF GREENLAND ICE SHEET

Because the sea-level contribution of the Greenland ice sheet will probably result from elevation of the snow line, ice sheet melting was assumed to occur only on the perimeter of the ice sheet. The grid approximation is given in figure 12.2 where 42 grids represent the region affected by ice sheet thinning. It was further assumed that all ice grids thinned by a uniform amount. This is not a requirement of the numerical model but represents the simplest case in the absence of information to the contrary. For this calculation the uniform thinning was assumed to be 477.1 metres. This (large) value was that needed to cause a eustatic (or oceanwide

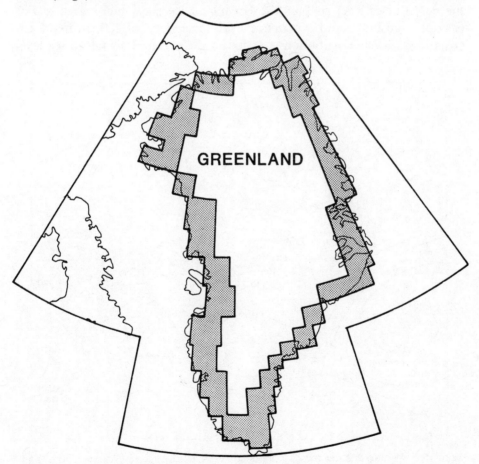

Figure 12.2 The Greenland ice sheet grid consisting of 42 elements in the shaded region

average) sea-level rise of exactly 100 cm. Because the sea-level model is linear the results can be scaled appropriately. For example, if thinning is actually only 119.3 m (25 cm eustatic sea-level rise), a more likely upper bound, then the resulting predictions would be exactly 25 per cent of those reported here. Hence the sea level response to *any* Greenland ice sheet melting history can be found from this one result provided the ice sheet thinned uniformly over the grid areas shown in figure 12.2. Sea-level predictions for ice sheet histories with non-uniform thinning are certainly possible but they would require another computer calculation.

The predicted global sea-level changes are summarised on figure 12.3. The contours are in centimetres of sea-level rise (where positive) or fall (where negative). These may also be considered percentage contours of the eustatic sea-level rise for the Greenland ice sheet melting case. For example, Iceland would experience a *fall* in sea level of 200 cm if 100 cm eustatic sea-level contribution is added to the ocean. This fall in sea level

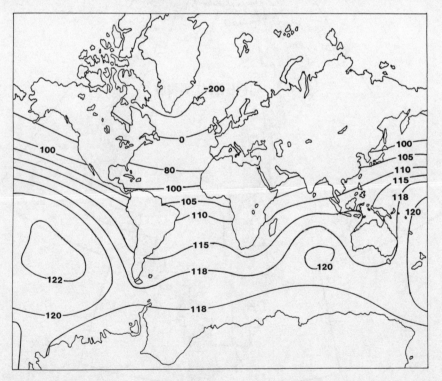

Figure 12.3   A map to show the amount of sea-level rise caused by the melting of part of the Greenland ice sheet. Contours are in centimetres if the eustatic sea-level rise is 100 centimetres. Alternatively, contours are in percent of eustatic sea-level rise

occurs because the Earth there will rise due to glacial unloading on Greenland and the geoid will lower from the reduced ice mass. England would observe no change in sea level but New Zealand would experience a 120 cm rise in sea level. Maxima for sea-level rise occur in the centres of oceans because loading of the oceans by meltwater causes the ocean floor to sag resulting in a pooling of water there.

Because continental coastlines are, by definition, boundaries between the oceans and the continents, differential tilting caused by the abrupt termination of meltwater loading occurs in these localities. The tilting occurs close to shorelines and so coastal sea-level changes may not be accurately portrayed on the generalized sea-level map. Therefore, in addition to the generalized map of sea-level changes, we have predicted sea-level changes for the 30 localities depicted in figure 12.4. Table 12.1 gives the predicted sea-level change for each locality.

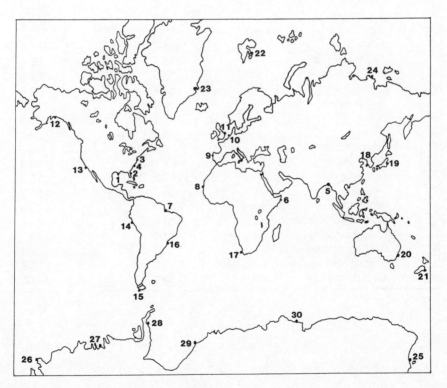

Figure 12.4 A map to show the locations of 30 discrete points where sea-level change is predicted. The values of the prediction are given in Table 12.1

Table 12.1   Predicted sea-level changes at discrete localities on continental coastlines. For both the Greenland and Antarctic cases the eustatic sea-level rise is 100 cm. Numbers refer to locations on figure 12.4.

	Location	Sea-level rise (cm) (− = fall)	
		Greenland Melting	Antarctic Retreat
1	Louisiana	91.2	115.8
2	East Florida	83.3	116.8
3	Chesapeake Bay	58.7	115.7
4	Cape Hatteras	73.2	115.0
5	Bangladesh	100.5	108.4
6	Somali	104.6	110.5
7	Amazon Delta	102.9	113.0
8	Mauritania	90.5	116.9
9	Portugal	57.6	115.4
10	Netherlands	30.4	109.4
11	London	22.9	111.3
12	Anchorage	69.4	117.2
13	San Diego	93.5	117.0
14	Lima	111.4	113.6
15	Tierra del Fuego	113.4	58.9
16	Rio de Janeiro	110.0	102.8
17	Cape Town	113.9	94.8
18	South Korea	99.9	111.8
19	Japan	107.2	120.0
20	Sydney	115.0	96.4
21	New Zealand	117.3	89.7
22	Spitzbergen	−98.1	113.9
23	Brewster	−1218.3	112.7
24	Tiksi	42.7	111.2
25	McMurdo	111.0	−123.0
26	across from McMurdo	113.2	−48.9
27	Pine Island Bay	112.4	−100.7
28	Filchner-Ronne west	112.6	−103.6
29	Filchner-Ronne east	110.8	−210.8
30	East Antarctica	113.1	−144.5

5.0 RESULTS: RETREAT OF THE ANTARCTIC ICE SHEET

In Antarctica there is reason to believe that ice sheet retreat would not be uniform because of differences in ice stream dynamics. We have therefore considered three regions in Antarctica shown in figure 12.5 which approximate those reported by Thomas (1985) as potential regions of enhanced ice sheet retreat. Some regions in East Antarctica which are grounded more than 500 m below sea level are also potentially unstable. Within each region uniform thinning of the ice sheet is assumed but between regions the thinning differs. Once again a total eustatic sea-level rise of 100 cm is used. Of this 100 cm rise 60 cm is assumed to come from region 'A' on figure 12.5 where the amount of thinning is thus 75.5 m uniformly spread over 30 grid points. The remaining 40 cm is derived from the Filchner-Ronne ice shelf region (20 cm; 104.3 m thinning; 23 grid points) and the Ross ice shelf region (20 cm; 82.9 m thinning; 18 grid points). This spatial variability in thinning differs from an earlier calculation of sea-level change resulting only from the contribution of the West Antarctic ice sheet (Clark and Lingle 1977). Scaling for other values

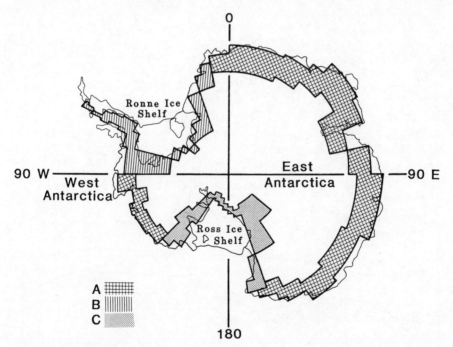

Figure 12.5 The Antarctic ice sheet grid. Non-uniform retreat occurs over the three regions A, B and C totalling 71 elements

of eustatic sea-level rise is, of course, valid assuming that 60 per cent of the rise comes from uniform thinning of region 'A' and 20 per cent comes from 'B' and 'C' respectively.

Figure 12.6 gives the global results for the case where the Antarctic ice sheet retreats. Here, in contrast to the Greenland case, the northern hemisphere experiences the greatest sea-level rise. Table 12.1 gives the corresponding predictions for the 30 coastal localities of figure 12.4.

6.0   DISCUSSION

It is likely that *both* the Antarctic and Greenland ice sheets may contribute to a sea-level rise. Predictions for this case are readily obtained by simple addition of the respective contributions. For example, suppose that by the year AD 2100 Greenland contributes 25 cm to the eustatic rise and Antarctica contributes 80 cm. These figures represent upper limits for the

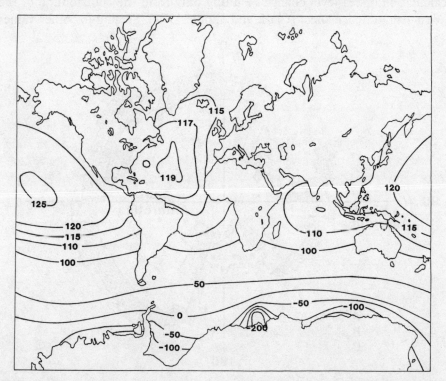

Figure 12.6   A map to show the amount of sea-level rise caused by the melting of part of the Antarctic ice sheet. Contours are in centimetres if the eustatic sea-level rise is 100 cm. Alternatively, contours are in percent of eustatic sea-level rise.

expected respective contributions. At Chesapeake Bay (locality No. 3) the observed sea-level rise would be 14.7 cm (25 per cent of 58.7 cm) resulting from Greenland ice sheet melting and 92.6 cm (80 per cent of 115.7 cm) from Antarctica's contribution. The total observed sea-level rise would thus be 107.3 cm for the 105 cm total eustatic sea-level rise. This rise in sea level would not occur instantaneously in time because the ice sheets would thin gradually over the next century. However if the rate of thinning is known, the results given here can be appropriately scaled. For example if 50 per cent of the ice sheet thinning is completed by the year AD 2050 then the observed sea-level rise would be 50 per cent of that value predicted here. These results are therefore quite general and can be applied in time-dependent cases even if ice sheet thinning magnitudes differ from those used in the calculation. This generality, of course, only applies if the initial assumption is good, that the Earth is a linear elastic material. Should viscous properties of the Earth be important on the century time scale then our predictions would be incorrect. Methods exist for solving the viscoelastic problem (Clark *et al.* 1978) but these assume that the viscous structure of the Earth is known.

In addition to the sea-level rise anticipated from meltwater additions to the ocean volume, the warming of the oceans themselves will decrease water density near the ocean surface. This density decrease will result in increased ocean volume but not of ocean mass. Making the good assumption that ocean mixing from currents will readily distribute the added heat uniformly throughout the oceans to a depth of about 100 m, Hoffman *et al.* (1983) have calculated the resulting rise in sea level expected by AD 2100. For a likely scenario they found that this temperature/density effect will result in a sea-level rise of approximately 72 cm with a range in estimates of 28 cm to 118 cm. To the extent that the assumption of uniform mixing is true, this rise in sea level will be uniform. Hence every locality will experience the same sea-level rise resulting from the temperature/density effect. Furthermore, since the amount of mass in the ocean is constant for this effect, neither the Earth's surface nor its geoid will be perturbed. One exception is the additional water loading that might occur as shorelines advance inland on a sloping continental shelf. This water load will be of small magnitude and affect only a very narrow strip of the Earth's surface. Therefore it probably has a negligible effect upon perturbation of the sea-level rise.

Studies of Holocene sea-level changes indicate that sea level has changed significantly during postglacial times with the magnitude of change differing among localities. For example on the coast of Brazil sea level has fallen approximately 4 m during the past 5000 years (Martin *et al.*

1979). At Chesapeake Bay on the eastern coast of the USA sea level has risen 10 m during that same time period (Belknap and Kraft 1977). We believe these Holocene changes result from the viscous response of the Earth to retreat of the ice sheets of the most recent ice age. If this belief is correct the expected rate of sea-level change at a given locality at present, independent of CO_2 effects, would be that found from extrapolation of data of past elevations of sea level indicated in the Holocene record to the present time. Although numerical models of the glacio-isostatic process exist, we believe this straightforward empirical approach to be much more reliable. For regions of the world where no Holocene record has been reported, model predictions could be employed (e.g. Peltier 1985).

The observed rise in sea level at any locality will be the algebraic sum of the contributions from ice sheet retreat, temperature/density effects, and continuing viscous response of the Earth to past ice sheets. The temperature/density contribution will be equal at all localities and so any spatial variation in the rate of sea-level rise will be caused by the effects of ice sheets – both past and present.

7.0   CONCLUSION

It is not certain that ice sheets will retreat during the next century; however if the projected CO_2 warming is valid such a retreat is likely. The predictions of sea-level changes, given here, can be applied to a large class of ice sheet thinning scenarios. A global tide gauge network could readily detect a eustatic sea-level change of 30 cm to 100 cm if it occurs over the next century and the results given here show that we should not expect the rise in sea level to be uniform. Observations of sea level rise would typically vary by 20 per cent from eustatic values and locally may differ by much greater magnitudes. This non-uniform rise in sea level could potentially be of great value in locating the dominant source of meltwater induced by CO_2 warming of the climate because the sea-level rise will vary in a systematic and known manner away from the water source.

ACKNOWLEDGEMENTS

This work was supported by the Environmental Protection Agency under contract No. 68–01–6558. The work was performed under subcontract 130.125 awarded to the National Aeronautical and Space Administration. We wish to express special thanks to Robert H. Thomas who motivated and encouraged us throughout this project and also provided his unpublished data.

Revised typescript received 1986, April.

REFERENCES

Belknap, D. F. and Kraft, J. C. 1977: Holocene relative sea-level changes and coastal stratigraphic units on the northwest flank of the Baltimore Canyon trough geosyncline, *J. Sediment. Petrol.*, 47, 610–29.

Bentley, C. R. 1983: The West Antarctic ice sheet: diagnosis and prognosis. In *Proceedings: Carbon Dioxide Research Conference: Carbon Dioxide, Science and Consensus*, Department of Energy CONF–820970, Washington DC, IV.3–IV.50.

Bindschadler, R. A. 1985: Contribution of the Greenland ice cap to changing sea level: present and future. In *Glaciers, Ice sheets, and Sea Level: effects of CO$_2$ induced climatic change*. Paper prepared for US Department of Energy, DOE/EV/60235–1, 258–66.

Charney, J., Chairman, Climate Research Board, 1979: *Carbon Dioxide and Climate: A Scientific Assessment*. Washington DC: National Academy of Sciences Press.

Clark, J. A., Farrell, W. E. and Peltier, W. R. 1978: Global changes in postglacial sea level: A numerical calculation, *Quat. Res.*, 9, 265–87.

Clark, J. A. and Lingle, C. S. 1977: Future sea-level changes due to West Antarctic ice sheet fluctuations, *Nature*, 269, 206–9.

Farrell, W. E. 1972: Deformation of the earth by surface loads, *Rev. Geophys. and Space Phys.*, 10, 761–97.

Farrell, W. E. and Clark, J. A. 1976: On postglacial sea level, *Geophys. J. Roy. Astr. Soc.*, 46, 647–67.

Hansen, J., Lacis, A., Rind, D., Russell, G., Stone, P., Fung, I., Ruedy, R. and Lerner, J. 1984: Climate processes and climate sensitivity, *Geophysical Monograph*, 29, American Geophysical Union, Washington, DC, 130–63.

Hoffman, J., Keyes, D. and Titus, J. 1983: *Projecting future sea-level rise: methodology, estimates to the year 2100, and research needs*, 2nd revised edition, US GPO No. 055–000–00236–3. Washington, DC: Government Printing Office.

Hollin, J. T. and Schilling, D. H. 1981: Late Wisconsin–Weichselian mountain glaciers and small ice caps. In G. H. Denton and T. J. Hughes (eds.), *The Last Great Ice Sheets*, New York: John Wiley and Sons, 179–206.

Hughes, T. J. 1973: Is the West Antarctic ice sheet disintegrating? *J. Geophys. Res.*, 78, 7884–910.

Hughes, T. J. 1977: West Antarctic ice streams. *Rev. Geophys. and Space Phys.*, 15, 1–46.

Hughes, T. J. 1983: The stability of the West Antarctic Ice sheet: What has happened and what will happen. In *Proceedings: Carbon Dioxide Research Conference: Carbon Dioxide, Science and Consensus*, US Department of Energy,

CONF–820970, Washington DC, IV.51–IV.73.

Martin, L., Suguio, K. and Flexor, J. M. 1979: Le Quaternaire marin du littoral Brésilien entre Cananéia et Barra de Guaratiba. In K. Suguio, T. R. Fairchild, L. Martin and J.-M. Flexor (eds.), *Proceedings of the 1978 International Symposium on Coastal Evolution in the Quaternary*. São Paulo, Brasil, 296–331.

Meier, M. 1984: Contribution of small glaciers to global sea level, *Science*, 226, 1418–21.

Menabe, S. and Wetherald, R. T. 1975: The effect of doubling the CO_2 concentration on the climate of a general circulation model, *J. Atmosph. Sci.*, 32, 3–15.

Mercer, J. H. 1978: West Antarctic ice sheet and CO_2 greenhouse effect: a threat of disaster, *Nature*, 271, 321–5.

Peltier, W. R. 1985: Climatic implications of isostatic adjustment constraints on current variations of eustatic sea level. In *Glaciers, Ice Sheets, and Sea Level: effects of CO_2-induced climatic change*. Paper prepared for US Department of Energy, DOE/EV/60235–1, 92–103.

Schlesinger, M. E. 1984: Atmospheric general circulation model simulations of the modern Antarctic climate. In *Environment of West Antarctica: Potential CO_2-induced changes*, Washington, DC: National Academy of Sciences Press for Polar Research Board, National Research Council, 155–96.

Smagorinsky, J., Chairman, Climate Research Board, 1982: *Carbon Dioxide: A Second Assessment*. Washington, DC: National Academy of Sciences Press.

Sugden, D. E. and Clapperton, C. M. 1980: West Antarctic ice sheet fluctuations in the Antarctic Peninsula area. *Nature*, 286, 378–81.

Thomas, R. H. 1985: Responses of the polar ice sheet to climate warming. In *Glaciers, Ice Sheets, and Sea Level: effects of CO_2 induced climatic change*, Paper prepared for US Department of Energy, DOE/EV/60235–1, 301–316.

Thomas, R. H. and Bentley, C. R. 1978: The equilibrium state of the eastern half of the Ross ice shelf, *J. Glaciol.*, 20, 509–18.

Thomas, R. H., Sanderson, T. J. O. and Rose, K. E. 1979: Effect of climatic warming on the West Antarctic ice sheet, *Nature*, 277, 355–8.

Titus, J. G. and Barth, M. C. 1984: An overview of the causes and effects of sea-level rise. In M. C. Barth and J. G. Titus (eds.), *Greenhouse Effect and Sea Level Rise: A Challenge for this Generation*, New York: Van Nostrand/Reinhold Co., 1–56.

Weertman, J. 1974: Stability of the junction of an ice sheet and an ice shelf, *J. Glaciol.*, 13, 3–11.

13

Conspectus of fundamental and strategic research on sea-level changes

Ian Shennan and Michael J. Tooley

1.0 INTRODUCTION

The literature on sea-level changes has grown exponentially in the past twenty-five years, and there has been some utility in grouping it under the two headings of fundamental and strategic research, and exploring the catalytic functions of various international organisations in promoting both exclusive and interlocking programmes of research on sea-level changes (chapter 1). Strategic research on the impact of projected sea-level rise on coastal lowlands demands a continuous investment in fundamental research on the evidence for and nature of sea-level changes in the past. The former invariably drives and stimulates the latter: the effects of the 1953 storm surge on the southern North Sea led in the Netherlands to fundamental research on the evidence for sea-level changes during the Holocene and long period subsidence (Anon. 1954, Jelgersma 1961) and in the United Kingdom to fundamental research on the incidence of coastal flooding and storm surges (Rossiter 1962, Heaps 1967) and on subsidence in south-eastern Britain (Dunham and Gray 1972).

In this chapter, the material treated by the authors of the chapters in this book is enhanced with published and unpublished material germane to a summary of recent fundamental and strategic research on sea-level changes.

2.0 FUNDAMENTAL RESEARCH

Fundamental research has addressed the problem of sea-level changes at different scales and over different time periods. Prior to the year 1976 when a paper by N.-A. Mörner on eustasy and geoid changes was published, the goal of many sea-level investigators was the construction of a graph to show an eustatic sea-level curve. Until 1980, the prime objective of Unesco/IGCP Project 61 was to define a single, globally-valid curve of sea-level variation. An examination of the *Atlas of Sea-level Curves* and the *Supplement* compiled by Bloom (1977, 1982) reveals that very few investigators quantified errors likely to affect the altitude of a dated sample but, at the same time, usually showed the dating error to one or two standard deviations of the mean date. Allowing for the likely error to have affected variates on one axis and not on the other is both illogical and unscientific, particularly as there are several examples in the literature of the use of error boxes qualifying the age *and* altitude of sea-level variates (Tooley 1986. See also discussion by Chappell in Chapter 10).

Godwin (1940) plotted 34 index points on a time/altitude graph, which showed relative land and sea-level changes in the Fenland, UK. Age ranges based on pollen analysis and archaeology were shown and altitudinal ranges for each index point were also shown either by arrows when the range was large and uncertain or by hatched areas when the range was more certain.

The advent of radiocarbon dating permitted greater precision on plotting the age of a sea-level index point, but three of the four earliest papers showing sea-level rise index points (de Vries and Barendsen 1954, Shepard and Suess 1956, Godwin *et al.* 1958) showed neither altitudinal nor temporal errors. This is suprising because not only had Godwin (1940) shown an acute awareness of the likely altitudinal and temporal errors to affect sea-level index points, but also van Straaten (1954) had considered likely errors arising from the radiocarbon dating method, compaction and tidal range, and shown each sea-level variable in an error box.

Following the examples set by Godwin (1940) and van Straaten (1954) a more cautious approach was adopted by other investigators. In the Netherlands, Jelgersma (1961) plotted only dated samples from basal peats that formed on Pleistocene age sands with a gentle, continuous gradient to overcome the problem of post-depositional changes in altitude caused by sediment compaction. Bloom (1964) represented each dated sample from the Hammock River estuary, Connecticut, USA by a rectangle the dimensions of which were probable errors arising from the sampling and dating techniques employed. A line showing the relative rise of high tide level was drawn through data points unaffected by consolidation, but errors in the precision of the date and the altitude were still estimated. Scholl (1964) and Scholl and Stuiver (1967) also considered age and altitude errors in establishing a submergence curve for Southern Florida and Grant (1970) summarized graphically all the sources of error likely to affect the age and altitude of index points on sea-level graphs.

Subsequently, curves were fitted through sea-level index points with little regard to the errors likely to have affected them. Fairbridge (1961) confidently drew a continuous line with an oscillating form through 57 index points derived from a range of materials from the world's coastlines and enhanced these dates subsequently with additional sea-level dates and dates from prehistoric middens in Brazil (Fairbridge 1976), yielding a modified curve, but without an allowance for the range of the data. Similarly Shepard (1960, 1963) employed 52 data points from stable areas on an age-altitude graph without an indication of errors likely to have affected both the age and altitude of each, but fitted an exponential sea-level curve. Local and regional sea-level investigations displayed the same confident interpretation of the data: for example in Schleswig-Holstein (Behre *et al.* 1979), in the Netherlands (Jelgersma 1961, 1979), in North-west England (Tooley 1974, 1979), in the Thames estuary, UK (Devoy 1979), the Barnstable estuary, Massachussetts, USA (Redfield 1967), the coastal plain of Delaware, USA (Kraft 1976), South Australia (Hails *et al.* 1983) and China (Yang and Xie 1984).

Error boxes, error bands and error-ellipses have been applied to each sea-level index point by some investigators in Australia (Thom and Chappell 1975), the United Kingdom (Akeroyd 1972, Devoy 1982, Kidson 1982 and Heyworth and Kidson 1982, Shennan 1982a, 1986a,b), The Netherlands (Louwe Kooijmans 1974, 1980), Hawaii (Easton and Olson 1976) and from four countries as part of the activities of IGCP 61 (Preuss 1979).

Enhancement of a sea-level data base with archaeological and historical data has been employed with effect by Godwin (1940), Akeroyd (1972), Louwe Kooijmans (1974), Fairbridge (1976), Flemming (1978, 1979–80), Gill and Lane (1985), Colquhoun and Brooks (1986) and Shennan (1986a,b), but these data require criteria different from geological samples to quantify their precision as sea-level indicators.

A single line on an age/altitude graph is a poor summary of sea-level changes if the variation in data points is not shown. Furthermore the interpretation of changes in sea level is scale dependent. Whether or not sea level has been characterised by low amplitude fluctuations during the Holocene is only important over the specific period of study, the area involved and the variables considered (Shennan 1982b). For time scales of the order of 1000 years the sea-level reconstruction may be generalised and alternations of periods of positive and negative tendencies may become insignificant as the time scale increases to 10 000 years. At this scale, sea-level altitude data are required in more general terms since the other variables that are studied, e.g. regional crustal movements, ice-sheet dimensions and ocean volumes, cannot be correlated precisely with sea level. As the resolution increases to 100 years the local scale variables contributing to the spread of the sea-level index points on the age/altitude graph increase in importance in the study, even though their precision of measurement is unchanged. Generalisations that were valid for the longer periods cannot now be made. Long-term variables may have changed their status from dependent to independent and the shorter term and local spatial scale variables from indeterminable to determinable. Thus the final summary of the sea-level data will vary according to its specified or potential application. Subsequent users of the information should be able to use the original sea-level index points rather than the curve which may be an inappropriate summary for their analysis.

In this book, the different forms of presentation of sea-level data on age/altitude graphs are illustrated. Continuous line sea-level curves from Brazil (figure 2.13), north-east Scotland (figure 3.12), the North Sea basin (figure 4.8), Japan (figure 6.2), the west coast of Africa (figure 8.6) and the east coast of Africa (figure 9.7) contrast with age/altitude graphs showing a range of errors for each variable or error bands from Brazil (figure 2.11), the Fenland, UK (figure 4.4) and Australia (figures 10.2, 10.5, 10.7 and 10.9).

Notwithstanding the aims of IGCP Projects 61 and 200 to standardise the approach to sea-level investigations as exemplified in the draft *Manual for Sea-level Research* (van de Plassche 1977) and the computer forms for radiocarbon-dated sea-level index points (van de Plassche and Preuss 1978), collectively the chapters in this book illustrate the range of approaches currently adopted not only in the display of sea-level data in particular, but also generally in the study of sea-level changes within the sphere of international cooperation fostered between 1974 and 1987.

The emphasis on standardization of data collection and presentation, the transfer of methodology and techniques from one country or environment to others, and an overall comparability of results are all possible, as exemplified by the preceding chapters. Such practices are necessary if objective and meaningful comparisons and correlations are to be made at any scale: local, continental or global. It is equally clear that the same practices are not universally adopted. Whilst total standardization of a too rigid methodology and technique is not feasible and, more significantly, is not desirable, it should be a realistic expectation that sea-level research workers reveal an awareness of the methodology and techniques applied elsewhere; of how the various data have been presented; of the interpretations made of individual site-based studies and how these data can be utilized beyond the site-based approach; of the necessity of comparison between different sites and different types of data; and of the development of ideas. This expectation will not always be realised. Some research remains intrinsically myopic and some investigators hibernate within their geographical and methodological areas and are unconcerned with developments elsewhere.

The scientific study of sea level during the past decade or so has been encouraged by a group of agencies, but progress has not always been clear. The approach adopted to solving problems associated with sea-level changes has largely, though not exclusively, been inductive and the subject remains mainly at the data-gathering stage. It could be argued that the subject would be advanced more satisfactorily by adopting the approach employed by Birks and Birks (1980) in the study of vegetational history by the falsification of hypotheses.

In many sea-level investigations, the hypothesis is implicit or is not clearly stated. The chief hypothesis of most studies is concerned with the identification of the components of crustal uplift or subsidence on the one hand, and ocean-level changes on the other. The hypothesis has been modified to accommodate locally distorting factors, such as sediment consolidation, variable rates of sedimentation, variable river discharge, water loading on continental shelves, neotectonics and palaeotidal changes. Recently, changes in the shape of the oceanic geoid have become a more fashionable explanation of non-synchronous altitudinal changes in sea level recorded on different temporal and spatial scales (Mörner 1981) with claims that these changes may be corroborated by empirical data from Brazil (Martin *et al.* 1985), from oceanic coral islands (Nunn 1986) and from the west coast of Africa (Giresse, this volume).

Along continental coasts, palaeo-geoidal changes have not been rigorously tested against processes likely to affect the altitude of the dated index points: such effects include within-estuary variations, changing river discharge, palaeo-tidal changes and changes in coastal configuration.

All the errors to which sea-level index points are subject (eloquently and economically reviewed by Kidson and Heyworth 1979 and Kidson 1982) preclude the assignment of an overriding control to explain relative sea-level change whether it is isostasy or geoidal-eustasy or the now abandoned term eustasy. Awareness of the errors has led both to geographical hibernation and the investigation of local, distorting factors. Whilst the detail of many recent sea-level investigations is exemplary, the lack of an agreed, objective methodology, universally applied, will prevent the realisation of correlation within and between regions which is the aim of IGCP 200.

Fundamental research in sea-level investigations in the future should be concerned with several interrelated areas. The first concerns the development and application of an objective methodology, discussed above and elsewhere (Shennan 1982a, 1983, 1986a,b, Shennan *et al.* 1983, Tooley 1982). The second concerns the acquisition of good quality data from areas deficient in sea-level information. Many areas of the African, Latin American and south-east Asian coasts are lacking in data, although a considerable body of new information has been synthesized from the coasts of China (Qin and Zhao 1986; reviewed in Tooley 1987). Sea-level data from oceanic islands, such as those assembled by Bloom (1970, 1974), Schofield (1977a,b), Nunn (1984), Pirazzoli (1985) and Pirazzoli and Montaggioni (1986) need to be extended and enhanced, and Nunn's (1984) conclusion, that the history of sea-level change on both islands and their continental coastal hinterlands is required to complete a regional picture, is to be applauded. The third area worthy of investigation is the accurate determination of differences in altitude of tide gauges located on different continents, using Very Long Baseline Interferometry (VLBI) and satellites of the Global Positioning System (GPS), to quantify variations in the rate of global sea-level rise (e.g. Carter *et al.* 1986), and the proportion attributable to steric changes (Thomson and Tabata, in press). An increase in the amount and quality of sea-level data from such fundamental research will provide a sound foundation for advances made in strategic research.

3.0 STRATEGIC RESEARCH

There have been many estimates of the rise of sea level consequent upon the complete melting of the remaining glaciers and ice caps of the Earth. Daly (1925) tabulated the range of estimates from Maclaren's (1842) estimated rise of 30 m to Humphreys' (1915) estimate of 40 m. Flint (1947) estimated a range of 20 m to 50 m, allowing for isostatic adjustment. There is little likelihood of complete deglaciation of the Earth because of the role that the high latitude ice caps and ice shelves play in the energy budget of the Earth but the estimated values remain a potential for the deglacial geoid of the Earth.

The impact of the increasing atmospheric concentration of carbon dioxide and other radiatively active gases on the temperature of the atmosphere and hence on the volume of ocean water, the stability of glaciers and ice sheets and on sea level itself has been the subject of many publications (for example, Barth and Titus 1984, National Research Council 1985, Robin 1986, Bolin *et al*. 1986, Clarke and Primus, this volume). The reviews of the likely effects on sea-level have yielded a series of four projected sea-level rise scenarios up to the year AD 2100 (Hoffman 1984) which are summarised in table 13.1. The values are given as mean, worldwide sea-level rise scenarios in which no account is taken of regional variations in the likely observed sea-level rise due to the redistribution of the mass within the Earth and of ice and water (see, Clark and Lingle 1977, Clark and Primus, this volume). Furthermore, accurate measurements of changing sea level may be the first reliable indicator of global warming due to the complicated noise, and incomplete coverage, of data monitoring global temperature changes (Maddox 1986).

Table 13.1 Estimated sea-level rise (in cm), AD 2000–2100 (after Hoffman 1984)

Year	Conservative estimate	Mid-range low	Mid-range high	High estimate
2000	4.8	8.8	13.2	17.1
2025	13.0	26.2	39.3	54.9
2050	23.8	52.3	78.6	116.7
2075	38.0	91.2	136.8	212.7
2100	56.2	144.4	216.6	345.0

The impact of projected sea-level rise on the coastal lowlands of the Earth was not considered until the 1970s. Mercer (1978) drew attention to the fact that the calculated rise in temperature at latitude 80°S, caused by the increased carbon dioxide content of the atmosphere, could result in a rapid deglaciation of West Antarctica and a 5 m rise of sea level, leading to a major disaster. The implications of a rise of sea level of this magnitude were considered for the United Kingdom (Tooley 1978), following earlier considerations of the impact of relative and absolute sea-level changes and flooding in the UK (Tooley 1970, 1971). Attention was drawn to the coastal location at low altitude of nuclear power station sites in the UK. The likely impact of projected sea-level rise on coolant water intakes from these stations and on effluent outlets from urban areas is worthy of further consideration. The disposal of hazardous waste in landfills in coastal floodplains would result in accumulations of toxic material that could be mobilised as sea level rose by a rise in the water table, increased storm damage and shoreline retreat. The need to establish the degree of risk from long period inundation has been enunciated: the scale and procedures for defining the risk await definition.

Flynn *et al.* (1984) have noted the location of eleven hazardous waste facilities in Charleston, South Carolina, all of which would lie within the 100-year flood zone in AD 2075. An increase in river salinity caused by sea-level rise would not only disrupt riparian wetlands but also result in saltwater contamination of adjacent aquifers dependent on river recharge. Hull and Titus (1986) have considered the likely effects of sea-level rise on the salinity of the Delaware River, and noted that the Potomac-Raritan-Magothy aquifer system, which is the principal source of water for the population and the industrialised areas of the coastal plain of southern New Jersey, would suffer from increased saltwater intrusion. A further impact of sea-level rise would be the inundation of sewage effluent and storm drain outlets that would need to be raised and feeder pipes relaid or pumps installed. Harbour facilities, especially lock sills and discharge sluices, would require reconstruction as sea-level rose (Goemans 1986).

An assessment of the impact of projected sea-level rise demands that the various sea-level rise scenarios resulting from the Environmental Protection Agency (EPA) research projects (Hoffman *et al.* 1983, Barth and Titus 1984, Seidel and Keyes 1983) are now formulated as hypotheses and tested in order to avoid criticisms such as those by Idso (1984) that some reports 'may thus turn out to be the most monumental gaffes ever produced by their sponsoring organizations'. An assessment also requires a measurement of probability for each scenario and the application of cost-benefit analyses (e.g. The Royal Society 1983): the finance required to raise sea defences protecting a nation's lowlands by two metres rather than one metre will be of major economic significance to that nation.

Ultimately, individual nation states will require data for planning purposes and these data will need to be at different scales. The EPA scenarios as modified by the non-uniform changes in sea-level altitude determined by Clarke and Primus (this volume) will serve at the continental scale, but local factors such as uplift, subsidence, river discharge, storm surge frequency and magnitude, tidal factors and sedimentation rates will need to be accommodated. Sea-level and coastal changes at the local scale will have to be determined so that a comparison of rates of change in the past with predicted rates of change in the future will give insights into the likelihood of specific outputs in terms of sedimentary and geomorphic consequences. However, data are lacking for the time period between the length of time over which tide gauge readings have been taken and the beginning of a dated sedimentary or landform record: this time period is at best 50 years and at worst 500 years.

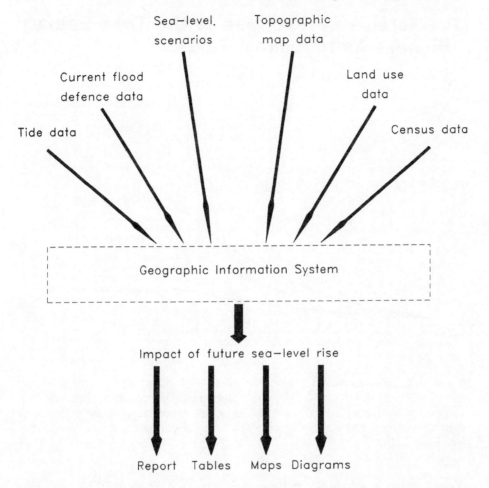

Figure 13.1 Organisation of a geographic information system used to provide data for future management of the impact of sea-level rise

An assessment of the impact of sea-level rise has been made at two scales: the detailed site scale reported by Barth and Titus (1984) in which the likely impact of each of the sea-level rise scenarios was evaluated for Charleston, SC and Galveston Bay, Te., USA and at the global scale analyses of Henderson-Sellers and McGuffie (1986). Neither of these scales permits rational planning decisions at the regional or national level, for which purposes a simple geographic information system has been developed and has been applied in the first instance to two high risk coastal lowlands in the United Kingdom – the Tees Lowlands and the Fenlands. The stages of data capture and presentation as applied to the

Predicted sea-level rise in the Tees Estuary (Highest Astronomical Tides)

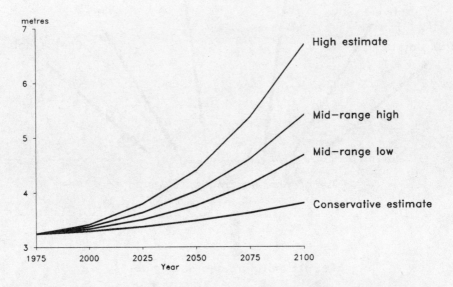

Figure 13.2 The sea-level rise scenarios of Hoffman (1984) modified for local tidal conditions (Admiralty Tide Tables 1985) and crustal movements (Shennan, this volume) for the Tees Estuary, Cleveland County, UK. All levels are related to Ordnance Datum for comparison with the topographic map data obtained for each ward (e.g. see figure 13.3)

Tees Lowlands are shown in figures 13.1 to 13.4. In figure 13.1 the input to the geographic information system is shown. Most of the data sets are not readily available in digitial form and manual acquisition adds a significant cost and time factor. For example, topographic data are obtained manually from Ordnance Survey 1:25 000 scale maps and collected for each census ward area, the areas of which are generated from digital files and are overlaid on the topographic maps. Digital contour and point data (spot altitudes and bench mark altitudes) and census data at the level of the enumeration district would be preferable. On figure 13.2 the sea-level rise scenarios of Barth and Titus (1984) are displayed graphically, modified for present tidal conditions in the River Tees: the graphs are plotted in relation to the High Astronomical Tide, which on the River Tees intersects the coast of +3.2 m O.D. Figure 13.3 shows the minimum altitude record for each ward in the County of Cleveland; the

Minimum height

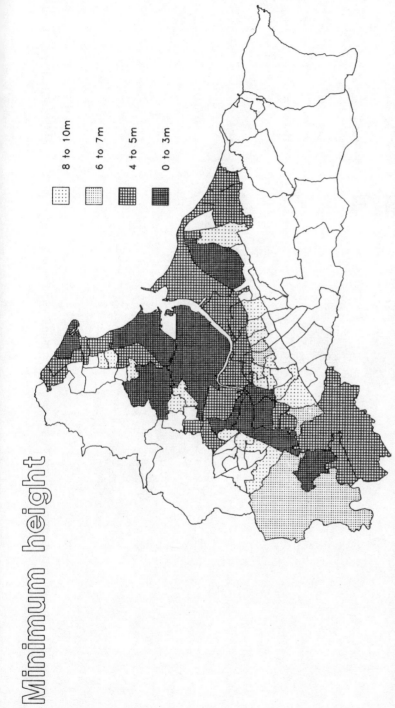

	8 to 10m
	6 to 7m
	4 to 5m
	0 to 3m

Figure 13.3 Minimum height recorded for each ward within the County of Cleveland. The minimum height shown will either be the lowest contour or the lowest spot height within the ward, shown on the latest 1:25 000 Ordnance Survey maps. A range of altitudinal data was collected, e.g. all spot heights, the three lowest and the maximum contours, so that various measures of the proportion of a ward below a particular altitude could be used. This map illustrates those wards which will be dependent on protection from flooding along the River Tees for any particular sea-level rise scenario. The use of minimum height indicates that the ward will be partly and not wholly affected. Unshaded areas are wards for which no detailed topographic data were collected since no part of the ward is below 15 m O.D

POPULATION

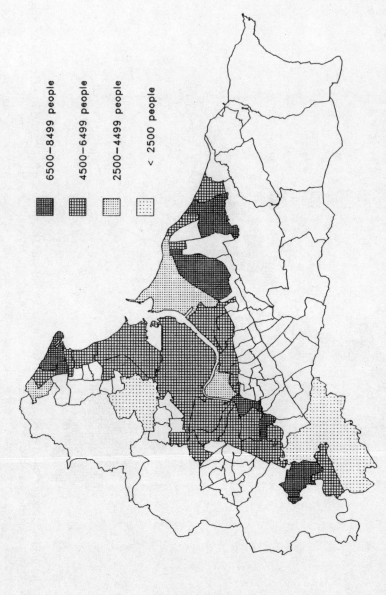

6500–8499 people

4500–6499 people

2500–4499 people

< 2500 people

Figure 13.4 Population distribution in the 40 wards with a minimum height of less than 7 m O.D. 1981 population census data have been employed

minimum value is defined either from the lowest contour value or lowest spot height in the ward. The map shows those wards which will require protection, the scale and extent of which is dependent on the time and altitude reached for the sea-level scenario specified. Because of the way in which the altitudinal data have been gathered, it may be that not all wards are equally affected because of the range of altitudes within their boundaries. Figure 13.4 shows the pattern of population in 1981 of the 40 wards with a minimum altitude of +7 m O.D. or less: a total of 229 456 people lived in those wards which would be affected given the high estimate sea-level rise scenario for AD 2100.

The ward and the enumeration district have been employed rather than the 1 km grid square or 1×1 degree cells because in the UK these are the basic units for the return of census data upon which planning decisions are taken. Additional vector data in the form of transport and service networks can be added.

Currently, impact maps and tables, utilising any of the UK 1981 census data can be produced for specified sea-level rise scenarios, modified for local conditions, for two major coastal lowlands in the UK – the Tees and the Fenlands. With the appropriate resources, this can readily be extended to the Thames Lowlands, and other coastal lowlands in the UK. This approach is recommended to other countries with extensive coastal lowlands, where sea-level rise is likely to disrupt agriculture, drainage, settlement, industrial and service activities.

The annual incremental rise of sea level is likely to be slow but inexorable. It is desirable from a planning point of view, for the needs of planning relocation, to give as much warning as possible. Whilst a catastrophic collapse of the West Antarctic ice sheet may not be imminent (Robin 1986) given a conservative sea-level rise scenario driven by thermal expansion of ocean water, melting of small glaciers and changes in water storage on land, such a rise may initiate changes in the stability of the Antarctic ice sheet. Denton *et al.* (1986) have put forward hypotheses to show the links between sea-level rise, the global ice sheet system, variations in atmospheric carbon dioxide and temperature. It remains important therefore to monitor the condition of the ice shelves on both coasts of the Antarctic Peninsula using satellite images as Mercer (1978) recommended. Thomas (in press) stressed the need to devise a kind of 'early warning system' for prompt detection of changes that will precede a detectable rise in sea level. The information required from satellite remote sensing would be: surface temperatures on land, oceans and ice sheets; sea-ice distributions; extent of summer melting on the polar ice sheets;

and the areal extent and surface elevations of the ice sheets in Greenland and Antarctica.

Having established an 'early warning system', several options are open to countries with coastal lowlands. These options have been grouped into active and passive approaches by Devoy (in press) and include the construction of costly sea defences and hazard zone mapping *i.a.* In the Netherlands, Goemans (1986) has estimated that if mean sea level rises by 2.0 m some 20 billion guilders (£UK 6.7 billion) will have to be expended over 100 years on raising the dykes and dunes, on water management and on rivers and ports, and this represents less than 0.1 per cent of the annual Dutch GNP. Newman and Fairbridge (1986) address the problem in three ways: evacuate the coastal lowlands, defend them or effect a fall in sea level by diverting freshwater into reservoirs, ground storage and interior basins.

The solution of problems related to sea-level rise that may affect the coastal lowlands of the Earth will be a fertile area for research of a strategic nature in the ensuing decades. But equally, testing the hypotheses against empirical data will be a challenge for those involved in fundamental research into sea-level changes at all scales.

Revised typescript received 1987, January.

REFERENCES

Akeroyd, A. V. 1972: Archaeological and historical evidence for subsidence in southern Britain. *Phil. Trans. R. Soc. Lond.*, A 272, 151–69.
Anon, (ed.) 1954: Quaternary changes in level especially in the Netherlands. A symposium, organised by the Geological Society, Royal Netherlands Geological and Mining Society, held at Utrecht, March 5 and 6, 1954. *Geologie en Mijnbouw*, 16, 147–267.
Barth, M. C. and Titus, J. G. (eds.) 1984: *Greenhouse Effect and Sea-level Rise: a challenge for this generation*. New York: Van Nostrand Reinhold.
Behre, K.-E., Menke, B. and Streif, H. 1979: The Quaternary geological development of the German part of the North Sea. In E. Oele, R. T. E. Schüttenhelm, and A. J. Wiggers, (eds.) *The Quaternary History of the North Sea, Acta Univ. Ups. Symp. Univ. Ups. Annum Quingentesimum Celebrantis* 2, 85–113, Uppsala.
Birks, H. J. B. and Birks, H. H. 1980: *Quaternary Palaeoecology*. London: Edward Arnold.
Bloom, A. L. 1964: Peat accumulation and compaction in a Connecticut coastal marsh. *Journal of Sedimentary Petrology*, 34, 599–603.
Bloom, A. L. 1970: Paludal stratigraphy of Truk, Ponape, and Kusaie, eastern Caroline Islands. *Geol. Soc. Am. Bull.*, 81, 1895–904.
Bloom, A. L. 1974: Geomorphology of reef complexes. In L. F. Laporte (ed.),

Reefs in Time and Space. Society of Economic Palaeontologists and Mineralogists. Special Publication No. 18, Tulsa, Oklahoma.

Bloom, A. L. (Compiler) 1977: *Atlas of Sea-level Curves.* IGCP Project 61, Cornell University, Ithaca, New York State.

Bloom, A. L. (Compiler) 1982: *Atlas of Sea-level Curves: supplement. Zone A curves and partial bibliography.* IGCP Project 61.

Bolin, B., Döös, B. R., Jäger, J. and Warrick, R. A. (eds) 1986: *International assessment of the role of carbon dioxide and of other greenhouse gases in climate variations and associated impacts.* Chichester: John Wiley.

Carter, W. E., Robertson, D. S., Pyle, T. E. and Diamente, J. 1986: The application of geodetic radio interferometric surveying to the monitoring of sea level. Paper given at the IAMAP/IAPSO Joint Assembly, Variations of Sea Level Symposium, Honolulu, Hawaii, August 7–8, 1985. *Geophys. J. R. Astr. Soc.*, 87, 3–13.

Clark, J. A. and Lingle, C. S. 1977: Future sea level changes due to West Antarctic ice sheet fluctuations. *Nature*, 269, 206–9.

Colquhoun, D. J. and Brooks, M. J. 1986: New evidence from the south-eastern US for eustatic components in the Late Holocene sea levels. *Geoarchaeology*, 1, 275–91.

Daly, R. A. 1925: Pleistocene changes of level. *Am. J. Sci.*, 10, 281–313.

Denton, G. H., Hughes, T. J. and Karlén, W. 1986: Global ice sheet system interlocked by sea level. *Quaternary Research*, 26, 3–26.

Devoy, R. J. N. 1979: Flandrian sea-level changes and vegetational history of the lower Thames estuary. *Phil. Trans. R. Soc. Lond.* B., 285, 355–407.

Devoy, R. J. N. 1982: Analysis of the geological evidence for Holocene sea-level movements in south-east England. *Proc. Geol. Ass.*, 93, 65–90.

Devoy, R. J. N. (in press): Sea-level applications and management. In Zhao Songling (ed.) *Proceedings of IGCP No 200 International Symp. on Sea-level Changes and Applications*, Qingdao, China.

Dunham, K. C. and Gray, D. A. (organizers) 1972: A discussion on problems associated with the subsidence of south-eastern England. 26–27 May 1971. *Phil. Trans. R. Soc. Lond.* A., 272, 79–274.

Easton, W. H. and Olson, E. A. 1976: Radiocarbon profile of Hanauma reef, Oahu Hawaii. *Geol. Soc. Am. Bull.*, 87, 711–19.

Fairbridge, R. W. 1961: Eustatic changes of sea-level. In L. H. Ahrens *et al.* (eds.), *Physics and Chemistry of the Earth* 4. London: Pergamon Press, 99–185.

Fairbridge, R. W. 1976: Shellfish-eating preceramic indians in coastal Brazil. *Science*, 191, 353–9.

Flemming, N. C. 1978: Holocene eustatic changes and coastal tectonics in the north-east Mediterranean: implications for models of crustal consumption. *Phil. Trans. R. Soc. Lond.* A, 289, 405–58.

Flemming, N. C. 1979–80: Archaeological indicators of sea level. *Oceanis*, 5, 149–65.

Flint, R. F. 1947: *Glacial geology and the Pleistocene epoch.* New York: John

Wiley and Sons, Inc.

Flynn, T. J., Walesh, S. G., Titus, J. G. and Barth, M. C. 1984: Implications of sea-level rise for hazardous waste sites in coastal floodplains. In M. C. Barth and J. G. Titus, (eds), *Greenhouse effect and sea-level rise.* New York: van Nostrand Reinhold Company, 271–94.

Gill, E. D. and Lane, L. N. 1985: Sea levels and aboriginal oyster midden at Lake Connewarre, Victoria, Australia. *Proc. R. Soc. Vict.*, 97, 95–100.

Godwin, H. 1940: Studies of the post-glacial history of British vegetation. III. Fenland pollen diagrams. IV. Postglacial changes of relative land and sea level in the English Fenland. *Phil. Trans. R. Soc. Lond.* B, 230, 239–303.

Godwin, H., Suggate, R. P. and Willis, E. H. 1958: Radiocarbon dating of the eustatic rise in ocean level. *Nature*, 181, 1518–19.

Goemans, T. 1986: The sea also rises. UNEP/EPA International Conference on the Health and Environmental affects of Ozone Modification and Climatic Change. Crystal City, Virginia. Roneo.

Grant, D. R. 1970: Recent coastal submergence of the Maritime Provinces, Canada. *Canadian Jl of Earth Sciences*, 7, 676–89.

Hails, J. R., Belperio, A. P. and Gostin, V. A. 1983: Holocene sea levels of Upper Spencer Gulf, South Australia. In D. Hopley (ed.), *Australian Sea levels in the last 15,000 years, a review.* Monograph Series, Department of Geography, James Cook University of North Queensland, Occasional Paper No 3, 48–53.

Heaps, N. S. 1967: Storm surges. In H. Barnes (ed.), *Oceanography and Marine Biology Annual Review*, 5, 11–47. London: Allen & Unwin.

Henderson-Sellers, A. and McGuffie, K. 1986: The threat from melting ice caps. *New Scientist*, 1512, 24–5.

Heyworth, A. and Kidson, C. 1982: Sea-level changes in south-west England and Wales. *Proc. Geol. Ass.*, 93, 91–111.

Hoffman, J. S. 1984: Estimates of future sea-level rise. In M. C. Barth and J. G. Titus (eds), *Greenhouse effect and sea-level rise: a challenge for this generation.* New York: Van Nostrand Reinhold Company.

Hoffman, J. S., Keyes, D. and Titus, J. G. 1983: *Projecting future sea-level rise: methodology, estimates to the year 2100 and research needs.* Washington, DC: US Environmental Protection Agency.

Hull, C. H. J. and Titus, J. G. (eds), 1986: *Greenhouse effect, sea-level rise, and salinity in the Delaware estuary.* Washington, DC: Environmental Protection Agency.

Humphreys, W. J. 1915: Changes of sea-level due to changes of ocean volume. *Journal of the Washington Academy of Sciences* 5, 445–46.

Idso, S. B. 1984: Review of Seidel, S. and Keyes, D. 1983: *Can we delay a greenhouse warming? Int. J. Remote Sensing*, 5, 839–40.

Jelgersma, S. 1961: Holocene sea-level changes in The Netherlands. *Meded. Geol. Sticht.* C VI., 7, 1–100.

Jelgersma, S. 1979: Sea-level changes in the North Sea basin. In E. Oele, R. T. E. Schüttenhelm and A. J. Wiggers (eds), *The Quaternary History of the*

North Sea. *Acta Univ. Ups. Symp. Univ. Ups. Annum Quingentesimum Celebrantis* 2, 233–48, Uppsala.

Kidson, C. 1982: Sea-level changes in the Holocene. *Quaternary Science Reviews*, 1, 121–51.

Kidson, C. and Heyworth, A. 1979: Sea 'level'. In K. Suguio, T. R. Fairchild, L. Martin and J.-M. Flexor (eds.), *Proceedings of the 1978 International Symposium on Coastal Evolution in the Quaternary*. São Paulo: Universidade de São Paulo, 1–28.

Kraft, J. C. 1976: The coastal environment. In J. C. Kraft and W. Carey (eds.), Selected Papers on the Geology of Delaware. *Transactions of the Delaware Academy of Science*, 7, 31–66. Newark: The Delaware Academy of Science.

Louwe Kooijmans, L. P. 1974: *The Rhine/Meuse Delta: four studies on its prehistoric occupation and Holocene geology*. Leiden: E. J. Brill.

Louwe Kooijmans, L. P. 1980: Archaeology and coastal change in the Netherlands. In F. H. Thompson (ed.) *Archaeology and Coastal Change*. Occasional Paper (N.S.) 1. London: The Society of Antiquaries of London, 106–33.

Maclaren, C. 1842: The glacial theory of Prof. Agassiz. *Am. Jl Science*, 42, 346–65.

Maddox, J. 1986: How to tell when the sea rises? *Nature*, 324, 105.

Martin, L., Flexor, J.-M., Blitzkow, D. and Suguio, K. 1985: Geoid change indications along the Brazilian coast during the last 7000 years. In *Proceedings of the Fifth International Coral Reef Congress, Tahiti* 3, 85–90.

Mercer, J. H. 1978: West Antarctic ice sheet and CO_2 greenhouse effect: a threat of disaster. *Nature*, 271, 321–5.

Mörner, N.-A. 1976: Eustasy and geoid changes. *The Journal of Geology*, 84, 123–51.

Mörner, N.-A. 1981: Space geodesy, paleogeology and paleogeophysics. *Ann. Geophys.*, 37, 69–76.

National Research Council 1985: *Glaciers, ice sheets, and sea-level effect of a CO_2-induced climatic change*. Report of a workshop held in Seattle, Washington, September 13–15, 1984. United States Department of Energy, Washington, DC DOE/ER/60235–1.

Newman, W. S. and Fairbridge, R. W. 1986: The management of sea-level rise. *Nature*, 320, 319–21.

Nunn, P. D. 1984: Occurrence and ages of low-level platforms and associated deposits on South Atlantic coasts: appraisal of evidence for regional Holocene high sea level. *Progress in Physical Geography*, 8, 32–60.

Nunn, P. D. 1986: Implications of migrating geoid anomalies for the interpretation of high-level fossil coral reefs. *Geol. Soc. Am. Bull.*, 97, 946–52.

Pirazzoli, P. A. 1985: Leeward Islands (Maupiti, Tupai, Bora Bora, Huahine) Society Archipelago. In B. De le Salle, R. Galzin and B. Salvat (eds.), Fifth International Coral Reef Congress, Tahiti 27 May–1 June 1985. Vol. I. *French Polynesian Coral Reefs, Reef Knowledge and Field Guides*. 17–72.

Pirazzoli, P. A. and Montaggioni, L. F. 1986: Late Holocene sea-level changes in the north-west Tuamotu Islands, French Polynesia. *Quaternary Research*, 25, 350–68.

Plassche, O. van de 1977: A manual for sample collection and evaluation of sea-level data. Amsterdam: Institute for Earth Sciences, Free University. Unpublished draft.

Plassche, O. van de and Preuss, H. 1978: Explanatory guidelines for completion of the computer form for sample documentation. Amsterdam and Hannover: IGCP 61. Unpublished typescript.

Preuss, H. 1979: Progress in computer evaluation of sea-level data within the IGCP Project no 61. In K. Suguio, T. R. Fairchild, L. Martin and J.-M. Flexor (eds.), *Proceedings of the 1978 International Symposium on Coastal Evolution in the Quaternary*. São Paulo: Universidade de São Paulo, 104–34.

Qin Yunshan and Zhao Songling (eds.) 1986: *China Sea-level Changes*. China Ocean Press.

Redfield, A. C. 1967: The ontogeny of a salt marsh estuary. In G. H. Lauff (ed.), *Estuaries*. Washington: American Association for the Advancement of Science, Publication 83, 108–14.

Robin, G. de Q. 1986: Changing the sea level. In B. Bolin, B. R. Döös, J. Jäger and R. A. Warrick (eds.), *International assessment of the role of carbon dioxide and of other greenhouse gases in climate variations and associated impacts*. Chichester: John Wiley.

Rossiter, J. R. 1962: Long-term variations in sea level. In N. M. Hill (ed.) *The Sea* 1. London: Interscience Publishers, 59–610.

Royal Society, The 1983: *Risk Assessment*. London: The Royal Society.

Schofield, J. C. 1977a: Late Holocene Sea level, Gilbert and Ellice Islands, West Central Pacific Ocean. *N. Z. Journal of Geology and Geophysics*, 20, 503–29.

Schofield, J. C. 1977b: Effect of Late Holocene sea-level fall on atoll development. *N. Z. Journal of Geology and Geophysics*, 20, 531–6.

Scholl, D. W. 1964: Recent sedimentary record in mangrove swamps and rise in sea level over the south-western coast of Florida: Part I. *Marine Geol.*, 1, 344–66.

Scholl, D. W. and Stuiver, M. 1967: Recent submergence of Southern Florida: a comparison with adjacent coasts and other eustatic data. *Geol. Soc. Am. Bull.*, 78, 437–54.

Seidel, S. and Keyes, D. 1983: *Can we delay a greenhouse warming?* Washington, DC: Government Printing Office.

Shennan, I. 1982a: Interpretation of Flandrian sea-level data from the Fenland, England. *Proc. Geol. Ass.*, 83, 53–63.

Shennan, I. 1982b: Problems of correlating Flandrian sea-level changes and climate. In A. F. Harding (ed.), *Climatic change in later prehistory*. Edinburgh: Edinburgh University Press, 52–67.

Shennan, I. 1983: Flandrian and Late Devensian sea-level changes and crustal movements in England and Wales. In D. E. Smith and A. G. Dawson (eds.),

Sea-level changes: a conspectus 389

Shorelines and Isostasy. London: Academic Press, Institute of British Geographers Special Publication No. 16, 255–83.

Shennan, I. 1986a: Flandrian sea-level changes in the Fenland. I: The geographical setting and evidence of relative sea-level changes. Journal of Quaternary Science, 1, 119–54.

Shennan, I. 1986b: Flandrian sea-level changes in the Fenland. II: Tendencies of sea-level movement, altitudinal changes, and local and regional factors. Journal of Quaternary Science, 1, 155–79.

Shennan, I., Tooley, M. J., Davis, M. J. and Haggart, B. A. 1983: Analysis and interpretation of Holocene sea-level data. Nature, 302, 404–6.

Shepard, F. P. 1960: Rise of sea level along north-west Gulf of Mexico. In F. P. Shepard, F. B. Phleger and T. H. van Andel (eds.), Recent Sediments, northwest Gulf of Mexico. Tulsa, Oklahoma: American Association of Petroleum Geologists, 338–44.

Shepard, F. P. 1963: Thirty-five thousand years of sea level. In T. Clements (ed.), Essays in Marine Geology in Honor of K. O. Emery. Los Angeles: University of South California Press, 1–10.

Shepard, F. P. and Suess, H. E. 1956: Rate of postglacial rise of sea level. Science, 123, 1082–3.

Straaten, L. M. J. U. van 1954: Radiocarbon datings and changes of sea level at Velzen (Netherlands). Geologie en Mijnbouw, 16, 247–53.

Thom, B. G. and Chappell, J. 1975: Holocene sea levels relative to Australia. Search, 6, 90–3.

Thomas, R. H. (in press): Future sea-level rise and its early detection by satellite remote sensing. In R. J. N. Devoy and R. W. Carter (eds.), Proceedings of a conference on the hydrodynamic and sedimentary consequences of sea-level change. 1986, 20–22 March. University College, Cork, Ireland.

Thomson, R. E. and Tabata, S. (in press): Steric heights at ocean station Papa in the northeast Pacific Ocean. Marine Geodesy.

Tooley, M. J. 1970: Floods risk in South. The Times, 8 September 1970, 3h.

Tooley, M. J. 1971: Changes in sea level and the implications for coastal development. Association of River Authorities Year Book 1971, 220–5.

Tooley, M. J. 1974: Sea-level changes during the last 7000 years in north-west England. Geogr. J., 140, 18–42.

Tooley, M. J. 1978: Sea-level changes. The Times, 11 February 1978, 15a.

Tooley, M. J. 1979: Sea-level changes during the Flandrian Stage and the implications for coastal development. In K. Suguio, T. R. Fairchild, L. Martin and J.-M. Flexor (eds), Proceedings of the 1978 International Symposium on Coastal Evolution in the Quaternary. São Paulo: Universidade de São Paulo, 502–33.

Tooley, M. J. 1982: Sea-level changes in northern England. Proc. Geol. Ass., 93, 43–51.

Tooley, M. J. 1986: Sea levels. Progress in Physical Geography, 10, 120–9.

Tooley, M. J. 1987: Sea levels. Progress in Physical Geography, 11.

Vries, H. de and Barendsen, G. W. 1954: Measurement of age by the Carbon-14 technique. *Nature*, 174, 1138–41.

Yang, Huai-jen and Xie, Zhiren 1984: Sea-level changes in East China over the past 20,000 years. In R. O. White (ed.), *The evolution of the East Asian Environment*. Hong Kong: University of Hong Kong, 288–308.

The Contributors

LARS-ERIK ÅSE Department of Physical Geography, University of Stockholm, S–106 91 Stockholm, Sweden.

JOHN CHAPPELL The Research School of Pacific Studies, Biogeography and Geomorphology, The Australian National University, GPO Box 4, Canberra, ACT 2601, Australia.

JAMES CLARK Department of Geology, Geography and Environmental Studies, Calvin College, Grand Rapids, Michigan 49506, USA.

THOMAS CRONIN United States Department of the Interior, Geological Survey, Reston, Virginia 22092, USA.

PIERRE GIRESSE Centre de Recherches de Sédimentologie Marine, Université de Perpignan, Avenue de Villeneuve, 66025 Perpignan, France.

B. ANDREW HAGGART Geography Section, Sir John Cass Faculty of Life and Environmental Sciences, City of London Polytechnic, Old Castle Street, London E1 7NT, United Kingdom.

STEPHEN IRELAND Department of Geography, University of Durham, Durham DH1 3LE, United Kingdom.

HIROSHI MACHIDA Department of Geography, Tokyo Metropolitan University, 3–2–1 Fukazawa, Setagaya–ku, Tokyo 158, Japan.

NILS-AXEL MÖRNER Grönby Independent Research Center, S–230 23, Anderslöv, Sweden.

YOTA OTA Department of Geography, Yokohama National University, 156 Tokiwadai, Hodogaya–ku, Yokohama 240, Japan.

PAOLO A. PIRAZZOLI Centre National de la Recherche Scientifique, Laboratoire d'information et de documentation en géographie, INTERGEO, 191, rue Saint-Jacques, 75005 Paris, France.

JOHN A. PRIMUS Department of Geology, Geograpy and Environmental Studies, Calvin College, Grand Rapids, Michigan 49506, USA.

IAN SHENNAN Department of Geography, University of Durham, Durham DH1 3LE, United Kingdom.

MICHAEL J. TOOLEY Department of Geography, University of Durham, Durham DH1 3LE, United Kingdom.

Author Index

394

Subject and Place Index

Related Titles: List of IBG Special Publications